TO BE
DISPOSED
BY
AUTHORITY

BEST STORIES OF THE NAVY

BEST STORIES OF
THE NAVY

edited with a Preface
by
THOMAS WOODROOFFE

FABER AND FABER LIMITED
24 Russell Square
London

First published in mcmxli
by Faber and Faber Limited
24 Russell Square London W.C.1
Second impression May mcmxli
Revised edition mcmxlvii
Reprinted October mcml
This new edition mcmlvi
Reprinted mcmlix
Printed in Great Britain by
Purnell and Sons Limited
Paulton (Somerset) and London

PUBLISHERS' NOTE

The publishers wish to thank the authors who have given permission to reprint their stories in this collection.

Acknowledgements and thanks are also due to: Messrs. Thomas Nelson & Sons, Ltd., for "The Promotion of the Admiral" and "The Settlement with Shanghai Smith" from *Salt of the Sea* by Morley Roberts; Messrs. Hutchinson & Co. (Publishers), Ltd., for "Seascape: Morning Off Lerwick" from *Sea Trails* by "Sea-Wrack"; Messrs. Hodder & Stoughton Ltd., for "Bad Weather" from *Endless Story* by "Taffrail"; Messrs. William Blackwood & Sons, Ltd., for agreeing to the inclusion in this book of "First Command" from *No Less Renowned* by Cdr. G. Hackforth-Jones; Messrs. William Kimber & Co., Ltd., for "Malta Convoy" from *Sea Flight* by Hugh Popham; Messrs. Rupert Hart-Davis Ltd., for "Far-Eastern Patrol" taken from *One of Our Submarines* by Edward Young.

The following stories first appeared in *Blackwood's Magazine*: "September Afternoon" by Lt. G. R. Colvin, "Shadi" by Cdr. T. A. Powell, and "Flotsam" by Ian Scott. "The Sailing of the *Ivy*" by T. Woodrooffe first appeared in the *Cornhill Magazine*.

The following stories are taken from the *Dittybox*: "A Case of Shock" by Bruce Waugh (November 1945); "Conforming to Tradition" by Lt.-Cdr. Julian Ginsbert (April 1946); "Ao Dghaisa" by John Davies (August 1946); "Eagles Fly High" by Cdr. Joseph Bartosik (December 1947); "In the Middle Watch" by T. Woodrooffe (October 1945); "A Trawler's Pig" by Lieut. Michael Parker (January 1947); "Brooklyn on Fire" by John Davies (December 1946); "Albert and the Germans" by Guy Morgan (January 1946); "Conversation in Valhalla" by E. M. Heard (October 1947).

5

PREFACE

The Navy is changing; but then it always has been. The high-charged ship gave way to the galleon; the stately three-decker sailed out to decide the fate of nations; and at one time the dreadnought seemed to have put an end to the argument. During every transition—from sail to steam, from coal to oil, from muzzle-loader to gun turret to the guided missile—there have been men who shook their heads and declared that the Navy wasn't what it was. Radar, remote control and Asdic may produce a different type of sailor, one to whom the running rigging of a square-rigged ship would be as much of a mystery as a high-pressure turbine would be to a smart topman of the old sailing Navy. But they are not so very different under their skins, because one thing is constant—the sea; and cathode tubes and super-heated steam are not as wonderful or as difficult to deal with as the element on which the sailor lives. It is that constant which most affects the character of the sailor—not a buntline or an arrester wire. The things sailors laughed about in the days of the first Queen Elizabeth were very much the same as the things they laugh about in these days of her successor. So in presenting a new selection of naval stories—better call them yarns—I do not apologise for keeping some that I chose for an earlier anthology, because the essential character of the Navy does not change so very much. In the preface to that other volume I wrote: "Few stories about the present war have yet been written, or if they have been will not pass the censor until it is over", and I went on to point out that the sailor was an inarticulate creature who never put pen to paper if he could possibly avoid it. As you will see, neither of these statements turned out to be correct. I have been able to include some yarns which appeared in the naval magazine

7

Dittybox during the war, stories written by sailors for sailors. These are not great literature, but they do show you the sort of man who sailed our ships for six long years. In them you will find no heroics, nothing horrific, and no laying on of sex with a trowel, not because sailors are saints—far from it—but because on the messdeck as in the wardroom these things just don't go down.

Anyhow, it is chiefly the fine days that you remember at sea, and even in a war you forget the horrors long before you forget the time the Skipper lost his new cap over the side. As to the other mis-statement: when the youth of a nation goes to war, a number of people who can write find themselves at sea, and, of course, being writers nothing can stop them writing. The first yarn in this book is about the sailing Navy at Frisco in the old days; the last about a submarine patrol in waters off Malaya in the late war. In between are yarns, written mostly by sailors, about peace or war, and the thread running through them all is gaiety—the gaiety born of a common discipline and knowledge of a job worth doing.

CONTENTS

9

CONTENTS

MORLEY ROBERTS

THE PROMOTION OF THE ADMIRAL

M r. Smith, who ran a sailors' boarding-house in that part of San Francisco known as the Barbary Coast, was absolutely *sui generis*. If any drunken scallawag of a scholar, who had drifted ashore on his boarding-house mud-flats, had ventured in a moment of alcoholic reminiscence to say so in the classic tongue, Shanghai Smith would have "laid him out cold" with anything handy, from a stoneware matchbox to an empty bottle. But if that same son of culture had used his mother tongue, as altered for popular use in the West, and had murmured: "Jerusalem, but Mr. Smith's the daisy o' all!" Smith would have thrown out his chest and blown through his teeth a windy oath and guessed he was just so.

"Say it and mean it, that's me," said Smith. "I'm all right. But call me hog and I *am* hog; don't you forget it!"

Apparently all the world called him "hog". For that he was no better than one, whether he walked, or ate, or drank, or slept, was obvious to any sailor with an open eye. But he was hard and rough and tough, and had the bull-headed courage of a mad steer, combined with the wicked cunning of a monkey.

"Don't never play upon me," he said often. "For 'get even' is my motter. There ain't many walkin' this earth that can say they bested me, not from the time I left Bristol in the old *Dart* till now, when I'm known the wide world over."

So far as ships and sailormen were concerned he certainly spoke the truth. He was talked of with curses in the Pacific from the Prybiloffs to the Horn, from San Francisco to Zanzibar. It was long odds at any given time in any longitude that some

seaman was engaged in blaspheming Shanghai Smith for sending him on board drunk and without a chest, and with nothing
better to propitiate his new shipmates with than a bottle of
vinegar and water that looked like rum till it was tasted. Every
breeze that blew, trade wind or monsoon, had heard of his
iniquities. He got the best of everyone.

"All but one," said Smith in a moment of weakness when a
dozen men, who owed so much money that they crawled to
him as a Chinaman does to a joss, were hanging upon his lips—
"all but one."

"Oh, we don't take that in," said one of the most indebted;
"we can 'ardly believe that, Mr. Smith."

Sometimes this unsubtle flattery would have ended in the
flatterer being thrown out. But Smith was now gently reminiscent.

"Yes, I was done brown and never got the best of one
swine," said the boarding-house keeper. "I don't ask you to
believe it, for I own it don't sound likely, me being what I am.
But there was one swab as give me a hidin', and he give it me
good, so he did."

He looked them over malignantly.

"I kin lick any of you here with one hand," he swore, "but
the man as bested me could have taken on three of you with
both hands. And I own I was took aback considerable when I
run against him on the pier at Sandridge when I was in Australia fifteen years ago. He was a naval officer, captain of the
Warrior, and dressed up to kill, though he had a face like a
figurehead cut out of mahog'ny with a broad-axe. And I was
feelin' good and in need of a scrap. So when he bumped agin
me, I shoved him over—prompt, I shoved him. Down he went,
and the girls that know'd me laughed. And two policemen
came along quick. I didn't care much, but this naval josser
picks himself and goes to 'em. Would you believe it, but when
he'd spoke a bit I seed him donate them about a dollar each
and they walked off round a heap of dunnage on the wharf,
and the captain buttoned up his coat and came for me. I never
seen the likes of it. He comes up dancin' and smilin', and he

kind of give me half a bow, polite as you like, and inside of ten seconds I knew I'd struck a cyclone, right in the spot where they breed. I fought good—you know me—and I got in half a dozen on his face. But I never fazed him none, and he wouldn't bruise mor'n hittin' a boiler. And every time he got back on me I felt as if I'd been kicked. He scarred me something cruel. I could see it by the blood on his hands. 'Twarn't his, by a long sight, for his fists was made of teak, I should say. And in the end, when I seemed to see a ship's company of naval officers around me, one of them hit me under the ear and lifted me up. And another hit me whilst I was in the air, and a third landed me as I fell. And that was the end of it, so far's I remember. When I came to, which was next day in a kind of sailors' hospital, I reached up for a card over my head, and I read 'concussion of the brain' on it. What's more, I believed it. If the card had let on that I'd been run over by a traction engine and picked up dead, I'd have believed it. And when I reely came to my senses, a med'cal student says as Captain Richard Dunn, of the *Warrior*, had bin to inquire when the funeral was, so's he could send a wreath. They said he was the topside fighter in the hull British Navy. And I'm here to say he was."

He breathed fierce defiance and invited any man alive to tell him he was lying.

"And you never got even?" asked the bar-tender, seeing that no-one took up the challenge.

"Never set eyes on him from that day to this," said his boss regretfully.

"And if you did?"

Smith paused, took a drink.

"So help me, I'd shanghai him if he was King of England!"

And one of the crowd, who had put down the *San Francisco Chronicle* in order to hear this yarn, picked it up again.

"S'elp me," he said, in a breathless excitement, "'ere's a bally cohincidence. 'Ere's a telegram from 'Squimault, saying as how the flagship *Triumphant*, Hadmiral Sir Richard Dunn, K.C.B., is comin' down to San Francisco."

"Holy Moses, let's look!" said Shanghai Smith.

13

He read, and a heavenly smile overspread his hard countenance. He almost looked good, such joy was his.

"Tom," he said to the bar-tender, "set up the drinks for the crowd. This is my man, for sure. And him an admiral, too! Holy sailor, ain't this luck?"

He went out into the street and walked to and fro rubbing his hands, while the men inside took their drink, and looked through the uncleaned windows at the boss.

"Holy Mackinaw," said Billy, who had drifted West from Michigan, "I reckon never to hev seen Mr. Smith so pleased since he shipped a crowd in the *Harvester*, and got 'em away that night and shipped 'em in the *Silas K. Jones*."

"He's struck a streak o' luck in his mind," said one of the seamen; "and it's this 'ere hadmiral. Now mark me, mates, I wouldn't be that 'ere hadmiral for the worth of California. Mr. Sir Blooming Hadmiral, K.C.B., et setterer, is going to 'ave a time."

He shook his head over the melancholy fate of a British admiral.

"Rot!" said one of the younger men; "'tain't possible to do nothin' to the likes of an admiral. Now, if 'twas a lieutenant or even a captain, I'm not sayin' as Mr. Smith mightn't do somethin'. But an admiral——"

"You mark me," said the older man, "I'd rather be as green as grass and ship as an able-bodied seaman with Billy Yates of the *Wanderer*, than be in that hadmiral's shoes. What do you say, Tom?"

Tom filled himself up a drink and considered.

"Wa'al," he answered after a long pause, "it's my belief that it won't necessary be *all* pie to be an admiral if the boss is half the man he used to be. For you see 'tis quite evident he has a special kind of respect for this admiral, and when Mr. Smith has been done by anyone that he respects, he don't ever forget. Why, you know yourselves that if one of you was to do him, he'd forgive you right off after he'd kicked the stuffing out of you."

This clear proof that Mr. Smith did not respect them and

was kind was received without a murmur. And as the boss did not return, the tide of conversation drifted in the narrower, more personal, channels of the marvels that had happened in the "last ship". And in the meantime H.M.S. *Triumphant*, known familiarly on the Pacific coast station as "the *Nonsuch*, two decks and no bottom", was bringing Rear-Admiral Sir Richard Dunn, K.C.B., to his fate in San Francisco.

"Was there ever such luck—was there ever such luck?" murmured Mr. Shanghai Smith. "To think of him turnin' up, all of his own accord, on my partic'lar stampin' ground! And I'll lay odds he's clean forgot me. I'll brighten up his mem'ry with sand and canvas and souji-mouji, so I will! Holy sailor, was there ever such luck?"

The morning of the following day H.M.S. *Triumphant* lay at her anchors off Saucelito in San Francisco Bay, and was glad to be there. For this was in the times when the whole British fleet was not absolutely according to Cocker. She leaked not a little and she rolled a great deal, and she would not mind her helm except upon those occasions when the officer in charge of the deck laid his money and his reputation on her going to starboard when, according to all rules, she should have altered her course to port. But though she was a wet ship with a playful habit of trying to scoop the Pacific Ocean dry, and though her tricks would have broken the heart of the Chief Naval Constructor had he seen her at them, she was the flagship in spite of her conduct, because at that time she was half the whole Pacific Squadron. The other half was lying outside Esquimault Dry Dock waiting for it to be finished. And when the *Chronicle* said that "Dicky Dunn" was the admiral, it had not lied. If any of that paper's reporters had known "Dicky" as his men knew him, he would have spread himself in a column on the admiral's character and personal appearance.

"He's the dead-spit of a bo'son's mate, to *be* sure," said the crew of the *Triumphant* when they received him at Esquimault. "An 'ard nut he looks!"

And a "hard nut" he certainly was. Though he stood five feet nine in height, he looked two inches less, for he was as broad as a door and as sturdy as the forebitts. His complexion was the colour of the sun when it sets in a fog for fine weather: the skin on his hands shone and was as scaly as a lizard's hide. His teeth were white and his eyes piercing. He could roar like a fog-horn, and sing, as the crew said, "like any hangel". There wasn't the match of "Dicky" on any of the seas the wide world over. The only trouble was that he looked so much like the traditional sailor and buccaneer that no-one could believe he was anything higher than a warrant officer at the most when he had none of his official gear about him.

Though the admiral did not know it, one of the very first to greet him when he set his foot on dry land at the bottom of Market Street was the man he had licked so thoroughly fifteen years before in Melbourne.

"Oh, it's the same," said Smith to his chief runner, who was about the "hardest case" in California. "He ain't changed none. Just so old he was when he set about me. Why, the galoot might be immortal. Mark him, now; will you know him any-where?"

"It don't pay me ever to forget," replied the runner. He had to remember the men who owed him grudges.

"Then don't forget this one," said Smith. "Do you find me a considerate boss?"

"Oh, well——" said the runner ungraciously.

"You've got to do a job for me, Billy."

"And what?"

"I'm goin' to have this hyer admiral shipped before the stick on the toughest ship that's about ready to go to sea," replied Smith.

Billy flinched.

"Sir, it's the penitentiary!"

"I don't care if it's lynchin'," said Smith. "Help—or get. I'm bossin' this job. Which is it?"

And Billy, seeing that he was to play second fiddle, con-cluded to help.

"And", he said to himself, "if we get nailed I'll split. Calls himself a 'considerate boss'. Well, Shanghai Smith *has* a gall!"

16

"Which do you reckon is the worst ship inside the Gate now?" asked Smith, after he had savoured his cunning revenge for a few minutes.

"The *Harvester* ain't due for a month, sir."

Smith looked melancholy.

"No, she ain't, that's a fact. It's a solid pity. Sant would have suited this Dunn first class." He was the most notorious blackguard of a shipmaster yet unhung, and the fact that Smith and he were bitter enemies never blinded Shanghai to the surpassing merits of his brutality.

"There's the *Cyrus G. Hake*."

Smith shook his head contemptuously.

"D'ye think I want to board this admiral at the Palace Hotel? Why, Johnson hasn't hurt a man serious for two trips."

"Oh, well, I thought as he'd sure break out soon," said Bill: "but there's the *President*. They do say that her new mate is a holy terror."

"I won't go on hearsay," said Smith decidedly. "I want a good man you and I know—one that'll handle this Dicky Dunn from the start. Now, what's in the harbour with officers that can lick *me*?"

"Well, I always allowed (as you know, Mr. Smith) that Simpson of the *California* was your match."

Smith's face softened.

"Well, mebbe he is."

At any other time he would never have admitted it.

"And the *California* will sail in three days."

"Righto," said Smith. "Simpson is a good tough man and so is old Blaker. Bill, the *California* will do. But it's an almighty pity the *Harvester* ain't here. I never knew a more unlucky thing. But we must put up with the next best."

"But how'll you corral the admiral, sir?" asked Bill.

"You leave that to me," replied his boss. "I've got a very fruitful notion as will fetch him if he's half the man he was."

Next evening Smith found occasion to run across a couple of the *Triumphant's* crew, and he got them to come into his house for a drink.

"Are these galoots to be dosed and put away?" asked the bar-tender.

"Certainly not," said Smith. "Fill 'em up with good honest liquor at my expense."

The bar-tender hardly knew where good honest liquor was to be found in that house, but he gave the two men-o'-war's men the slowest poison he had, and they were soon merry.

"Is the admiral as dead keen on fightin' with his fists as he was?" asked Smith.

"Rather," said the first man.

"Oh no, he's tired," said the second. "'E allows 'e can't find no one to lick 'im. 'E never could."

"Oh, that's his complaint, is it?" said Smith. "And is he as good as he was?"

"I heerd him tell the first luff on'y the other day as 'e reckoned to be a better man now than he was twenty years ago. And I believes 'im. 'Ard? Oh my! I do believe if 'e ran agin a lamp-post he'd fight through it."

It was enough for Smith to know that the admiral was still keen on fighting. To draw a man like that would not be so difficult. When he had turned the two naval seamen into the street, he called for the runner.

"Have you found out what I told you?"

"Yes," replied Bill. "He mostly comes down and goes off at eleven."

"Is he alone?"

"Mostly he has a young chap with him. I reckon they calls him the flag-lieutenant; a kind of young partner he seems to be. But that's the only one so far. And the *California* sails day after ter-morrer, bright and early."

"Couldn't be better," said Smith. "After waitin' all these years I can't afford to lose no time. Thish-yer racket comes off to-night. Look out, Mr. Bully Admiral! I'm on your track."

And the trouble did begin that night.

Mr. "Say-it-and-mean-it" Smith laid for Admiral Sir Richard Dunn, K.C.B., etc. etc., from ten o'clock till half-past eleven, and he was the only man in the crowd that did not hope the victim would come down with too many friends to be tackled.

"It's a penitentiary job, so it is," said Bill. And yet when the time arrived his natural instincts got the better of him.

The admiral came at last; it was about a quarter to twelve, and the whole water-front was remarkably quiet. The two policemen at the entrance to the Ferries had by some good luck, or better management, found it advisable to take a drink at Johnson's, just opposite. And the admiral was only accompanied by his flag-lieutenant.

"That's him," said Smith. "I'd know the beggar anywhere. Now keep together and sing!"

He broke into "Down on the Suwannee River", and advanced with Bill and Bill's two mates right across the admiral's path. They pretended to be drunk, and as far as three were concerned, there was not so much pretence about it after all. But Smith had no intention of being the first to run athwart the admiral's hawse. When he came close enough, he shoved the youngest man right into his arms. The admiral jumped back, and landed that unfortunate individual a round-arm blow that nearly unshipped his jaw. The next moment everyone was on the ground, for Bill sand-bagged the admiral just as he was knocked down by the lieutenant. As Sir Richard fell, he reached out and caught Smith by the ankle. The boarding-house master got the lieutenant by the coat and brought him down too. And as luck would have it, the youngster's head hit the admiral's with such a crack that both lay unconscious.

"Do we want the young 'un too?" asked Bill, when he rose to his feet, swinging his sandbag savagely. And Smith for once lost his head.

"Leave the swine, and puckarow the admiral," he said. And indeed it was all they could do to carry Sir Richard without exciting any more attention than four semi-intoxicated men would as they took home a mate who was quite incapacitated.

But they did get him home to the house in the Barbary Coast. When he showed signs of coming to, he was promptly dosed and his clothes were taken off him. As he slept the sleep of the drugged, they put on a complete suit of rough serge toggery and he became "Tom Deane, A.B."

"They do say that he is the roughest, toughest, hardest nut on earth," said Bill: "so we'll see what like he shapes in the *California*. I dessay he's one of that lot that lets on how sailormen have an easy time. It's my notion the *California* will cure him of that."

By four o'clock in the morning, Tom Deane, who was, as his new shipmates allowed, a hard-looking man who could, and would, pull his weight, lay fast asleep in a forward bunk of the *California's* fo'c'sle as she was being towed through the Golden Gate. And his flag-lieutenant was inquiring in hospital what had become of the admiral, and nobody could tell him more than he himself knew. So much he told the reporters of the *Chronicle* and the *Morning Call*, and flaring headlines announced the disappearance of a British admiral, and the wires and cables fairly hummed to England and the world generally. At the same time the San Francisco police laid every water-front rat and tough by the heels on the chance that something might be got out of one of them.

"What did I tell you?" asked Bill in great alarm, as he saw several intimate friends of his being escorted to gaol.

"Are you weakenin' on it?" said Smith savagely. "If I thought you was, I'd murder you. Give me away, and when I get out, I'll chase you three times round the world and knife you, my son."

And though Bill was so much of a "terror", he could not face Smith's eyes.

"Well, I ain't in it, anyhow," he swore.

But certainly "Tom Deane, A.B.," was in it, and was having a holy time.

When the admiral woke, which he did after half an hour's shaking administered in turns by three of the *California's* crew, who were anxious to know where he had stowed his bottle of rum, he was still confused with the "dope" given him ashore. So he lay pretty still and said—

"Send Mr. Selwyn to me."

But Selwyn was his flag-lieutenant, and was just then the centre of interest to many reporters.

"Send hell: rouse out, old son, and turn to," said one of his new mates. And the admiral rose and rested on his elbow.

"Where am I?"

"On board the *California*, to be sure."

"I'm dreaming," said the admiral, "that's what it is. To be sure, I'm dreaming."

There was something in his accent as he made this statement that roused curiosity in the others.

"No—you ain't—not much," said the first man who had spoken; "and even if you was, I guess Simpson will wake you. Rouse up before he comes along again. He was in here an hour back inquiring for the trumpet of the Day of Judgement to rouse you. Come along, Deane! Now then!"

"My name's Dunn," said the admiral, with contracted brows.

"Devil doubt it," said his friend: "and who done you? Was it Shanghai Smith?"

The admiral sat up suddenly, and by so doing brought his head into violent contact with the deck above him. This woke him thoroughly, just in time to receive Mr. Simpson, mate of the *California*, who came in like a cyclone to inquire after his health.

"Did you ship as a dead man?" asked Mr. Simpson, "for if you did, I'll undeceive you."

And with that he yanked the admiral from his bunk, and dragged him by the collar out upon the deck at a run. Mr. Simpson was "bucko" to his finger-tips, and had never been licked upon the high seas. But for that matter Vice-Admiral Sir Richard Dunn, K.C.B., had never hauled down his flag either to any man. It surprised him, as it would have surprised any of his crew, to find that he took this handling almost meekly. But then no one knows what he would do if the sky fell; and as far as the admiral was concerned, the entire world was an absurd and ridiculous nightmare. He rose at the end of his undignified progress and stared at the mate.

"Who—who are you?" he said.

Mr. Simpson gasped.

"Who am I—oh, who am I? Well, I'll oblige you by statin' once for all that I'm mate of this ship, and you're my dog."

But the "dog" shook his head.

"Nothing of the sort," he said, as he staggered with the remains of the opiate. "I'm a British admiral, and my name's Sir Richard Dunn. Where's my ship?"

Any ordinary kind of back answer or insubordination received only one kind of treatment on board the *California*, and when a man had been beaten to a jelly, he rarely recovered enough spirit to inquire why he had been hammered. But this was a new departure in back talk.

"Oh, you're an admiral—an admiral, heh?" said Simpson.

"Of course," said Sir Richard, and a sudden gust of rage blew the last opium out of him. "Why, damn it, sir, what the devil do you mean by laying your filthy paws on me? Where's your captain, sir? By all that's holy, I'll smash you if you so much as look at me again."

Now it is a remarkable fact that the utterly and entirely unexpected will sometimes shake the courage of the stoutest heart. It is possible that a tiger would itself turn tail if a lamb rushed at him with open mouth. And though Mr. Simpson would have tackled a prize-fighter, knowing he was a prize-fighter, the fact that one of the kind of men whom he was accustomed to wipe his boots on now turned upon him with entirely strange language and a still stranger air of authority, for a moment daunted him utterly. He stood still and gasped, while the admiral strode aft and went up the poop ladder. He was met there by the captain, who had been the terror of the seas as a mate. A narrow escape of a conviction for murder had partially reformed him. He had also become religious, and usually went below when Simpson or the second "greaser" was hammering anyone into oblivion and obedience.

"What is this?" asked Captain Blaker mildly, yet with a savage eye. "Mr. Simpson, what do you mean by allowing your authority (and mine delegated to you) to be disregarded?"

"Sir——" said Mr. Simpson, and then the admiral turned on him.

"Hold your infernal tongue, sir," he roared. "And sir, if you are the master of this vessel, as I suppose, I require you to put about for San Francisco. I am a British admiral, sir: my name is Sir Richard Dunn."

"Oh, you're an admiral and you 'require'?" said Blaker. "Wa'al, I do admire! You look like an admiral: the water-front is full of such. Take that, sir."

And the resurgent old Adam in Blaker struck the admiral with such unexpected force that Dunn went heels over head off the poop and landed on Simpson. The mate improved the opportunity by kicking him violently in the ribs. When he was tired, he spoke to the admiral again.

"Now, you lunatic, take this here ball of twine and go and overhaul the gear on the main. And if you open your mouth to say another word I'll murder you."

And though he could not believe he was doing it, Sir Richard Dunn crawled aloft, and did what he was told. He was stunned by his fall and the hammering he had received, but that was nothing to the utter and complete change of air that he experienced. As he overhauled the gear he wondered if he was an admiral at all. If he was, how came he on the maintop-gallant-yard of a merchant ship? If he wasn't, why was he surprised at being there? He tried to recall the last day of his life as an admiral, and was dimly conscious of a late evening somewhere in San Francisco at which he had certainly taken his share of liquor. A vague sense of having been in a row oppressed him, but he could recall nothing till he had been yanked out of his bunk by that truculent devil of a mate then patrolling the poop.

"I—I must be mad," said the admiral.

"Now then, look alive there, you dead crawling cat," said Mr. Simpson, "or I'll come up and boot you off the yard. Do you hear me?"

"Yes, sir," said the admiral quickly, and as he put a new mousing on the clip-hooks of the mizzen-topmast-staysail-tripping-line block, he murmured: "I suppose I never was an admiral after all. I don't seem to know what I am." And the hardest nut among the admirals of the Active List wiped away a tear with the sleeve of his coat as he listened to the sacred Commination Service with all its blessings, intoned in a down-east twang by the eminent Mr. Simpson.

"He's crazy," said Simpson to the second greaser. "Says he's an admiral. I've had the Apostle Peter on board, and a cook who said he was St. Paul, but this is the first time I've run against an admiral before the mast."

"Does he look like it, sir?" asked Wiggins, laughing.

"He looks the toughest case you ever set eyes on," said Simpson. "But you'd have smiled to see the way the old man slugged him off the poop. And yet there's something about him I don't tumble to. I guess that's where his madness lies. Guess I'll cure him or kill him by the time we get off Sandy Hook. —Now then, you, admiral, come down here and start up the fore rigging, and do it quick, or I'll know the reason why."

And the Knight Commander of the Bath came down as he was bid, and having cast a perplexed eye over Simpson and Wiggins, who sniggered at him with amused and savage contempt, he went forward in a hurry.

"This is a nightmare," he said; "I'm dreaming. Damme, perhaps I'm dead."

When he had overhauled the gear at the fore—and being a real seaman he did it well—Wiggins called him down to work on deck, and he found himself among his new mates. By now they were all aware that he believed he was an admiral, and that he had spoken to Simpson in a way that no man had ever done. That was so much to his credit, but since he was mad he was a fit object of jeers. They jeered him accordingly, and when they were at breakfast the trouble began.

"Say, are you an admiral?" asked Knight, the biggest tough on board except Simpson and Wiggins.

And the admiral did not answer. He looked at Knight with a gloomy, introspective eye.

"Mind your own business," he said, when the question was repeated.

And Knight hove a full pannikin of tea at him. This compliment was received very quietly, and the admiral rose and went on deck.

"Takes water at once," said Knight; "he ain't got the pluck of a mouse."

But the admiral went aft and interviewed Mr. Simpson.

"May I have the honour of speaking to you, sir?" he said, and Simpson gasped a little, but said he might have that honour.

"Well, sir," said Sir Richard Dunn, "I don't know how I got here, but here I am, and I'm willing to waive the question of my being a British admiral, as I can't prove it."

"That's right," said Simpson. "Ah, I'll have you sane enough by and by, my man."

The admiral nodded.

"But I wish to have your permission to knock the head off a man called Knight for'ard. It was always my custom, sir, to allow fights on board my own ship when I considered them necessary. But I always insisted on my permission being asked. Have I yours, sir?"

Simpson looked the admiral up and down.

"Your ship, eh? You're still crazy, I'm afraid. But Knight can kill you, my man."

"I'm willing to let him try, sir," said the admiral. "He hove a pannikin of tea over me just now, and I think a thrashing would do him good and conduce to the peace and order of the fo'c'sle."

"Oh, you think so," said Simpson. "Very well, you have my permission to introduce peace there."

"I thank you, sir," said the admiral.

He touched his hat and went forward. He put his head inside the fo'c'sle and addressed Knight,—

"Come outside, you bully, and let me knock your head off. Mr. Simpson has been kind enough to overlook the breach of discipline involved."

And Knight, nothing loth, came out on deck, while Simpson and Wiggins stood a little way off to enjoy the battle.

"I'd like to back the admiral," said Wiggins.

"I'll have a level five dollars on Knight," said Simpson, who remembered that he had, on one occasion, found Knight extremely difficult to reduce to pulp.

"Done with you," said Wiggins.

And in five minutes the second mate was richer by five dollars, as his mates carried Knight into the fo'c'sle.

"I don't know when I enjoyed myself more," said Simpson, with a sigh—"even if I do lose money on it. While it lasted it was real good. Did you see that most be-ewtiful upper cut? And the right-handed cross counter that finished it was jest superb. But I'll hev to speak to the victor, so I will."

And he addressed the admiral in suitable language.

"Don't you think, because you've licked him, that you can fly any flag when I'm around. You done it neat and complete, and I overlook it, but half a look and the fust letter of a word of soss and I'll massacre you myself. Do you savvy?"

And the admiral said—

"Yes, sir."

He touched his cap and went forward to the fo'c'sle to enter into his kingdom. For Knight had been "top-side joss" there for three voyages, being the only man who had ever succeeded in getting even one pay-day out of the *California*. The principle on which she was run was to make things so hot for her crew that they skipped out at New York instead of returning to San Francisco, and the fresh crew shipped in New York did the same when they got inside the Golden Gate.

"I understand," said the admiral, as he stood in the middle

26

of the fo'c'sle, "that the gentleman I've just had the pleasure of knocking into the middle of next week was the head bully here. Now I want it thoroughly understood in future that if any bullying is to be done, I'm going to do it."

All the once obedient slaves of the deposed Knight hastened to make their peace with the new power. They fairly crawled to the admiral.

"You kin fight," said one.

"I knew it jest so soon as you opened yer mouth," said another. "The tone of yer voice argued you could."

"It's my belief that he could knock the stuffin' out o' Mr. Simpson," said the third.

"'Twould be the best kind of fun," said another admirer of the powers that be, "for Blaker would kick Simpson in here, and give the admiral his job right off. He's got religion, has Blaker, but he was an old packet rat himself, and real 'bucko' he was, and believes in the best men bein' aft."

And though the admiral said nothing to this, he remembered it, and took occasion to inquire into its truth. He found that what he knew of the sea and its customs was by no means perfect. He learnt something every day, and not the least from Knight, who proved by no means a bad sort of man when he had once met his match.

"Is it true," asked the admiral, "what they say about Captain Blaker giving anyone the mate's job if he can thrash him?"

"It used to be the custom in the Western Ocean," said Knight, "and Blaker was brought up there. He's a real sport, for all his bein' sort of religious. Yes, I'll bet it's true." He turned to the admiral suddenly. "Say, you wasn't thinking of takin' Simpson on, was you?"

"If what you say's true, I was," said the admiral. "It don't suit me being here."

"Say now, partner," put in Knight, "what's this guff about your being an admiral? What put it into your head?"

And Sir Richard Dunn laughed. As he began to feel his

feet, and find that he was as good a man in new surroundings as in the old ones, he recovered his courage and his command of himself.

"After all, this will be the deuce of a joke when it's over," he thought, "and I don't see why I shouldn't get a discharge out of her as mate. Talk about advertisement!"

He knew how much it meant.

"Look here, Knight," he said aloud, "I *am* an admiral. I can't prove it, but my ship was the *Triumphant*. I don't want to force it down your throat, but if you'd say you believe it, I should be obliged to you."

Knight put out his hand.

"I believes it, sonny," he said, "for I own freely that there's suthin' about you different from us; a way of talk and a look in the eye that ain't formiliar in no fo'c'sle as I ever sailed in. And if you was lyin', how come you to lie so ready, bein' so drunk when Simpson hauled you out o' yer bunk? No, I believe you're speakin' the trewth."

And Sir Richard Dunn, K.C.B., shook hands with Charles Knight, A.B.

"I won't forget this," he said huskily. He felt like Mahomet with his first disciple. "And now, in confidence," said the admiral, "I tell you I mean to have Simpson's job by the time we're off the Horn."

"Good for you," cried Knight. "Oh, he kicked me somethin' cruel the time him and me had a turn-up. Give it him, old man. And here's a tip for you. If you get him down, keep him down. Don't forget he kicked you, too."

"I don't forget," said Sir Richard—"I don't forget, by any means."

Yet he did his duty like a man. Though many things were strange to him, he tumbled to them rapidly. One of his fads had been doing ornamental work even when he was an admiral, and he put fresh "pointing" on the poop ladder rails for Blaker in a way that brought everyone to look at it. There was no-one on board who could come within sight of him at any fancy work, and this so pleased Simpson that the admiral never had a cross word till they were south of the Horn. Then by chance the mate and the captain had a few words which ended in Simpson getting much the worst of the talk. As luck would have it, the admiral was the handiest to vent his spite on, and Simpson caught him a smack on the side of his head that made him see stars.

"Don't stand listenin' there to what don't concern you, you damned lazy hound," he said. And when the admiral picked himself off the deck, Simpson made a rush for him. The admiral dodged him, and shot up the poop ladder. He took off his cap to the captain, while Simpson foamed on the main-deck and called him in vain. At any other time Blaker would have gone for the seaman who dared to escape a thrashing for the moment by desecrating the poop, but now he was willing to annoy Simpson.

"Well, what do you want?" he roared.

The admiral made a really elegant bow.

"Well, sir, I wanted to know whether Western Ocean custom goes here. I've been told that if I can thrash your mate, I shall have his job. They say forward that that's your rule, and if so, sir, I should like your permission to send Mr. Simpson forward and take his place."

There was something so open and ingenuous in the admiral that Captain Blaker, for the first time on record, burst into a shout of laughter. He went to the break of the poop and addressed the mate.

"Do you hear, Mr. Simpson?" he inquired genially.

"Send him down, sir," said Simpson.

"Are you sure you can pound him?"

Simpson gritted his teeth and foamed at the mouth.

"Kick him off the poop, sir."

The admiral spoke anxiously.

"I'm a first-class navigator, sir. Is it a bargain?"

And Blaker, who had never liked Simpson, laughed till he cried.

"Are you willing to stake everything on your fightin' abilities, Mr. Simpson?"

And when Simpson said "Ay" through his teeth, the admiral jumped down on the maindeck.

Now, according to all precedents, the fight should have been long and arduous, with varying fortunes. But the admiral never regarded precedents, and inside of ten seconds Mr. Simpson was lying totally insensible under the spare topmast. To encounter the admiral's right was to escape death by a hair's-breadth, and it took Charles Simpson, Able Seaman (*vice* Mr. Simpson, Chief Officer), two hours and a quarter to come to.

"And I thot he could fight," said the disgusted skipper. "Come right up, Mr. What's-your-name; you're the man for me. There ain't no reason for you to trouble about my second mate, for Simpson could lay him out easy. All I ask of you is to work the whole crowd up good. And I don't care if you are an admiral, you are the right sort all the same. I guess that Simpson must have reckoned he struck a cyclone."

And Blaker rubbed his hands. Like Simpson at the fight between the admiral and Knight, he did not know when he had enjoyed himself more. He improved the occasion by going below and getting far too much to drink, as was his custom. And the promoted admiral took charge of the deck.

"Ability tells anywhere," said Sir Richard Dunn. "I didn't rise in the service for nothing. Ship me where you like, and I'll come to the top. If I don't take this hooker into New York as captain and master, I'll die in the attempt."

He had come to himself and was beginning to enjoy himself. His natural and acquired authority blossomed wonderfully when he took on the new job, and as Blaker never swore, the admiral's gift of language was a great vicarious satisfaction to him. Wiggins accepted the situation without a murmur. Even Simpson himself bore no malice when his supplanter not only showed none, but after knocking the bo'sun's head against a bollard, gave his place to the former mate. Though he kept the men working and got the last ounce out of them, none of them were down on him.

"I tell you he's an admiral, sure," they said.

"He's got all the ways of one, I own," said Bill, an old man-o'-war's man. "I spoke to an admiral myself once, or rather he spoke to me."

"What did he say?" asked the rest of his watch.

"He said," replied Bill proudly, "he upped and said, 'You cross-eyed son of a dog, if you don't jump I'll bash the ugly head off of you.' And you bet I jumped. Oh, he's all the ways of *some* admirals, he has."

"Well, admiral or none," said the rest of the crowd, "things goes on pleasanter than they done when you was mate, Simpson."

And Simpson grunted.

"And he gets more work out of us than you done either, Simpson, for all your hammerin' of us."

"I'll likely be hammerin' some of you again shortly," said Simpson. And as he was cock of the walk in the fo'c'sle, whatever he was in the ship, the others dried up.

Nothing of great interest happened till they were well east of the Horn and hauled up for the northward run. And then Blaker took to religion (or what he called religion) and rum in equally undiluted doses.

"I'm a miserable sinner, I am," he said to the admiral, "but all the same, I'll do my duty to the crowd."

He called them aft and preached to them for two hours. And when one man yawned, he laid him out with a well-directed belaying pin. The next day, when it breezed up heavily and they were shortening sail, he called all hands down from aloft on the ground that their souls were of more importance than the work in hand.

"Come down on deck, you miserable sinners," said Blaker through a speaking-trumpet. His voice rose triumphantly above the roar of the gale. "Come down on deck and listen to me. For though I'm a miserable sinner too, there's some hopes for me, and for you there's none unless you mend your ways, in accordance with what I'm telling you."

Even with the speaking-trumpet he could hardly make

himself heard over the roar of the increasing gale and the thunderous slatting of the topsails in the spilling-lines.

"Don't you think, sir, that they'd better make the topsails fast before you speak to them?" said the admiral.

"No, I don't," replied Blaker—"not much I don't, not by a jugful. For if one of 'em went overboard, I'd be responsible before the throne. And don't you forget it."

"Damme, he's mad," said Sir Richard—" mad as a march hare. She'll be shaking the sticks out of her soon."

He leant over the break of the poop, and called up Wiggins.

"Mr. Wiggins, one word with you."

Wiggins came up, as Blaker roared his text through the trumpet.

"Will you stand by me, Mr. Wiggins, if I knock him down and take command?"

"I will; but mind his gun," said Wiggins. "When he's very bad, he'll shoot."

It was not any fear of Blaker's six-shooter that made the admiral hesitate. To take the command, even from a madman, at sea is a ticklish task and may land a man in gaol, for all his being a shanghaied admiral.

"I tell you, Mr. Wiggins, that Simpson is a good man. I'll bring him aft again."

And Wiggins made no objection when Simpson was called up by the admiral.

"Mr. Simpson," said the mate, "this is getting past a joke. Have you any objection to taking on your old job if I secure this preaching madman and take command?"

Simpson was "full up" of the fo'c'sle, and as he had a very wholesome admiration for the admiral, he was by no means loth to return to his old quarters.

"I'm with you, sir. In another quarter of an hour we shall have the sticks out of her."

And still Blaker bellowed scripture down the wind. He was still bellowing, though what he bellowed wasn't scripture, when Simpson and Wiggins took him down below after five minutes of a row in which the deposed captain showed something of his ancient form as the terror of the Western Ocean. As they went, the admiral, now promoted to being captain of a Cape Horner, picked up the battered speaking-trumpet and wiped some blood from his face, which had been in collision.

"Up aloft with you and make those topsails fast," he roared. "Look alive, men, look alive!"

And they did look alive, for "Dicky" Dunn never needed a speaking-trumpet in any wind that ever blew. When things were snugged down and the *California* was walking north at an easy but tremendous gait, he felt like a man again. He turned to Simpson and Wiggins with a happy smile.

"Now we're comfortable, and things are as they should be, Mr. Simpson, let the men have a tot of grog. And how's Mr. Blaker?"

"Wa'al," said Simpson cheerfully, "when we left him he warn't exactly what you would call religious nor resigned."

But if Blaker was not happy, the admiral was thoroughly delighted.

"Now you see what I said was true," he declared at dinner that night; " if I hadn't been an admiral and a man born to rise, how could I have been shipped on board this ship as a foremast hand and come to be captain in six weeks? I'll be bound you never heard of a similar case, Mr. Simpson."

And Simpson never had.

"Was it Shanghai Smith, do you think, as put you here?" he asked.

The admiral had heard of Shanghai Smith in the fo'c'sle.

"When I get back I'll find out," he said. "And if it was, I'll not trouble the law, Mr. Simpson. I never allow any man to handle me without getting more than even."

"You don't," said Simpson. If his manner was dry, it was sincere.

"But I don't bear malice afterwards. Your health, Mr. Simpson. This kind of trade breeds good seamen, after all. But you are all a trifle rough."

Simpson explained that they had to be.

"When the owners' scheme is to have one man do three men's work, they have to get men who will make 'em do it. And when the owners get a bad name and their ships a worse, then men like Shanghai Smith have to find us crews. If you could get back to San Francisco and hammer an owner, some of us would be obliged to you, sir."

"Ah, when I get back!" said the admiral. "This will be a remarkable yarn for me to tell, Mr. Simpson. I still feel in a kind of dream. Would you oblige me by going to Mr. Blaker and telling him that if he continues to hammer at that door I'll have the hose turned on him."

And when Simpson went to convey this message the admiral put his feet on the table and indulged in a reverie.

"I'll make a note about Shanghai Smith, and settle with him in full. But I shall rise higher yet. I know it's in me. Steward!"

"Yes, sir," said the steward.

"I think I'll have some grog."

He drank to the future of Admiral Sir Richard Dunn, master of the *California*.

MORLEY ROBERTS

THE SETTLEMENT WITH
SHANGHAI SMITH

It is easy to understand that there was something more than a flutter in shipping circles in San Francisco, to say nothing of the sailors' boarding-houses, when a telegram reached that city from New York which was expanded as follows:

"*THE LOST ADMIRAL*

"*Admiral Sir Richard Dunn, whose mysterious disappearance in San Francisco three months ago caused such great excitement, has arrived at New York in command of the ship* California. *He was, it appears, assaulted, and drugged, and put on board that vessel, and owing to a series of exciting incidents during the passage, finally took charge of her. The admiral is in good health. He states that he has no idea who was responsible for the outrage.*"

The bar-tender at Shanghai Smith's house was the first to spot this cable. He put his hand on the bar and vaulted it.

"Say, Billy, see this."

He shook up the runner, who was taking a caulk on a hard bench, having been engaged between four and six in getting three drunken men on board the *Wanderer*. It is often easier to get a dozen amenable to reason than three, just as it is easier to handle many sheep than few. He was very tired and sulky.

"Well, wo'd's up now?" he grunted.

"Hell is up, and flamin'," said Tom. "You ain't forgot the admiral by any chance, now?"

Billy woke as suddenly as if he had been sleeping on the look-out and had been found hard and fast by the mate.

35

"Eh, what, has the *California* turned up?"

"You bet she has," said Tom. And he burst into laughter. "What d'ye reckon he was on board of her when she came to N'York?"

"Cook's mate?"

"No, captain, captain! Think of that. And he says he don't know who laid him out and put him aboard of her."

Billy rose.

"Here, gimme the paper. You're drunk."

He read the telegram with protruding eyes.

"By the holy frost, but he must be a dandy. Say, Smith must know this."

He marched to Smith's bedroom and induced his boss to sit up and hear the news, after Smith had used more bad language with his eyes shut than most men in San Francisco could lay their tongues to when wide awake.

"Don't I tell you it's about the admiral," expostulated Billy; "it's about Dunn, as you shoved on the *California*."

But now Shanghai was wide awake. He looked at Billy with wicked eyes.

"As *I* shoved in the *California*, eh? Say that again and I'll get up and knock the corners off of you. You miserable Tar-head, if I hear you whisper that I had the last joint of the little finger of my left hand in the game, I'll murder you."

Billy fell back from the bed in alarm. Though he looked big enough to have eaten Shanghai Smith, he lacked the "devil" which had made his boss what he was—the terror of the "coast" and of sailormen, and a political power in his quarter of the city.

"Oh, very well then, Mr. Smith, but who done it?"

"Understand that no one knows who done it, you dog," said Smith, reaching for what he called his "pants", "but if anyone done it, it was you. And don't you forget it. I hire you to do the work, and I'll see you does it. Don't get me mad, or you'll be runnin' to the penitentiary howlin' for ten years to get away from me."

And Billy went back to Tom.

"He's fair luny, that's what he is. But if he reckons I'm goin' to the calaboose for him, he'll run up agin a snag."

And presently Smith came out to breakfast with a face as black as a near cyclone. Billy and Tom jumped when he spoke, and all those men in his house who were in a leeshore, as regards dollars, got away from him and adorned a neighbouring fence.

"What's wrong wiv Shang'ai?" asked a Londoner; "'e's a black 'un, but I never seed 'im so rorty as this!"

And no one answered him. They were a sick crowd at any time, and now, when their slave-owner roared, their hearts were in their boots.

But Smith was only trying to keep up his own courage. Not once, but many times since he had got even with the man who had given him a thrashing, he had regretted his method of revenge.

"I'd best have bashed him and left him laying on the Front," said Smith, "and here's Tom and Bill know the whole racket. I've half a mind to have them put out of the way. In such a place as this, who *can* a man trust? Bah, it sickens me, it does. It fair sickens me."

He was virtuously indignant with an ungrateful world. Even his revenge had been a failure. How in the name of all that was holy and unholy had the admiral managed to rise from the fo'c'sle to the command of the *California?*

"And I thought Blaker and Simpson was both men!" said Smith with disgust. "There ain't any trustin' to appearances, nor to reputation neither. But how could the swine have done it?"

An early evening paper had the whole story, and as Shanghai was still up town, all his crowd of crimps and slaves roared over the yarn.

"He fo't the mate and was give 'is billet," said one. "I say, but old Blaker was a sport. That's real old Western Ocean packet law. And then Blaker went luny with psalm-singing and the hadmiral locked 'im up. 'Strewth, but it must 'ave bin a picnic! I'd 'ave give a month's wages to see the show. But 'oo was it Shang'aied a hadmiral?"

He spoke with bated breath.

"Who'd it be but Smith?" asked the speaker's mate sulkily. "He's a devil, a notorious devil, as *we* know. He'd shanghai his father for a quarter, if he was dry. And a month back my own brother that shipped in the *Cyrus F. Brown* told me as Shanghai had a down on this very man."

"Then I wouldn't be Smith for all 'is money. This'll be a Government business."

It would have been if the admiral had been any other kind of man. But Admiral Sir Richard Dunn was one of those, and they get rarer every day, who prefer handling their own affairs. He had a gift of humour, too, and was mightily pleased with himself.

"Whoever it was that laid for me, he never meant to make me master of the *California*," he said, as he came west on the cars. "And whoever he was, I will fix him. The mate was pretty certain it was this Shanghai Smith. If it was——"

If it was, it seemed a healthy thing for Mr. Smith to leave San Francisco and hide somewhere in the Islands. But all his interests kept him where he was, even when H.M.S. *Triumphant* came down again from Esquimault and lay waiting for the admiral off Goat Island.

The crew of the *Triumphant*, being very proud of their own special admiral, were in so furious a rage against anyone connected with crimping in the city that no "liberty" was granted to any one of them.

"It's hall very fine," said the *Triumphants* unanimously, "but these 'ere Americans are too smart by 'alf. Them and huss'll part brass-rags one of these fine days. But ain't it fine to think that Dicky went to sea as a man before the stick, and come out right on top?"

They chortled with exceeding pleasure—with pleasure founded on his achievements and on the unexpected experiences he had had of sea-life.

"To think of Dicky bunking it among a crowd of merchant Jacks," said the crew. "We'd give a lot to 'ave seen him shinning up aloft for dear life."

But all the same they loved him dearly, and when he came alongside five days later, not all their sense of discipline prevented their breaking into a storm of cheers that rang out across the bay and was almost heard at Oakland. Hard as Dicky Dunn was, he went to his cabin rather in a hurry. For once in his life he could hardly trust himself to speak. But he received the congratulations of the captain and officers, including young Selwyn, who had been with him when he had been kidnapped, with the greatest calm.

"Yes, I've had some experience," he said, "and I don't know that it has done me any harm. I know more of the conditions on board merchant vessels than I did before."

"And what do you propose to do, Sir Richard?" asked Selwyn, an hour later. "The authorities and the police seemed very anxious to do what they could."

The admiral lighted one of his own cigars, and found it more to his taste than the ship's tobacco of the *California*.

"I don't propose to trouble the police," he said, "nor need there be any international correspondence so far as I'm concerned. I'll play my own game. I think, Selwyn, that I know who laid for us that night. And from what I learnt in the *California* (I learnt a lot, by the way) I've a notion that ordinary justice would never get hold of the man, at least not in San Francisco, not even if I paid for it."

"Then what——"

But Dicky Dunn interrupted him.

"I've a notion," he said significantly.

And that afternoon he sent Selwyn ashore with a very polite note to the chief of the San Francisco police, saying that Rear-Admiral Sir Richard Dunn would be very glad to see that gentleman on board the *Triumphant* late that evening, if he could make it convenient to come.

"Let the band begin to play!" said Mr. Peter Cartwright: "it looks as if I'd better face the music. I wonder if he has any kinkel as to the man who did it? It's more than I have, unless it was Smith, or Sullivan."

As he drew his five thousand dollars a year and pickings

39

partly through the grace of both the notorious boarding-house keepers that he mentioned, he did not relish running against them. Nevertheless, it was better to do that than run against a mightier snag. He looked, with a groan, at the pile of correspondence which had accumulated since the admiral's disappearance.

"And here's the British Consul wants to see me to-morrow!" he cried. "They'll clinch me if they can get no-one else."

And he went on board the *Triumphant* feeling as if he was out of a job.

The admiral received him courteously, and was alone.

"This has been a bad business, admiral, sir," said Mr. Cartwright, "and as chief of police of this city I feel it as a personal slur. Your request to see me anticipated me by no more than twelve hours. I proposed to seek an interview with you to-morrow morning."

"I am obliged to you," said the admiral. "Will you have anything to drink?"

"It *was* rather cold on the water," replied Cartwright.

And when the chief of police had a tumbler of hot whisky and water in both hands, the admiral opened up.

"I've sent for you, Mr. Cartwright," he began, "to tell you that I don't want any proceedings taken about this matter."

Cartwright opened his mouth and stared at the admiral in surprise. Then he began to imagine he understood. Sir Richard Dunn had evidently been somewhere on the night of his disappearance which would not suit him to have known.

"Ah, I see," said Cartwright, with a subtle smile.

"I've my own notions as to the brand of justice dispensed in this State, Mr. Cartwright. It is considerably milder than the native liquors. I want your assistance in doing without the law, and in administering justice myself. Have you any notion of the gentleman who shipped me in the *California*?"

"It was probably a boarding-house master," said Cart-wright.

"Of course."

"It might have been Sullivan, or the Sheeny, or Williams, or Smith."

"Is that the scoundrel they know here as Shanghai Smith?" asked the admiral.

And Cartwright nodded.

"The crew of the *California* put it down to him at once."

"I don't know that it was necessarily him," said Cartwright pensively; "though he has the worst name, he's no worse than the others. For my own part, I reckon the Sheeny—he's a Jew boy, of course—is a deal tougher than Smith."

And just then Selwyn, who knew the chief of police was on board, put his head into the admiral's cabin.

"Could I speak to you a moment, Sir Richard?"

And Dicky Dunn went outside.

"I thought, as you had this Cartwright with you, sir," said Selwyn, "that I ought to tell you a queer yarn that has just been brought me by one of the quartermasters. It seems that one of the men has a story that you once had a fight with Shanghai Smith and hurt him badly. It was in Australia, I believe—in Melbourne."

"Stay a minute," said the admiral; "let me think. Yes, by Jove, I did have a row on Sandridge Pier years ago, and I broke the man up so that he had to go to a hospital. And his name—yes, it *was* Smith. Thanks, Selwyn, I'll see if this man ever was in Australia."

He went back to Cartwright.

"Now as to the Sheeny, admiral," said Cartwright, who was beginning to feel comfortable.

"Never mind the Sheeny, Mr. Cartwright," said his host; "do you know Smith's record? Where did he come from?"

"He came from Melbourne," replied the chief.

And the admiral slapped his leg.

"That's the man, I believe."

"Why?"

"Never mind why," said Dunn. "But supposing it was, could we prove it against him?"

"I doubt it," said Cartwright cheerfully. "Probably no-one would know it but his runner. And Bill Haines would perjure himself as easy as drink lager."

"But if we did prove it?"

"There'd be an appeal, and so on," said the chief.

He indicated large and generous delay on the part of the merciful American law by a wave of his hand.

"You see we couldn't prove, anyhow, that he knew you was you," said Cartwright, "and if I know my own business, it would come down to a matter of assault and so many dollars."

"That's what I imagined," said the admiral. "So I propose to take the matter in hand myself and relieve you of it. For though Smith, or the real man, might come off easily, if I choose to have it made an international business someone will have to pay who is not guilty."

"That's likely enough," said Cartwright uneasily. "On the whole, admiral, I'd rather you took the job on yourself, provided it was put through quietly. What do you propose?"

Dunn put his hands in his pockets, and "quarter-decked" his cabin.

"I want to be sure it's Smith—morally sure. How can I be made sure? I'll tell you now what I know about him."

He repeated what Selwyn had said, and told him the story of his having fought a man on Sandridge Pier at Melbourne fifteen years before.

"His name was Smith."

"It fits as neat as a pair of handcuffs," said the chief of police. "I'll think it over and let you know. Stay, sirree, I've got it now. Look here, admiral, now you mark me. This is a scheme. It'll work, or my name's Dennis. I'll have it put about in the right quarter that though there ain't evidence to touch the real man who worked the racket on you, it is known who actually corralled you and shoved you on the *California*. I'll get the proper man to give it away that a warrant is being made out. And next day I'll have all the runners of all the chief boarding-houses arrested. Do you see?"

"No, I don't," said the admiral.

"Oh come," cried Cartwright. "The man we don't arrest will be the man who done it."

"Yes, but——"

"Well," said Cartwright, "I understand you didn't particularly hanker to catch the understrapper."

"Ah," said the admiral. "Of course I see. You mean——"

"I mean the boarding-house boss will shove the runner that did it out of sight. And then you'll know him by reason of the very means he takes not to be given away. For of course he'd reckon that the runner on being held would squeal."

"It's a good plan," said the admiral. "And when I know, what kind of punishment would Mr. Smith like least of all?"

"Provided you remember he's an American citizen, I don't care what you do," replied the chief. "But if you asked me, I should get him served the way he's served you. Shanghai Smith among a crowd of sailormen in an American ship, such as the *Harvester* (and the skipper of the *Harvester* hates him like poison)—and *she* sails in three days—would have a picnic to recollect all his life. For, you see, they know him."

"I'll think it over," said the admiral. "Your plan is excellent."

"So it is," said Cartwright, as he was rowed ashore, "for Smith ain't no favourite of mine, and at the same time it will look as if I gave him the straight racket, anyhow."

He sent an agent down to the water-front that very night. The man dropped casual hints at the boarding-houses, and he dropped them on barren ground everywhere but at Shanghai Smith's.

"Jehoshaphat," said Smith, "so that's the game!"

Peter Cartwright had, in his own language, "reckoned him up to rights"; for the very first move that Smith played was to make a break for Billy's room. As the runner had been up most of the night before enticing sailormen off a Liverpool ship just to keep his hand in, he was as fast asleep as a bear on Christmas Day, and he was mighty sulky when Smith shook him out of sleep by the simple process of yanking his pillow from under his head.

"Ain't a man to get no sleep that works for you?" he demanded. "What's up now?"

"Hell is up, and fizzling," replied Smith. "I've had word from Peter Cartwright that you'll be arrested in the mornin' if you don't skin out. It's the admiral. I wish I'd never set eyes on him. Come, dress and skip: 'twon't do for you to be gaoled; mebbe they'd hold you on some charge till you forgot all you owe to me. There ain't no such thing as real gratitude left on earth."

Billy rose and shuffled into his clothes sullenly enough.

"And where am I to skip to?"

"To Portland," said Smith; "the *Mendocino* leaves in the mornin' for Crescent City and Astoria, don't she? Well, then, go with her and lie up with Grant or Sullivan in Portland till I let you know the coast is clear. And here's twenty dollars: go easy with it."

He sighed to part with the money.

"I'd sooner go down to Los Angeles," grunted Billy.

But Smith explained to him with urgent and explosive blasphemy that he was to get into another State in order to complicate legal matters.

"You've the brains of a Flathead Indian, you have," said Smith, as he turned Billy into the street on his way to find the *Mendocino*. "What's the use of havin' law if you don't use it?"

And in the morning, when Smith heard that ten runners at least had been urgently invited to interview Mr. Peter Cartwright, he was glad to be able to declare that Billy was not on hand.

"He's gone East to see his old man," he said drily. "And as his father is a millionaire and lives in the Fifth Avenue, N' York, he couldn't afford to disregard his dyin' desire to see him."

"You are a daisy, Smith," said the police officer who had come for Billy. "Between you and me, what have you done with him?"

Smith shook his head.

44

"I shot him last night and cut him up and pickled him in a cask," he said with a wink. "And I've shipped him to the British Ambassador at Washington, C.O.D."

"You're as close as a clam, ain't you, Smith? But I tell you Peter is havin' a picnic. This admiral's game was playin' it low down on Peter, whoever did it. There are times when a man can't help his friends."

Smith lied freely.

"You can tell Peter I had nothin' to do with it."

"Yes, I can *tell* him!" said the police officer. And he did tell him. As a result the chief of police wrote to the admiral:

"Sir,—I have interrogated all the runners but one belonging to the chief boarding-houses, and have succeeded in obtaining no clue. The one man missing was runner to Mr. William Smith, commonly known as 'Shanghai' Smith. Under the circumstances, and considering what you said to me, I am inclined to wait developments. If you will inform me what you wish me to do, I shall be glad to accommodate you in any way.

Yours truly,
PETER CARTWRIGHT.

"P.S.—If you could write me a letter saying you are quite satisfied with the steps I have taken to bring the offender to justice, I should be obliged.

"P.S.—If you wish to meet Mr. John P. Sant, captain of the *Harvester*, now lying in the bay and sailing the day after to-morrow, I can arrange it."

But both the postscripts were written on separate pieces of paper. Mr. Cartwright was not chief of police for nothing. He knew his way about.

Dicky Dunn, on receiving Peter's letter, called in his flag-lieutenant.

"When they shanghaied me, they knocked you about rather badly, didn't they, Selwyn?"

Selwyn instinctively put his hand to the back of his head.

"Yes, Sir Richard. They sand-bagged me, as they call it, and kicked me too."

"I'm pretty sure I know who did it," said the admiral, "and I'm proposing to get even with the man myself. It seems that it will be a difficult thing to prove. Besides, I'm not built that way. I don't want to prove it and send the man to gaol. I like getting even in my own fashion. What would you do if I could tell you who it was that laid the plot against us that night?"

Selwyn was a clean-skinned, bright-eyed, close-shaven young fellow, as typical an Anglo-Saxon salted in the seas as one could meet. His eyes sparkled now.

"I—I'd punch his head, sir."

The admiral nodded.

"I believe I did punch his head, years ago, Selwyn. But he was looking for a fight and found it, and ought to have been satisfied. Between you and me and no-one else, the chief of police here and I have fixed this matter up between us. He says that he has no evidence, and the only man who might have given the affair away has been shipped off somewhere. I'm going to show Mr. Smith that he didn't make a bucko mate of me for nothing. And I want you to help. I've got a scheme."

He unfolded it to Selwyn, and the young lieutenant chuckled.

"He used to be a seaman," said the admiral, "but for twelve years he's been living comfortably on shore, sucking the blood of sailors. And if I know anything about American ships—and I do—he'll find three months in the fo'c'sle of this *Harvester* worse than three years in a jail. Now we're going to invade the United States quite unofficially, with the connivance of the police!"

He lay back and laughed.

"Oh, I tell you," said the admiral, "he ran against something not laid down in his chart when he fell in with me. You can come ashore with me now and we'll see this Cartwright. American ways suit me, after all."

"Then I understand, Mr. Cartwright," said the admiral, an hour later, "that there won't be a policeman anywhere within hail of this Smith's house to-morrow night?"

"I've got other business for them," said Peter.

"And I can see Mr. Sant here this afternoon?"

"I'll undertake to have him here if you call along at three."

He spent the interval at lunch with the British Consul.

"I tell you what, Stanley," said the admiral, "I don't care what they did to me, for it's done me no harm. But after this you should be able to make them enforce the laws. If they would only do that, the Pacific Coast wouldn't stink so in the nostrils of shipmasters and shipowners."

The consul explained the local system of politics. It appeared that everyone with any business on the borders of crime insured against the results of accidents by being in politics.

"And if the thieving politicians appoint the man to control them, what's the result?"

"The result is—Shanghai Smith," said the admiral. "Well, I'll see you later. I've an appointment with Mr. Sant, of the *Harvester*."

The consul stared.

"What, with Sant? Why, he got eighteen months' hard labour for killing a man six months ago."

"But he's not in prison?"

"Of course not," said the consul. "He was pardoned by the Governor."

"He's just the man I wish to see," cried Dicky Dunn.

He found Sant waiting at Cartwright's office. He was a hard-bitten, weather-beaten gentleman, and half his face was jaw. That jaw had hold of a long cigar with his back teeth. He continued smoking and chewing, and did both savagely. What Peter had said to him did not come out, but by agreement the admiral was introduced as Mr. Dunn.

"You have reason not to like Shanghai Smith?" said Peter.

"That's so," nodded Sant.

"Mr. Dunn does not like him either. Could you make any use of him on board the *Harvester*?"

"I could," said Sant, grinning; "he'd be a useful man."

"If you imagined you missed a man to-morrow morning just as you were getting up your anchor, and someone hailed you and said they had picked one up, you would take him aboard?"

"Wet or dry," said Sant.

"I'll undertake he shall be wet," said the admiral. "Eh?" And he turned to Selwyn.

"Yes, sir," replied the lieutenant, "that could be arranged."

"Very well, Mr. Sant," said the admiral.

"And it's understood, of course," said Peter, "that you gentlemen never saw each other and don't know each other when you meet, it being a matter of mutual obligation."

"I agree," said Sant. And the admiral shook hands with a gentleman who had been pardoned by an amiable Governor.

"And of course," Cartwright added as he escorted the admiral and Selwyn into the passage, "if there *should* be a shindy at Smith's and any of your men are in it, we shall all explain that it was owing to your having been put away. And two wrongs then will make it right. I guess the newspapers will call it square."

"Exactly so," said the admiral.

And when he reached the *Triumphant* he had very nearly worked out the plan by which the row at Shanghai Smith's was to occur.

"I'll just go over it with you, Selwyn," he said, when he reached his cabin again. "Now you must remember I rely on your discretion. A wrong step may land us in trouble with the authorities and the Admiralty. There never was a Government department yet which wouldn't resent losing a fine chance of a paper row, and if they catch me settling this matter out of hand, my name is Dennis, as the Americans say. And I don't want your name to be Dennis either."

"Well, what do you propose, Sir Richard?" asked Selwyn.

"This is rightly your show and mine," said the admiral. "I won't have anyone else in it, that I can help. I ought to speak to Hamilton, but I won't. I'll keep him out of the

trouble"—for Hamilton was the captain of the *Triumphant.*
"I suppose the men here *are* really fond of me?" said the
admiral interrogatively.

"They have no monopoly of that," said Selwyn.

"Is there any one of them you could drop a hint to, that
you could trust?"

"Of course," said Selwyn; "there's Benson, whose father
works for mine as gardener. We used to fight in the tool-
house at home, and now he would jump overboard if I asked
him."

"Do you mean Benson, my coxs'n?"

"Yes, sir."

"He's the very man. You might let him know that if he
should get into any trouble, he will be paid for it. I leave the
rest to you. You can go ashore now, with this note to Stanley.
That will give you a chance to take Benson with you and
speak to him on the quiet. I don't know that I care particularly
to hear any more about it till the day after to-morrow, unless
I have to. Ultimately all the responsibility is mine, of course."

And by that Selwyn understood rightly enough that Dicky
Dunn, for all his cunning, had no intention of shirking trouble
if trouble came. He went ashore and took Benson up town
with him.

"Do the men think it was Shanghai Smith that laid for us,
and put the admiral away, Benson?" he asked as they went
up Market Street.

"There ain't the shadder of a doubt 'e done it, sir," said
Benson.

"And they don't like it?"

"Lord bless you, sir. It's very 'ard 'avin' all liberty stopped,
but between you and me it was wise to stop it. They would
'ave rooted 'is 'ouse up and shied the wreckage into the bay."

"It's a pity that you and about twenty more couldn't do
it," said Selwyn. "And if one could only catch hold of the
man himself and put him on board an outward bound ship,
it would do him good."

Benson slapped his leg.

"Oh, sir, there ain't a man on board the *Triumphant* that wouldn't do six months with pleasure to 'ave the 'andlin' of 'im.''

"No?"

"For sure, sir."

"I was lying awake last night thinking of it," said Selwyn; "at least, I believe I was awake—perhaps I was dreaming. But I seemed to think that a couple of boats' crews were ashore, and that you went to Shanghai's place for a drink."

"I've done that same, sir," said Benson, "and the liquor was cruel bad."

"And I dreamed—yes, I suppose it was a dream—that you started a row and made hay of his bar and collared him, and took him in the cutter and rowed him round the bay till about four in the morning."

"You always was very imaginary and dreamy as a boy, sir, begging your pardon, sir," said Benson.

"And I dreamed you came to the *Harvester*——"

"Her that's lying in the bay—the ship with the bad name among sailormen?"

"That's the ship," said Selwyn; "and you hailed her and asked the captain if a man had tried to escape by swimming. And he said 'Yes', and then you said you'd picked him up."

Benson looked at him quickly.

"But he wouldn't be wet, sir."

"Oh yes, he would, Benson. You could easily duck him overboard."

Benson stared very hard at the lieutenant.

"Of course. I could very easily duck him—and love to do it, too. And did the captain of the *Harvester* own to him, sir?"

Selwyn nodded.

"He would, Benson—I mean he did, of course."

"I suppose," asked Benson, with his eyes on the pavement, "that it had been arranged so?"

"In the dream, yes," said the lieutenant.

"Was it for to-morrow evening, sir?"

"I thought so," said Selwyn. "And the curious thing about

MORLEY ROBERTS

it was that the whole thing was done as quietly as possible.
All you men went to work in silence without as much as a
hurrah. And one of the boats brought me ashore and the
other brought the admiral. And it was only after you had put
the man on board the *Harvester* that you came back for the
admiral at five in the morning, Benson."

"And what about the boat as brought you, sir?"

"I came back at twelve and went on board with them,
after the fight, and while you were rowing Mr. Smith about
the b̶ ̶ ̶ ̶ ̶ ̶ing him up."

"W̶ ̶ ̶ ̶ ̶ ̶ ̶ ̶ ̶ ̶ ̶sir?"

"N̶ ̶ ̶ ̶ ̶ ̶ ̶ ̶ "only that I forget whether it
cam̶ ̶ ̶ ̶ ̶ ̶ ̶ said it was a game all of their
own̶ ̶ ̶ ̶ ̶ ̶n sure—that if anyone got into
tro̶ ̶ ̶ ̶ ̶ ̶fter all."

c̶ ̶ ̶ ̶ ̶," said Benson warmly. "I wish it
c̶ ̶ ̶ ̶ ̶u never know your luck, sir."

̶ ̶ ̶ ̶:sn't," said Selwyn.

̶ ̶ ̶ ̶t on board again and had a long
̶ ̶ ̶ ̶ ̶oats' crews, there was a unanimous
̶ ̶ ̶ ̶at Mr. Smith had piled his ship up
̶ ̶ ̶ ̶ he ran against a British admiral.

̶ ̶ ̶no weepons," said Benson—"nothin'
̶ ̶ ̶ ̶n' than a staysail 'ank as a knuckle-
I don't recommend. An odd stretcher
̶ ̶ ̶s there will do the job. And the word is
̶ ̶ ̶n."

"M̶ ̶ ̶ ̶ ̶l," said the men. And like the children
that they were, they wrought the whole ship's company into
a frenzy of excitement, by dropping hints about as heavy as
a half-hundred-weight on everyone who was not in the game.
Had there been much longer to wait than twenty-four hours,
they must have told, or burst. And if they had not burst, the
others would have finally reached the truth by the process of
exhaustion.

It was nine o'clock on the following evening that the
admiral went on shore to dine with the British consul. He

51

told Benson that he might be later than eleven. And as Benson touched his cap he took the liberty of believing he might be as late as five in the morning. And just about eleven Selwyn came ashore in another boat with papers which had to go to the admiral. That is what he said to the first lieutenant. Captain Hamilton was sleeping the night at the house of a cousin of his in San Francisco.

"I shall be back in an hour, Thomas," said Selwyn. And the two coxs'ns were left in command of the cutting-out expedition. The whole business was nearly wrecked at the outset by the settlement of the question as to who was to be left in charge of the boats. Finally Thomas and Benson ordered two men to stay, and the defrauded men sat back and growled most horribly as the rest moved off towards Shanghai Smith's in loose order.

"Look 'ere," said Billings to Graves as they were left alone, "it's hobvious one must stay with the boats; but one's enough, and on an hexpedition like this, horders ain't worth a damn. I'll howe you a quid, a whole quid, and my grog for a month if you'll be the man to stay."

"No, I'll toss you, the same terms both sides."

And the spin of the coin sent Billings running after the rest. He was received by Benson with curses, but he stuck to the party all the same.

"Very well, you report me! You know you can't," he said defiantly. "And I've give Graves a thick 'un and my grog for a month to be let come."

This awful sacrifice appealed even to Benson.

"All right," he said. "But if I can't report you for this, I can the next time."

"Next time be damned," cried Billings; "'oo cares about next time, now?"

And they hove in sight of Shanghai Smith's.

It was the first time a bluejacket had been near the place since a day or two before the admiral's disappearance. And at first when Shanghai saw them come he regretted that Billy, his best fighting man, was by now well on his way to Portland.

But for at least ten minutes the *Triumphants* behaved very well. Benson had a good head and had arranged matters very neatly.

"You look 'ere," he had said; "the thing to look out for is the barman. He keeps a gun, as they calls it 'ere, on a shelf under the bar. Smith, 'e'll 'ave one in his pocket. So when I says, 'This rum would poison a dog', don't wait for no back-answer, but lay the barkeeper out quick, with a stone match-box or anything 'andy. And the nearest to Smith does the same to 'im. He'll likely not be be'ind, but if 'e is, bottle 'im too, and not a word of jaw about it first or last."

They stood up to the bar, and Benson ordered drinks for himself and three particular pals of his.

"Ain't this Mr. Smith's?" he asked.

"I'm Smith," said Shanghai.

"'Ere's to you. I've often heard of you," said Benson. And three or four merchant seamen sitting about the room sniggered and passed a few sneering remarks among themselves about "Liberty Jack".

Smith, who had taken enough that night to make him rash, referred to the admiral.

"So your admiral has come back, has he?"

"He has," said the *Triumphants*. "And Dicky Dunn is lookin' for the man that played that dirty game on him."

And Smith shrugged his shoulders as he half turned away.

"'Tain't half so dirty as this rum," said Benson; "it would poison a dog."

And as the words left his mouth the ball opened with a sudden and tremendous crash. Two heavy matchboxes went for Tom behind the bar; one laid him out as quietly as if he had been hocussed; the other smashed a bottle which held a liquor known on the Barbary Coast as brandy, and starred the mirror behind the shelves. Thomas at the same moment stooped and caught Shanghai Smith by the ankles and pitched him on his head. He never had time to reach for his "gun". The merchant seamen jumped to their feet and made for the door.

"Stop them!" said Benson, and half a dozen bluejackets

hustled them back again. "No you don't, Johnnies; you can stay and 'ave free drinks, and look after the man behind the bar. Drag out that Smith and get 'im in the open air." And Thomas dragged Smith into the darkness by his collar.

"There's to be no drinkin' for us," said Benson. "Smash what you like, and taste nothin'." And in less than a minute Shanghai's place was a lamentable and ghastly spectacle.

"Sarves him right," said one of the merchant seamen, as he salved a bottle of poison. "Oh, ain't he a sailor-robbing swine?"

"Fetch him in and let him look at it," said Benson, with a wink.

Thomas had been primed.

"He's come to and run like billy-oh!" he cried.

But Smith was incapable of running. He was being carried by two bluejackets.

"After 'im, after 'im," said Benson; and in another moment the whole house was clear.

When Tom came to, he found the place a wreck, and four boarders too far gone in free liquor to offer any useful explanation of what had occurred since the rum had been pronounced fit to poison a dog.

"All I know is," said the soberest, "that he fit and we fit and fit and fit, and then 'e run."

And when Tom sought for the police, it was very odd that there was not one to be found in the quarter of San Francisco which most needs clubbing to keep it in order. There was not even one to bear witness that a crowd of bluejackets and an American citizen had come along the waterfront at midnight. But five minutes after midnight a British lieutenant could have taken his oath that both crews were in their boats and at least moderately sober.

"I've seen the admiral, Benson," said Selwyn, as he stepped into his boat and sat down, "and he *may* be later than he said."

"Very well, sir," replied Benson.

And as soon as Selwyn had disappeared into the darkness,

the boat with Mr. Shanghai Smith in followed suit. And the bay of San Francisco is not so well policed that they had anyone inquiring what they were doing as they pulled across to Saucelito, and laid up quietly till three o'clock.

"He ain't dead, we hopes," said the crew of the boat.

"Not 'e," said Benson; "'is 'eart beats all to rights, and 'is head is perfectly sound, bar a lump the size of a 'en's egg. That upendin' dodge of Thomas' is very fatal in a row—oh, it's very fatal."

It was nearly two o'clock before Shanghai made any motion. But when he did begin to get conscious, he found his mind and his tongue with surprising rapidity.

"That 'ead of yourn must be made of five-eighths boiler-plate, Mr. Smith," said Benson, as Smith sat up suddenly.

"What am I doin' here?" asked Smith.

"'Ow do we know?" asked the delighted crew. "You *would* come. It warn't no good excusin' of ourselves."

Smith put his hand to his head.

"Who hit me?" he demanded savagely.

"No one," said the crew unanimously; "you tried to stand on your 'ead."

"Put me ashore," said Smith. "What are you goin' to do?"

"We're waitin' to see the '*Arvester* yonder 'eave 'er anchor up," replied Benson. "We're in the sailor-supplyin' line, we are, same as you was."

"He don't like to hear that," said Billings; "we're cutting him out of a job. And this time we ain't supplyin' admirals."

"No, we ain't. Yah, you man-buyin', sailor-robbin' swine! And 'twas you dared touch our admiral. Oh, you dog, you!"

They all took a turn at him, and Smith saw he was in the tightest corner he had ever occupied. This was satisfactorily expressed for him.

"Say, Shanghai, did you ever hear of Barney's bull?"

And when Smith refused to answer, they answered for him.

"He was jammed in a clinch, and so are you. You're goin' to 'ave the finest time of all your life. Did you ever 'ear of Sant of the '*Arvester*?"

And Smith, for all his brutal courage, shook in his boots.

"I'll give you chaps a hundred dollars to put me ashore," he cried. "I never touched Sir Richard Dunn."

"Dry up," said Benson, "and don't lie. We wouldn't part with you, my jewel, not for a thousand. What made you desert from the 'Arvester, a comfortable ship like that, with sich a duck of a skipper?"

"I'll give you a thousand," said Smith desperately.

"At four o'clock you're goin' on the 'Arvester—and 'tis nigh on three now. Sant wouldn't miss a man like you, so smart and 'andy, for all the gold in Californy. Own up as you shanghaied the admiral?"

Smith grasped at any chance of avoiding the *Harvester*. For Sant had a dreadful name, and both his mates were terrors.

"If I own I put him away, will you take me ashore and hand me over to the police?"

He was almost in a state of collapse.

Benson looked at the man, and in the faint light of far-off day still below the horizon the boat's crew saw him wink.

"We'll vote on it, if you owns up. What d'ye say, chaps?"

"Ay, we'll vote," said the men. "Say, did you do it?"

But Smith saw how the voting would go, and refused to speak. They heard six bells come across the water from many ships. And then they heard seven. There was a grey glint in the east. The sand-dunes on the verge of the Ocean Pack whitened as they pulled for the *Harvester*. They heard the clank of her windlass brakes and the bull voice of her mate, as he encouraged his men to do their best by threatening them with three months of hell afloat.

Smith offered Benson two thousand dollars.

"I wouldn't part with you except to Sant for all you ever robbed men of," said Benson—"and what that is, on'y you knows. Pull, boys; her cable's up and down. No, hold on a moment; he must be wet, of course."

In spite of his struggles they put him over the side and soused him thoroughly. When they pulled him on board again, he sat cursing.

"Now, boys, bend your backs."

And when he came up alongside the *Harvester* she was just moving under the draught of her loosed topsails.

"*Harvester*, ahoy!" cried Benson.

"Hallo!" said Sant. "What is it?"

"You don't happen to have lost one of your crew, tryin' to desert by swimmin', sir?"

"Have you picked him up? What's his name, does he say?"

"It's Smith, sir."

"That's the man," said Sant. "I want him badly."

But Smith cried out—

"This is kidnappin', Mr. Sant. I refuse to go."

"Oh, Smith," said Sant, "I'll take all the chances of its bein' anythin' you like. Throw them a rope."

And the *Triumphants* towed alongside.

"Up you go," said Benson.

"I won't," said Smith.

"Won't you?" asked Benson. "We'll see about that. Hook on there, Billings."

And the next moment Smith was jammed in a running bowline round his waist.

"Sway him up," said Benson; and the crew of the *Harvester* hoisted the notorious robber with about the only feelings of pleasure they were likely to know till they reached New York. And the *Triumphants* pushed off as they heard the mate address Mr. Smith in language which did his reputation and the reputation of the ship most ample justice.

"There's talk and there's a fore-topsail-ahoy voice for you," said Benson. "Oh, Mr. Smith will be looked after, he will. Now, chaps, pull for it, or the admiral will be waitin', and if that 'appens, 'twill be 'Stand from under'."

SEASCAPE: MORNING OFF LERWICK

When people talk about courage—I always think of Webster. Yet I shall never forget my complete bewilderment when first we met, for by some strange chance Webster was drafted to our destroyer as an officer's steward.

He arrived when we were boiler-cleaning alongside the old depot-ship, and when I went up on deck to inspect him, hoping against hope that there would be awaiting me a smart young steward who could and would stand up to destroyer life, I was horrified to find myself confronting a distinguished-looking, elderly gentleman of about fifty.

I groaned. There must have been some mistake. This dear old boy, whom I should have expected to encounter in Bond Street, wearing a silk hat, was so very obviously miscast for the rôle of steward in a destroyer. How on earth the drafting office had come to make such a mistake was immaterial. Webster had arrived. Moreover, I soon discovered that he had never been to sea before—let alone in a destroyer. I groaned again. It looked to me like pure homicide. Officially, he was R.N.V.R., but, actually, he was a distinguished artist with four pictures in the Paris salon.

I sought out the Captain, and my only consolation was the expression on *his* face when he, himself, sighted Webster.

But we were all wonderfully, marvellously, hopelessly wrong.

For the days passed into weeks, and the weeks into months, and Webster was still with us. Moreover, incredibly and amazingly, he had turned out to be the kind of steward that morose first lieutenants of destroyers dream of and ponder on, at sea, while jammed in between the empty mess-stove and a handy bulkhead, eating ice-cold sardines out of the tin in lieu of a hot breakfast which is not available because the decks are not safe for traffic.

Other boats in the flotilla cast envious and covetous eyes at Webster. Gradually, his fame spread. He performed incredible feats in collaboration with the cook, for he brought to his novel job a first-class intelligence and the enthusiasm of an artist; and, strangely enough, he was as popular with the cook in the galley for'ard as he was with the hands in the fo'c'sle mess decks.

We ourselves, I think, offered up a prayer every time we met that distinguished, spruce figure reeling along the sea-infested upper deck, where the wet corticine offered but precarious foothold. Yet, somehow, when Webster glanced benignly, but with something of disapproval, at the tempestuous waves, the weather seemed to moderate at once. His innocence of all forms of sea-life, and his dignity, were stupendous. And in steady, never-failing stream all the while at sea, hot meals flowed aft, punctual, appetizing, and perfectly served: and they came *via* a ward-room pantry which gleamed and shone in a cleanliness akin to that of the Captain's quarters in a crack battleship.

And the peculiar thing about it all was that Webster, the landsman, who had never been to sea, was never seasick.

As time went on, we found ourselves glancing furtively at one another. Webster was too good to be true. He would blow up. The ship would blow up. Something would happen, and our incomparable steward would disappear, wafted away to some higher plane; for were sea-going mortals ever favoured like this without some frightful disaster suddenly shattering their Utopian comfort?

Then, one day, we were ordered to Lerwick, in the Shetland Isles. Up there things had been happening: two destroyers had been lost escorting the Norwegian convoy, but we did several trips without incident, until . . .

One fine, misty morning we were returning to harbour after a sticky ten days at sea, when I woke up suddenly in my bunk, knowing immediately that something was wrong. My head was buzzing, for I had had the middle watch from twelve to four, and also, the cabin-flat atmosphere was foul. Glancing at my watch I saw that we should be close to harbour. The engines had stopped—it was that that had awakened me.

In a moment I was up on deck, shivering. I glanced for'ard and then round the mist-laden sea. It was just getting light. A voice hailed me from the bridge. Quickly I walked out to the port side. It was the Captain. He said quietly:

"Stay there, No. 1. There's a big mine bumping down the port side and another one against the starboard hull abreast the after torpedo-tubes."

My blood ran cold. I peered along the port side.

There it was! A huge, spherical mass, bump, bumping, with a hollow sound against our frail plates. Unconsciously I noted the three detonator horns: they looked devilish somehow, and prehistoric in the half-light, set there like eyes on stalks on that rusty, bloated body. I didn't trouble to walk over and look at the starboard mine. I took the "owner's" word for it.

And then a voice, close by, spoke; and I jumped nearly out of my skin.

"Nasty things, sir," said Webster from the ward-room hatch; and I think he was carrying in his hands a pot of tea. But at the moment I was too concerned to reply.

As I stood there on the tiny quarter deck of the destroyer, not much more than eighteen feet across just there, it struck me suddenly that the surgeon-probationer was still in his hammock below.

Webster advanced cautiously from the ward-room hatch and came towards me. He had a habit of twirling his iron-grey moustache, and I remember that as he came towards me he carried the tea-pot in one hand and twirled his moustache with the other. Silently, I indicated to him the other mine, which was now giving our starboard plates some far too hearty bumps near the third and after funnel. Webster did not drop the tea-pot, but he stood for a moment tense and still.

"Another, sir?" he breathed to me.

I nodded back, then I whispered to Webster:

"The surgeon-probationer is still below, I believe, Webster. Do you know?"

Webster's answer was to tiptoe back to the ward-room hatch, but first he put down carefully on the quarter deck the small tea-pot he had been carrying, and I remember noting with a kind of wonder that his hand was as steady as a rock. It was one of those ludicrous incidents that sometimes occur—providentially, perhaps—in the midst of some pressing danger, and which ease the strain.

I concentrated on that tea-pot for a moment. It seemed such a homely, friendly object, seated there so primly on the sea-bleached corticine.

Webster only hesitated a moment at the ward-room hatch, then he skirted the canvas shelter above the Captain's quarters, and went forward to the cabin-hatch beyond. Very quietly, he disappeared down the ladder and I heard the murmur of voices; he was warning the surgeon-probationer. By then, the port-side mine was almost abreast of him—not more than fifteen feet away—and it loomed gigantic in the light of dawn, standing quite four feet out of the water.

The whole ship was strangely quiet. Under my feet the propellers were now revolving slowly; the starboard engine going ahead, the port one astern.

I looked forward and up at the bridge. I seemed to have been standing there a long time in a cold grey world filled suddenly with the most ghastly threat. The Captain was leaning over the after bridge rails and his face was set and determined; occasionally, he signalled to the sub and the signalman, standing by the engine-room telegraphs and revolution-indicator, ordering the ship's engines at slow revolutions with a concentrated, fateful caution. Faintly, the tinkle of the telegraph bells came floating aft to me. Suddenly, he called to me again:

"Stay there, No. 1," he said, "I can't get away from that damned port-side mine—there's a current shoving it up against the hull, and if we roll——" he made a gesture of finality.

Then he added: "I can't see the starboard one very well, it's lower in the water; keep me informed of its position, and stand by because I'm going to try to bump it away—otherwise it's a thousand pounds to a rotten apple that that port-side blighter will foul the propeller-guard.

I said: "Ay, ay, sir," but when I started to move cautiously towards the starboard rail, I found my knees were strangely sagging and my feet seemed to be made of lead—and very cold lead at that. However, I got to the rail and looked over; and there was the mine, nestling under our hull, and bumping, bumping—I've never cared to hear anything bump with quite that deadly sound ever since.

The next few seconds were really unpleasant. I heard the rattle of the steering engine, as the helm went over hard a-starboard, and the deck quivered as the starboard engine-revolutions increased. The Captain was trying out his wheeze. And it worked, but that must have been the most patient, the most long-suffering German mine that ever found its way into Northern waters; for we caught it some really hearty cracks, and the last one cracked it some ten feet out from the ship's side.

I waved my hand for'ard towards the bridge, and a smile of relief came slowly over the "owner's" face. He looked about ten years older than he did the previous day.

Haltingly, I dragged my insubordinate feet back to the port side and there I was joined by Webster. He said: "The surgeon-probationer's gone for'ard, sir; there's no-one else aft."

I said: "Thank you, Webster; that's a great relief. You'd better go for'ard yourself now."

But the old paladin was horrified.

He said: "I must be near my pantry, sir. What are you all going to do for breakfast if the pantry's wrecked?"

It was a ludicrous speech, standing there together as we were literally within a plank's breadth of death, and I'm afraid I giggled weakly.

I said: "Webster, don't you realize that if that damned thing does an extra bump or fouls the propeller-guard, you and I and your confounded pantry will go sky-high, and we shan't want breakfast, no, nor lunch, nor tea either, for a very, very long time?"

"Ah, sir," said Webster, "I'm afraid you take a pessimistic view of the situation." Then he said: "Could we not push the mine away, sir, with a boathook?"

I replied somewhat tersely: "Do you know, Webster, what these mines are made of? Do you realize that the detonator underneath that little spur is composed of fulminate of mercury, which patient and brave men test under armour-plate by tickling the beastly stuff with a feather?"

But Webster had an answer to that too.

He said: "It's a chance, sir. If we can keep our boathook away from the detonating horns, we might shove it away, don't you think, sir?"

I thought not, and said so emphatically. But just at that moment the Captain hailed me quietly again from the bridge-

"It's no go, No. 1," he said. "I can't get away from the port-side mine and she's too far aft now to risk my coming astern and letting the mine bump right for'ard. Can you suggest any. thing?"

To my amazement, I heard myself answering: "Webster and I, sir, might try pushing the thing off with a padded boathook—enough, anyhow, to prevent it fouling the propeller-guard."

The Captain pondered, while the mist gradually dispersed, and looking ahead, I saw a few miles away, opening up, the harbour of Lerwick—and, oh, so fair and desirable a harbour it seemed at that moment!

Then slowly the "owner" said: "I don't like it, but we've got to do something. I have an idea that that port-side mine is a nasty customer: I don't like the look of him, so for Heaven's sake be careful."

I said fervently: "We will, sir!" Then I turned to Webster, rather sourly, I'm afraid.

"Come on now," I said, "that bearing-out spar over there is better than a boathook. Bring it over here, then nip down

63

to your pantry and bring up every dish-cloth and rag you've got."

Hastily, when he returned, we converted the end of the spar into what looked like an enormous swab. Then, cautiously, we lifted our strange weapon and advanced to the attack; I having impressed upon my enthusiastic helper that he was on no account to push or do anything until I gave the order; and I also warned him of the vital necessity for avoiding any roll of the mine, as it was probably fitted with a rolling detonator as well as an impact one.

I can assure you that those few moments seemed to spin themselves out into years.

We began almost catastrophically, for when, very gingerly, I had placed the head of our spar against the middle of the mine and told Webster to shove, he shoved so heartily that the head of our weapon slipped on the slimy metal of the mine-casing and both he and I almost went over the side on top of it.

In a horrified voice, from the bridge, the Captain urged caution.

Sweat poured off my face as I turned and rent the old artist. Then we had another shot, this time with more success.

The mine was appallingly heavy. It must have weighed nearly a ton, but pushing and shoving with—speaking for my-self—our hearts in our mouths, we eventually did manage to shove the thing out a few feet.

Then a frightful thing happened, the memory of which is vivid still. The mine suddenly whirled in, spinning vigorously like a top, towards the ship's side and, after bumping heavily, it made a beeline for the propeller-guard—as if animated by some perverse, impish spirit.

Whether caught in an eddy, or in some way still foul of its moorings, we did not stop to inquire, I yelled at Webster:

"Quick, man! we've got to bear it off before it gets there!"

Rushing aft, we shoved our spar out over the side and braced ourselves up like frantic cavemen awaiting the charge of some fearsome monster, armed only with a spear.

Luck was with us this time; for the mine, rolling in a perfectly horrible manner, thudded right on to the end of our padded spar and jarred us both to the marrow. Then, straining, sweating, we held it off and eased it carefully round the curve of the propeller-guard, which stuck out for two vital feet from the ship's side. Those were a ticklish few seconds, for the mine seemed to be doing its best to slip round the pad and crash into the propeller-guard. It was then I blessed my stars for Webster's thirteen stone or so, which he used to the full.

At last, I croaked in a hoarse voice to the steward: "She's going!" I cried to him, "we've got the darned thing clear. One last heave now!"

We gave that heave: the pad slipped. I let go with one hand and signalled frantically to the Captain. The mine rolled, span, and escaped the pad—all in one breadth, but it was just too late. Surging in towards the stern, it grazed the propeller-guard and dashed towards the very curve of the sheer right aft. But, simultaneously, the propellers thrashed madly; the destroyer suddenly gathered way, leaping forward, and Webster and I, losing our balance, came down heavily in a heap on the corticine deck.

I stayed there for a moment, feeling distinctly shaky, but Webster helped me up, and then stared out over the rail astern and to the east'ard, where dawn was breaking.

I watched him, curiously. His face was now pale and his expression still and set; but he wasn't looking at the mine now bobbing twenty-five yards astern in our wake. He looked to me like a man who has seen a vision.

"Jove, sir," he murmured to me, "what a morning, what a sky! If a man painted that, people would not believe; they would laugh; but some time . . . I will try."

Then he turned to me and walked forward and picked up the tea-pot. The routine official Webster, our well-known paragon, had reappeared. "I will make you some fresh tea, sir," he said, saluting; "when you come back from the bridge it will be ready."

SEASCAPE: MORNING OFF LERWICK

Years later, I met Webster again; and, strangely enough, it *was* in Bond Street and he *was* wearing a silk hat, but this time it was I who took off my hat to him.

Later still that same day, I stood in a small picture gallery where Webster had a show of his paintings.

In front of me, dominating the wall, was a large seascape, and, as I looked at it, my breath suddenly caught; for its title was *Morning off Lerwick*.

It was a lovely piece of work: just sea and sky and a wedge of duck flying low and fast across the foreground. It reminded me of Somerscales' "Dawn". There was about that picture a wonderful sense of space and dignity and harmony.

A hand on my arm recalled me.

"Jove! I was frightened to death that morning," Webster murmured in my ear.

I looked at him in amazement.

"You were, really?" I said. "I thought you were wonderful."

"No!" he smiled at me, "not wonderful; just scared to death! You see, while I was hanging about the naval barracks—an old dodderer of fifty whom nobody knew what to do with—they gave me a three months' course on mines at the Mining School."

W. P. DRURY

"JOHN ECUADOR"

Captain Cholmondeley Bompas, M.V.O., R.N., having quitted the Admiralty by its north-west exit, crossed the Mall, climbed the Duke of York's steps, and laid his course for the "Senior". The day being hot, he proceeded, as he would have expressed it, under easy steam; yet his weather-bitten face betrayed an eager anticipation that ill accorded with his leisurely locomotion. For when, as a penalty of exalted rank, a man has suffered three years' splendid isolation in the after-cabin of a cruiser in the Pacific, his soul craves for that environment where he may unbend in cryptic periods to clay of his own high caste.

At the first glimpse of the great Service clubhouse, however, the face of Captain Cholmondeley Bompas fell. The building was surrounded by ladders, from which honest protégés of Mr. Keir Hardie, with a lofty scorn for the claims of Capital upon their time, strenuously debated the Free Everything Bill. A triple reek of paint, shag, and whitewash pervaded the atmosphere, while sheeted settees, like crinolines in a faded daguerreotype, loomed dimly through the dusty windows of the reading-room. Round the corner in Pall Mall the general ichabod was emphasized by the fast-closed entrance doors; and the chagrined mariner realized that he had returned at that regularly recurring season when the "Senior" is closed for repairs, and its bellicose outcasts seek sanctuary within the Athenæum across the way. With rapidly rising choler he turned his footsteps thither.

"What! Saul also among the prophets?"

A stentorian acquaintance in the sister Service chanced at the moment to be issuing from the academic portals.

Bompas plucked him by the lapel of his best frockcoat.

"Yes," he retorted, "and plaguily out of the picture Saul feels! Plain living at sea don't necessarily give one a taste for high thinking ashore. Damme!"—he shied violently as he focused a shovel hat lying on a hall chair—"the place is a blooming bishop warren!"

The soldier laughed profanely. "Some Methody ferret must have cleared it out, then," he opined. "The only right reverend bunny I've seen here this morning is the brand-new Bish. of Exborough."

"I'll borrow a gun and have a pot at him," grinned the Post-Captain. "Look here. You'd imagine, wouldn't you, that you could dodge the whole bench of bishops on an ocean that was big enough for the moon to come out of?"

The other courteously, but firmly, disengaged the grip upon his creased lapel. "One would think so," he conceded.

"So I should have said a few months ago," snorted Bompas, "and yet you may take it from me that I had bishop enough in the Pacific in a single week to last me a brace of lifetimes!"

In the dim religious light appropriate to Minerva's vestibule the choleric Captain, fresh from the sunlight without, cannoned against a gaitered dignitary in quest of his headgear.

The Churchman apologized.

"My fault entirely," snapped the seaman. "I ought to have kept a better look-out in unfamiliar waters. The Bishop of Exborough, I think?"

"The Dean. Your friend unwittingly gave me brevet rank. May I hope that your grievance does not embrace the deanery?"

"My grievance?"

"Against the episcopate. Pardon me if I seem to have been eavesdropping, but I could hardly help hearing, could I?"

"The Colonel has a voice like a megaphone—he should take something for it," growled Bompas.

The Dean laughed. "As these are strange waters," he said, "perhaps you will let me do pilot. This is our reading-room—so called, you will say, because no-one apparently reads here. The heat, I suppose. Have you seen to-day's *Times*?"

Bompas, it transpired, had not. "But Mr. Dean," he presently blurted out, "I think that, in self-justification, I should spin you the yarn of that Bishop."

The other glanced at his watch. "I shall be charmed to hear it," he said. "I have a young friend lunching with me at half-past one; meanwhile"—he indicated a couple of arm-chairs in a cool recess by the window—"here's an ideal confessional."

"In spite of my remarks to the Colonel," began Bompas, when they had ensconced themselves, "no-one has a greater veneration for the clergy of the Established Church, *as a body*, than I."

The Dean courteously inclined his head.

"As a body. But"—the Captain vindictively gripped the arms of his chair—"I'd gladly give a hundred pounds to see a certain limb of it reduced by the Court of Arches to the rank of perpetual curate."

The Dean glanced nervously at a thermometer hanging in the window, and bethought him of the doctrine that salvation lies in humouring the sun-stricken brain. "Yes, yes," he purred. "He's a bishop, I think you said?"

"Was," corrected Bompas, "for the inside of a nightmare week. But"—he mopped his brow with a red silk handkerchief—"*nous avons changé tout cela maintenant.*"

"A foreign prelate, I presume?"

"Foreign? Not much! As Anglican a scamp as his god-fathers and godmothers could make him."

The Dean cudgelled his memory. But not even a "Dr." Clifford could have recalled a scandal among the spiritual peers that has entailed dethronement. "Of course," he mused, "you are speaking of some colonial, or perhaps suffragan, bishop. Which, may I ask, was his see?"

"The one spelt with an *a*," said Bompas, "and I wish he was at the bottom of it. But I'll spin you the whole lurid chronicle."

The Dean cast an apprehensive glance round the deserted

room. Assured, however, that no-one was within earshot, his face relaxed in an expectant smile; and, joining his outspread finger-tips upon the rolling plateau of his decanal waistcoat, he leaned back in lazy contemplation of a game of blind-fly's-buff that was in progress near the ceiling.

"It was as nearly five months ago as be damned—I mean as nearly as one can remember without reference to the log," corrected Bompas, "that I was heading one afternoon, at something more than economical speed, for the north-west coast of South America. The extra consumption of coal was ustified by a brace of unavoidable circumstances. The ship was within the tropics, and her ensign was half-masted."

"In the midst of life——" sighed the Dean to the blue-bottles.

"A falling halliard block," completed Bompas, "is apt to prove a very literal bolt from the blue. Even now I always cut off the top of my breakfast egg instead of cracking it."

The other edged his chair a trifle nearer the door. "So do I," he protested nervously.

"But not for the same reason, probably, that I do. A battered shell still reminds me of the skull on which the block had pitched. In the usual course I should have buried the poor fellow (an ordinary seaman) at sea. But we had just picked up the land; and, knowing what a fetish a tombstone is upon the lower deck, as soon as the anchor had been let go I sent a lieutenant ashore in the whaler to make arrangements for a funeral in the local cemetery."

"It was an act of humanity", commented the Dean, "which did you and the British Navy the highest credit."

The Post-Captain blushed beneath his sunburn. "The humanity", he rejoined, "stopped short at the British Navy. The town was Spanish, with the concentrated prejudice of all Spain against heretics. The authorities would not permit a British seaman's corpse to desecrate their tuppenny-ha'penny graveyard!"

The Dean nodded. "I have always heard", he said, "that the memory of Drake is still held accursed by the Roman

Church in those latitudes. So you had to give the dead man a sailor's grave after all?"

"Wrong first guess. You are evidently unaware, Mr. Dean, that it is contrary to the tradition of the Service to climb down in the face of a rebuff. I sent the officer ashore a second time, with powers to treat with the garlic-eating bigots for the purchase of a plot of ground as remote from their precious cemetery as they pleased. British gold proved more effectual than appeals to their Christian charity, and within an hour I had signed the necessary documents. Then I sent for"— Bompas swallowed with difficulty—"my parson.

"He had only just joined the Service as a temporary chaplain under the new scheme, and had come out to the ship direct from a country curacy. He was homesick, lovesick and seasick, and he bleated about the decks like a bewildered wether in the lambing season. Naturally I thought he was a fool."

"Naturally," echoed the Dean.

"Well, he wasn't. Things—including sheep-faced curates —are not always what they seem. I explained the situation, and told him the funeral was fixed for one bell in the second dog.

"'What hour is that?' he inquired.

"'The last-joined boy on the lower deck will tell you,' I retorted.

"'I will ask him,' he said. 'After all, it is not so much the time as the place that matters.'

"'I have yet to learn', I replied, 'that anything matters in this ship, when once it has been decided on by ME.'

"'In this ship, I grant you,' he bleated.

"'Or on shore,' I thundered, bringing my fist down with a bang upon the writing-table. 'What have you to say against my new cemetery?'

"'You have spilt the ink', he sniggered, 'and I have nothing to say, either for or against your new cemetery, except that I cannot read the Burial Service in it.'

"'Indeed!' I sneered. 'Perhaps you also object to read it on the quarter-deck at sea?'

"'Not at all,' he simpered; 'the two cases are not parallel. The "Burial of the Dead at Sea" is specially provided for by the Prayer Book, and the Prayer Book is to me what the Admiralty Instructions are to you. I can find no clause in my Instructions authorizing me to bury one of my flock in unconsecrated ground.'"

"Nevertheless," interpolated the Dean, "that contingency is also provided for."

"Not in the Prayer Book," snapped Bompas; "if I had found it there—and I hunted all night—I'd have put him under arrest."

"Not in the Prayer Book, perhaps," assented the Dean, "but——"

"How was I to know anything about the Burial Laws Amendment Act? They didn't teach ecclesiastical history in the *Britannia*. What I do know is", added Bompas, "he had me all round!"

"I fear that he had," smiled the Dean.

"Yes, but mark time a bit. 'Your quibble', I told him, 'is easily disposed of. You shall go ashore five minutes ahead of the funeral party, and consecrate the ground beforehand.'

"Never in my life has anything driven me so near justifiable homicide as the smile of pity with which he received the suggestion.

"' I fear', he said, shaking his head, 'that you are ignorant of the very rudiments of canon law. No one but a bishop can do what you propose.'

"Even at sea, Mr. Dean, laymen endeavour to restrain their language in the presence of your cloth. But to be heckled in my own cabin by a curate as if I was a mothers' meeting, was a new experience for me. I swore."

"Poor mothers' meeting!" laughed the Dean. "I think we may absolve it. Even I—— Yes, please go on."

"'If you imagine you have come to sea to browbeat post-captains,' I told him, 'you never made a bigger mistake in all your foolish life. I accept your assertion—at all events, until I can verify it. The ground *shall* be consecrated by a bishop.'

"That obviously staggered him!

"'Before the funeral?' he asked.

"'Before the funeral.'

"'I hope you haven't forgotten', he went on doubtfully, 'that your bishop must be an Angli——'

"'Get out of my cabin,' I shouted. 'And come back in ten minutes' time.'

"As soon as he had gone I sent for the Assistant Paymaster who acted as my clerk, and, before the ten minutes expired, the latter had drawn up a certain document at my dictation. I was in the act of signing it when the parson reappeared.

"'As you seem to be a bit of a sea-lawyer,' I began, 'you shall test the legality of this document step by step. The King, I believe, is the head of the Established Church?'

"'I believe so,' he murmured.

"'And, on board this ship, I represent the King?'

"'An admirable understudy,' he giggled.

"'When I desire your criticism I will ask for it,' I retorted. 'As the representative of the head of the Established Church, then, and to meet the present emergency, I raise you temporarily to the bishopric. Here is your *Acting Rate of Bishop*, duly made out and signed by me. You can now consecrate the cemetery, and read the Burial Service afterwards.'

"He looked the paper through, folded it, and carefully placed it in his pocket.

"'You may rest assured', he said (and from the first I mistrusted his Sunday-school grin), 'that I shall use my utmost endeavours to live up to the high estate to which it hath pleased you to raise me.' A moment later I was rid of him."

With a retrospective sign of relief, Captain Bompas paused.

"I congratulate you", said the Dean, "on a British seaman's resourcefulness."

"Your congratulations", snapped the British seaman, "are premature. About an hour later I heard the galley called away. What would *you* say, if the deanery carriage were piped away without your orders?"

"Nothing," returned the Dean earnestly; "I never argue with my wife. But where is the connection?"

"The galley of a man-o'-war", explained Bompas, "is the Captain's own boat, and no-one else uses her without his special permission. I rang for the officer of the watch.

"'Who called the galley away?' I asked.

"He seemed surprised. 'I did, sir,' he replied. 'The Chaplain went ashore with the funeral party in the pinnace; but he told me the galley was to be sent in to fetch him off, and that he had your sanction for saying so.'

"'Oh! he said that, did he?' I spluttered. 'Send the reverend gentleman to me the instant he returns on board!'

"I will not repeat, Mr. Dean, what the gulls heard *me* say from the stern gallery as I watched my galley coming alongside the ship. The boat's crew were grinning from ear to ear, and well they might. For the clerical lubber in the stern-sheets had as much notion as an agitated nursemaid of handling a six-oared boat. He was sawing at the yoke-lines as though he were doing Sandow exercises, with the result that he fouled the accommodation ladder and stove in the galley's bows. A moment later, as if nothing had happened, he was simpering in the cabin doorway, two fingers of his right hand raised above his head.

"'*Pax tecum*,' he grinned.

"For the first time in a fairly eventful life I found myself utterly unequal to the occasion, and, before I could pull myself together, he had flung himself with a sigh of contentment into my favourite arm-chair.

"'*Bonum est*,' he smirked, with an upward roll of the eyes—'*optimum est episcopari!*'

"'You've been drinking,' I retorted, though I knew he hadn't.

"'Oh, fie!' he moaned, shaking his forefinger at me, 'to say what you know to be untrue. Nevertheless, after that dangerous boat of yours, I should welcome a little wine for the stomach's sake.'

"'Silence!' I howled, with a smack on the table that made him skip. 'Any more of this jack-acting, and I place you under arrest. Clergyman or not, as an officer of the ship under my command you are "a person subject to the Naval Discipline Act", and only my respect for your cloth has so far restrained me from posting a sentry over you.'

"'On what charge?' he lisped.

"'On half a dozen,' I thundered. 'In the first place, what the devil do you mean by stoving in the bows of my galley?'

"'It was an error of judgement,' he giggled. 'I pulled the wrong string.'

"'I heartily wish,' I rejoined, 'that you had got it into a hangman's knot, and pulled it round your silly neck instead. How dare you come off in the galley at all—wasn't the pinnace good enough?'

"'Not for a bishop,' he murmured.

"'Oh,' I said, 'so that's how the land lies! Suffering from swollen head, eh? Well, I'll soon cure that. I gave you the acting rate to enable you to perform a certain duty. The moment that duty was completed, you reverted to your original rank.'

"He slowly shook his head. 'I cannot agree with you,' he said. 'Once a bishop, always a bishop.'

"'We'll see about that,' I retorted. 'If I can rate a man a bishop, I can disrate him; and I jolly well disrate you now!'

"'I fear', he rejoined, with that exasperating smirk of his, 'that, not being Primate of All England, you imagine a vain thing. His Grace of Canterbury is the only man in the Empire who can deprive an Anglican bishop of his see.'

"Although I was careful to give no hint of it, for the first time an uneasy suspicion crossed my mind that I had done a foolish thing.

"'I will consider the point,' I said. 'Meanwhile you can return to the wardroom.'

"But he still lolled in my arm-chair. 'It is most unfortunate,' he grinned, 'but you seem to be fated always to propose the impossible.'

"'Impossible to go back to your own mess?' I stammered. The fellow took all the wind out of my sails!

"'Utterly!' he insisted. 'The case is in a nutshell. In relative rank a prelate takes precedence even of a post-captain, so, you see, I am really performing an act of condescension.'

"'I don't follow you.'

"'Graceful condescension,' he sniggered, 'in consenting to mess with you.'

"'To mess with me!' I shouted, springing from my chair. 'Have you the audacity to propose that I shall hobnob for the rest of the commission with a blithering, brummagem bishop?'

"'A bishop of your own creation,' he corrected, 'and the commission will pass like one o'clock. I'll teach you canon law in the evenings after dinner.'

"Mr. Dean, what was I to do? I had neither the means of testing his outrageous claims, nor any one whom I could consult. In his pocket lay that infernal episcopal warrant, given under my hand and seal; and any friction between the ecclesiastical authorities and the Admiralty would inevitably have resulted in the loss of my command. I played for safety. I bade him stay where he was and be—blessed!

"He stayed; and, if you were a layman, I should have less difficulty in finding an adequate adjective to describe the time that followed. He took his title, if you please, from the State in which the newly consecrated cemetery lay, and wrote me a pastoral letter signed '*John Ecuador*'. He babbled from morning to night of his late curacy in Devonshire, and, as I have already told you, when he was not seasick he was love-sick. Indeed, I don't know which maddened me most—his Latin grace at breakfast, his episcopal blessing at bedtime, or the intervening rhapsodies on the daughter of the Vicar of Plymbridge."

As though impelled by a pin, the Dean suddenly sat upright in his chair. "Of Plymbridge?" he echoed.

"Of Plymbridge," repeated Bompas—"a pompous but harmless old boy beating up for preferment."

The Dean reddened. "Really, sir——" he began.

"It's not my description," said Bompas, "I'm quoting his drivelling curate, and if the strain had lasted much longer I should have become as drivelling as the curate. But one evening towards the end of the week, after a fatuous *tête-à-tête* dinner that had nearly choked me, I suddenly discovered that there was method in his madness."

"Had I been a layman I'd have bet on it," said the Dean.

"It's easy to be wise after the event," sneered Bompas.

"And sometimes before it," laughed the other.

"I don't follow you," growled Bompas. "Anyway, his bargain was this. A certain fat living in the gift of my brother, Sir Boreas Bompas, was, so he said, about to fall vacant. He would burn his bishop's commission and descend to the wardroom that night if I would get him the rectory and thereby enable him to marry old Pomposity's daughter.

"'Then the Rectory is as good as yours,' I assured him. 'I will cable to Sir Boreas the moment we get into harbour to-morrow morning.'

"'In that case,' he grinned, '*nolo episcopari.*'

"'I'm sick of your eternal Greek—I want a translation,' I said."

"Which was precisely what *he* didn't," laughed the Dean. "*Nolo episcopari!* Well, well, he is evidently a young man who will attain many things—among them, I begin to suspect, the hand of 'old Pomposity's' daughter. But my guest should be here by now, and I think he would interest you. I should be so glad if you would join us at lunch."

"You are such an intelligent listener", said Bompas enthusiastically, "that nothing would please me more. Unfortunately, I have to return to the Admiralty, so the pleasure, I fear, must be postponed."

Five minutes later the Dean was shaking hands with his guest in the hall. "I am glad you have come," he exclaimed; "I began to fear you might shy at the dismal prospect before you."

"The—er—dismal prospect?"

"Of a *tête-à-tête* meal with a pompous but harmless old boy 'beating up for preferment'."

For an appreciable moment the ex-curate's face lost its sheep-like expression. But only for a moment. "I congratulate you and the Church, sir," he grinned, "on the King's recognition of your scholarship. I gather that you have met an old pirate who taught me more original profanity in a single week than the average layman acquires in a lifetime."

"How far it was original," laughed the Dean, "I have no means of judging. But, after hearing the narrative of his sufferings, I, for one, can find it in my heart to condone the—the language."

"And the pastoral letter, I trust, sir?" added the young man a little anxiously.

"I am sure", said the Dean evasively, "that you would now like to hear about Mary."

In the after-cabin of the port guard-ship at Plymouth, Captain Cholmondeley Bompas, M.V.O., R.N., sat at his table, glaring at a newly arrived invitation card. It was silver-edged, and bore in silver lettering a legend to the effect that the gallant addressee's presence was desired by the Dean of Exborough and his wife on the occasion of the marriage of their daughter Mary with the Rector of St. Dunstan-in-the-Wold.

"I suppose I shall go," muttered Bompas, "but it's like his dam' cheek to add *that!*"

The Post-Captain's glare focused itself on a portion of the card where the chaste bridal lettering had been marred by a parenthesis in prosaic ink. For, immediately after the bridegroom-elect's name, and in an all too familiar calligraphy, had been inserted the two words "*John Ecuador*".

"TAFFRAIL"

BAD WEATHER

I

I have sometimes been asked what it is like to be in a
real gale of wind in a destroyer. It is rather a difficult
question to answer. So much depends upon the strength
of the gale, the height of the sea, the size of the destroyer, and
whether one is steaming with the sea or against it.

In the days before the war, serving in the old 27- and 30-
knotters of something under 400 tons, we had our fair share of
bad weather. These little ships, with their sharp bows and
low turtle-back forecastles, used sometimes to dive through
the seas, bringing them green and solid on to the bridge, and
drenching us with spray in anything approaching a stiff
breeze. They were lively, too. On the other hand, none of our
cruises were really long. We were generally going from port to
port in the British Isles, and, if the weather was really bad,
we could usually run for shelter. If we did have to weather out
a gale at sea, we could choose our own speed.

The average destroyers of the war period were ships of about
1,000 tons, craft far more weatherly and roomier than the
older ones built between 1894 and 1899 in which most
of us had served our early apprenticeship in the destroyer
service.

In war, however, we could not run for shelter when things
became really uncomfortable. We were generally in company
with battleships and cruisers as an anti-submarine screen, and
if they could stick the weather, we had to. Moreover, we could
not choose our own speed, but had to steam the speed of the
fleet or squadron.

It was no unusual thing for destroyers to have their bridges knocked flat, and most of us suffered damage at one time or another. Read what Captain the Hon. Barry Bingham says in writing of the 780-ton *Tigress*—he himself was serving in her sister ship, the *Hornet:* "To steam 20 knots with the battle-cruisers in practically all weathers was no sinecure, and, while these enormous ships were slipping along comfortably, the unhappy destroyers were having a bad time of it. One could only marvel at the way they jumped and dodged the waves of a long head sea. But every now and then you would catch a huge wave in the wrong stride, and a sheer wall of green sea would fall over the whole ship. When the bridge started carrying away, we thought it was time to 'submit' this fact to the admiral, requesting permission to ease down a few knots.

"The *Tigress*, one of the destroyers in my division—in fact, my sub-divisional mate—encountered one of these enormous seas, which struck her fair and with sufficient force to drive the bridge rails about four feet aft on the compass and to pin her captain, Lieutenant-Commander Paul Whitfield, between the two. He broke two ribs and sustained some internal damage, yet nevertheless continued in command."

But even when alone it was not advisable for destroyers to be too leisurely. "Fritz," the ubiquitous German submarine, used sometimes to slam in a torpedo at anything he saw provided he had a fair chance of hitting. I remember one of the Harwich Force destroyers, the *Moorsom*, being torpedoed off the Maas Lightship, a favourite lurking-ground for U-boats. The *Moorsom* was steaming 20 knots when hit, and the torpedo duly exploded in an upheaval of smoke and spray. But nobody can have been more surprised than the submarine's commander when the destroyer steamed off at 15 knots until she was out of harm's way. The torpedo had exploded against her rudder, detaching the A bracket of one propeller from the hull, and loosening the other. Her escape was one of the many lucky ones of the war. Had it struck amidships—indeed, almost anywhere else—she must have been brought to a standstill, when another shot would have finished her.

Apart from one or two expeditions to the Skager Rack, when we had a severe pounding, I think the worst trip I ever experienced in a destroyer was in January 1918, when, in the *Telemachus*, we were ordered to proceed north-about from the Firth of Forth to Avonmouth for our biennial refit. Avonmouth was at the very opposite end of the British Isles—690 miles if we went round the north of Scotland and through the Irish Sea; about 60 miles more via the east coast of England and the Channel.

Having arrived in harbour at 7 a.m. after three days' buffeting at sea, we received orders a few hours later to sail at 5.30 p.m. The weather was vile, with a strong north-easterly breeze and occasional flurries of snow and sleet, so thick that they shut out all view of the Forth Bridge, about half a mile downstream. It was a filthy day. The needle of the aneroid had been travelling anti-clockwise for thirty-six hours, and still continued to fall. I heard the quartermaster of the forenoon watch, a hoary-headed mariner, sucking his teeth with astonishment when he gazed at it at about noon to enter the reading in the deck log.

"What's the matter, Jevons?" I asked him.

"I can't make it out no'ow, sir," he replied, tapping the glass with a gloved finger. "I've never seen the likes of it—goin' backwards all the time. Maybe it's out of order, sir."

I shook my head. The aneroid was telling a dismal tale; but it was a true one.

We were in for a dusting.

We got it.

II

By 5.40 p.m., at which time it was dark, we were steaming under the great arch of the Forth Bridge with the white, red, white lights glimmering high overhead to show that the inner anti-submarine net had been lowered for our benefit. Steaming on past a line of lighted buoys to starboard, we came to the inner boom, its southern entrance marked by trawlers showing red and green lights. We passed on through the outer gate, increased speed to 20 knots, and were soon abeam of Inchkeith, whose searchlight promptly demanded our name. There were still the outer anti-submarine defences to be negotiated, the heavy boom and nets between Eli and Fidra Island, almost at the entrance to the Firth.

Getting in or out of the Firth of Forth in wartime was not particularly easy. Four separate systems of anti-submarine defences had to be passed through. It was as well. On September 2nd, 1914, late at night, the German submarine U.21, commanded by Lieutenant Hersing, had crept up as far as the Forth Bridge before she was detected. Unable to attack the men-of-war above it, she was forced to retreat, and three days later sank the first man-of-war ever destroyed by a torpedo fired from a submarine. This was the light-cruiser *Pathfinder*, torpedoed off St. Abb's Head on the afternoon of September 5th, 1914.

About two hours after leaving our buoy we were passing May Island, the light on which was shown for our especial benefit. We fixed our position accurately, switched off navigation lights, steamed on for a mile or two, and then altered course to the northward up the Scottish coast.

Shore lights were not ordinarily displayed in wartime as they helped enemy submarines. There were no outlying dangers, however, beyond the Bell Rock, of which we were steering well clear. We had asked for the lights at Girdleness, near Aberdeen, and Rattray Head and Kinnaird Head, farther north, to be shown between certain stated times, allowing for a speed of 20 knots. The wind, still blowing very hard, was in the north-north-west. We were anxious to make good going while under the lee of the coast. Once past Kinnaird Head and into the open stretch of water off the Moray Firth, we might expect a heavy sea. I was aiming to make Duncansby Head, at the eastern end of the Pentland Firth, soon after daybreak.

For over a hundred miles the going was good, for there was nothing really vicious about the sea. But the cold was uncomfortable. The thermometer was well below 32°, with the spray freezing as it fell. Moreover, we had frequent snow squalls, until the bridge and mast were well covered in ice.

We duly sighted Girdleness, Rattray Head, and Kinnaird Head lights, and at about 1.20 a.m. altered course to the north-north-west for Duncansby Head, about eighty miles on. Almost as soon as we left the shelter of the land the sea became heavier and steeper, and the old ship began to tumble about with a violent corkscrew motion as only a destroyer can. We had eased to 14 knots; but, even so, the ship was pitching heavily into the head sea, flinging her bows dizzily into the air at one moment, and under water the next. Occasional green seas smashed over the forecastle and thudded against the bridge, while the spray drove over in sheets and stung our faces like hail.

It was blowing very hard, with the wind booming and shrilling through our scanty rigging. Ahead, the sea was faintly phosphorescent. I could see nothing but a confused maelstrom of leaping white, and the foaming summits of the nearer waves as they drove towards us. The upper deck was constantly buried in breaking water as they surged on board and went racing madly aft. The ship was bumping badly, sometimes flinging her stern out of water until the propellers raced madly in air. There was nothing for it but to ease down.

We tried her at 12 knots; but even this was too much. We eased to 10, at which she no longer crashed and threatened to break herself in halves. She rode easier, though the motion was still frightful.

Pyke, the pale-faced, seasick signalman, was crouched over a bucket in the tail of the bridge. He was never happy at sea, poor fellow, and, glancing at him, I thought of what it must be like on the fœtid, sloppy mess-decks under the forecastle. Contrary to popular belief, a good many sailors are still seasick, even destroyer sailors.

Turning the ship over to the officer of the watch, I retired to the chart house below the bridge, to find the usual scene of desolation. The violent rolling and pitching had unshipped every movable fitting from its place and had hurled it on to the deck. A trickle of dirty water from a faulty pipe connection in the roof dripped steadily on to the cushioned settee which served as my bed. The two steel doors, normally water-tight, admitted streams of water every time a sea broke on board.

It was cold and damp and miserable. The drawers under the chart-table containing the chart folios were slowly disgorging their contents on to the already littered deck covered with six inches of dirty water swishing dismally from side to side. It was a gruesome sight.

I salved some books, some bound copies of Sailing Directions, an unbroken cup, a tin of biscuits, my spare sea-boots, the sub-lieutenant's sextant, a pair of parallel rulers, and a tin of cigarettes. But no sooner had I wedged them in what I fondly imagined were safe positions than they fell down again. Rather than wedge the books in the bookshelf over the settee, where, as likely as not, they would work themselves loose and descend in an avalanche on my head as I tried to sleep, I let them lie.

Taking off my dripping oilskins and sodden muffler, I arrayed myself in a tolerably dry "lammy-coat" and tapped on the little window of the wireless-office behind the chart house.

It flicked open, to display the red face of Biddle, the leading telegraphist, with a pair of telephone receivers clipped over his ears. Biddle enjoyed what is popularly known as a "fug". His cubby-hole was perhaps six feet square, littered all over with the mysterious instruments of his calling, and with just sufficient room on the deck for a chair, a desk, and a box of confidential books. With all his ventilators tight shut, the electric light blazing, the radiator full on, and the ship rolling and pitching drunkenly, he was literally stewing in his own juice. Biddle had a hardened stomach, and was even smoking. But the wave of heated air which smote me in the face caused me to step back hastily. It smelt of overheated humanity, damp serge, acrid cigarette smoke, and the stench of hot metal.

"Aren't you rather hot in there?" I asked him.

Biddle laughed. Indeed no, he replied, it was just nice and snug.

"Has anything been coming through?" I enquired.

"Nothing much, sir," he answered. "Some of the destroyer patrols in the Pentland Firth have been reporting very bad weather, that's all. They've been ordered to return to base."

I groaned inwardly. In eight hours or so we should be in the Pentland Firth ourselves. If the patrols had been withdrawn, it meant we were in for a real snorter.

III

When daylight came at about 7.30 land was in sight on the port bow. It was not until two hours later, however, that we rounded Duncansby Head and altered course to the westward through the Pentland Firth.

It was a grey morning, with a few stray gleams of wintry sunlight flickering through the dark snow-clouds scurrying down from windward on the wings of the gale. The sea, with the wind blowing against the tide, was very confused. The waves rose and fell in no regular cadence, rearing themselves up perpendicularly to topple in yeasty white. At times, charging furiously together, the spray of their impact went hurtling to leeward in sheets of flying spindrift. The wind, if anything, had increased.

We staggered on through the Firth. Land lay on both sides. On the starboard bow, within a mile and a half, was the rocky islet of Swona, veined with the snow lying in its gullies and its low summit covered with a mantle of white. Beyond, from right ahead to well abaft the starboard beam, lay Hoy, Flotta Island, and South Ronaldshay, the southern islands of the Orkney group guarding the great expanse of Scapa Flow. Looking through glasses, one could see masts just

85

showing over the distant hills, for inside, in the landlocked anchorage, lay the Grand Fleet.

The hills and mountains looked very bleak and barren, tier upon tier of white-capped hummocks fading into the dim distance, their lower slopes streaked with lying snow. The mountains of Hoy, fine on the starboard bow, shone intensely white when touched by the errant gleams of sunlight, then disappeared altogether as the dense snow flurries drove down from the northward.

On our port bow lay Stroma with its lighthouse, and beyond, terminating to the west in the bold mass of Dunnet Head, was the mainland of Scotland, Caithness. It was a forbidding-looking shore, the wind-driven water surging madly against the rocks off the sheer cliffs.

The Pentland Firth had always had an evil reputation among seamen. Its tides are strong; its eddies and whirlpools uncertain. Even great battleships, for no apparent reason, have been suddenly swirled through a right angle or more out of their course. But in a gale of wind its dangers are magnified a hundredfold. The tide sometimes runs at 10 knots, and the wind, blowing against it, is apt to raise a toppling sea sufficient to overwhelm an ill-found vessel. Many a light-cruiser or destroyer has limped into Scapa Flow with her bridge beaten flat, and boats, and possibly men, washed overboard. Even a battleship, steaming westward against a gale, had her bridge completely removed by an enormous sea which broke on board in a liquid avalanche and flooded the ship with hundreds of tons of water.

So it behoved us to be careful.

It would be dark by 4.0 p.m. I had no wish to struggle on during the night through the Minch and Little Minch, between the Outer Hebrides and the west coast of Scotland. Lights were few and far between, and the Shiant Islands lay right in mid-channel. If we did ask for the lights to be shown, we might never sight them if it really came on to snow. What we had in mind was to push on as fast as possible during the day, so as to arrive before dark at Loch Ewe, some fifty miles down the coast from Cape Wrath. There we could spend the night.

Alas for our good intentions!

Once out of the lee of the Orkneys the sea rapidly got worse. We were steaming along towards Cape Wrath with the gale on our starboard beam and nothing between us and Iceland. Seldom have I experienced such motion. Yawing wildly in her course, the ship was rolling as much as fifty degrees to leeward. We had to lash ourselves on to the bridge rails to remain upright.

One is accused of exaggeration if one describes a sea as "mountainous", though mountainous, compared with ourselves, this sea certainly seemed to be—great hills of grey water streaked and topped with white which seemed to reach as high as our masthead as we sank into the valleys between them. The ship, borne skywards on a crest, leant drunkenly over on her side and seemed to slide down the next watery abyss. Occasionally, as a comber caught her bows and drove her off her course, the forecastle buried itself in the water and the stern was well in the air, with the rudder and propellers useless, while her midship portion, straddled awkwardly across the back of the wave, would be overwhelmed in a boiling cataract eight feet deep. Then, as the sea drove on and the bows lifted, the stern fell into the next hollow, and another watery avalanche broke over our tail.

We were battened down, with life-lines rigged along the deck. Even so, it was only possible to get from aft forward, or vice versa, by watching for a lull and taking a chance of being washed overboard. If anyone had gone, no boat could have been lowered to rescue him. We should have had to try picking him up from the ship.

The sea had already made a clean sweep of the canopies over the wardroom and cabin hatches in the stern. I had no wish to see the flimsy circular hatches beaten in, and the stern compartments flooded.

But what could one do?

The helmsmen did their utmost to keep the ship on her course. If they could keep her from yawing, things were more or less satisfactory beyond the rolling, and we took no heavy water on board. The wheel was never still; but there was no holding her within thirty or forty degrees of her course as she was buffeted alternately on bow and stern. She was here, there, and everywhere. Wet through and numb with cold, the quartermasters were soon tired out. We had them relieved every half-hour.

We were moving along in a sort of zigzag crawl. It was manifestly impossible to reach Loch Ewe before dark. What should we do?

I made up my mind to anchor in some sheltered anchorage that we could reach before dark, and to sail again next morning. Whatever happened, I was determined not to attempt the Minches by night.

Going down to the chart house and hanging on by our eyelids, the first lieutenant and myself hauled out a chart or two and examined the Sailing Directions. The nearest anchorage was twelve miles down the coast from Cape Wrath, and its name was Loch Inchard. It was a narrow fiord about four miles long, "little used by shipping," said the Sailing Directions, "partly in consequence of the entrance being difficult to make out from seaward". Moreover, it seemed that the average width of the loch was little more than 600 yards, while within half a mile of the entrance lay the unmarked Bodha Ceann na Saile, a submerged rock with a least depth of twelve feet. The *Telemachus* drew fourteen and a half feet of water to the tips of her propellers.

On the whole, Loch Inchard did not sound particularly inviting, though it did afford a sheltered anchorage farther up which should be unaffected by any wind that blew. But it was literally the only port in a storm—Hobson's choice. We made up our minds to go there.

We staggered on towards Cape Wrath—rolling, lurching, and pitching, flung about like an empty cask in the great seas. The snow seemed to be increasing, for frequent squalls shut down the visibility to a few hundred yards. In the intervals we could see the coast to port. Its snow-covered mountains, dark cliffs, and welter of breaking water looked grim and menacing, altogether horrible.

The distance from the Pentland Firth to Cape Wrath is a bare sixty miles. It was the longest sixty miles I have ever travelled!

The galley fire had long since been put out by a sea, so that hot food was impossible. When I sent for the coxswain to enquire as to what had been done about the men's dinner, he grinned sadly and replied that most of them required no nourishment at all. They wished to lie down and die, and that speedily. For those who were strong enough to eat, we contrived hot cocoa and thick bully-beef sandwiches—that and their rum ration. My own lunch, eaten on the bridge, consisted of slightly thinner sandwiches well flavoured with seawater.

It was not until 2.30 that we saw the irregular hummock of Cape Wrath with the lighthouse on its summit. Seldom have I seen a spectacle to compare with the sight of the huge seas breaking against that wall of dark cliff. Great hillocks flung themselves at its rocky base, to burst in upheavals of spray a full seventy feet high. The body of each wave, recoiling seaward after its fruitless effort to breach the solid rock, impacted against its successor, so that the coast was fringed with half a mile of whitened, leaping water which rioted in all directions, tumbling, playing madly. It was fascinating to watch. I began to realise then why some mediaeval mariner, clawing his way round that promontory in his crazy sailing-ship, had christened it Cape Wrath.

Passing it by, we gradually hauled round to the southward. I looked anxiously aft as we turned, for the alteration of course would bring the stern swinging into the sea. For a few moments all went well. Then, as luck would have it, the bows lifted on the back of a huge wave, and the stern sank into the next hollow. A hillock of grey water, steep and sheer like a wall, white capped and foaming, towered up astern and started gradually to overtake us. I watched it, fascinated. For a few breathless moments it hung there, its crest over-hanging the quarterdeck by fully twenty feet. It came nearer —nearer. Would the stern never rise?

Then the after part of the ship started to lift ever so slowly. But it was too late. The curling summit of the sea tottered, fell on board with a crash which made the whole ship tremble.

For what seemed an eternity the after part of the ship remained buried in the heart of the sea. All I could see was the mizzenmast standing up out of the whitened water. We had sent down a message for nobody to remain on the upper deck before we altered course, and I prayed fervently that no man was on the quarterdeck when that wave overwhelmed it. Then the stern rose, the water cascading forward and over-board in a miniature Niagara.

We increased speed to 15 knots. The ship yawed wildly; but the increase certainly saved us from being "pooped" again.

The shore, composed of peculiar reddish cliff, was only a couple of miles or so to port. We sped by a ten-fathom patch upon which the seas, suddenly checked in their deep-water stride, burst furiously. We passed a little rocky island, its rounded summit almost obliterated in sheets of flying spray.

But half an hour later we had steered in towards the land and were steaming by Eilean an Róin—the Island of the Seal —at the entrance to our harbour. Once under the lee of the land the sea started to go down, and a few minutes later we were travelling up the narrow inlet of Loch Inchard with the snow-covered hills on either side. The gale, whistling round the gullies, sent the powdery snow flying. But in the sheltered loch the water was flat calm. The ship was on an even keel again.

We steamed on, hugging the shore to port to avoid the rocks in mid-channel, and passing two little clusters of houses which looked more like Eskimo *igloos* than civilised habitations. The ship's company, rubbing their eyes, came on deck and looked about them. Their cigarettes and pipes appeared.

A boatswain's pipe twittered:

"Ha-ands bring ship to an anchor!"

Five minutes later the engines were stopped, and the anchor went to the bottom with the cheerful rattle of cable.

I fixed the position of the ship on the chart by cross-bearings, waited until she had "got" her cable, and then left the bridge. Half-way down the ladder I had an inspiration, and called to the coxswain.

"Sir?"

"Issue an extra rum ration at supper-time."

"Extra rum ration, sir!" he started to object. "We can't——"

"We will!" I cut him short. "If the powers that be ask you why, refer them to me."

"Aye, aye, sir," he replied, not at all displeased.

I went to my cabin to change into something dry, perhaps to have a bath. But the moment I saw the stern at close quarters I knew the worst. Practically everything except the after gun had been swept overboard, even the after binnacle.

The wardroom, two feet deep in water, was a scene of chaos. I swallowed some raw whisky, and retired to my cabin, to find it even worse. My steward, busy with a bucket and my bath sponge, was trying to compete with the flood. All my most treasured possessions had been hurled to the deck. Books, boots, and clothing had joined forces on the floor with my typewriter, all the contents of the drawers in my writing-table, and the half-finished manuscript of a book whereof all the typing had run.

It was a grisly scene.

I got my bath two hours later.

The thermometer was still below freezing.

I did not escape a raging cold in the head, which lasted the whole of my ten days' leave.

My typewriter was never quite the same afterwards. Undoubtedly it was our worst journey.

IV

At eight next morning, fortified after a night's rest, we resumed our journey southward. The gale still raged furiously, but the wind and sea were astern. In the intervals between the snow-squalls the sun shone out in a pale blue sky.

We went on to 20 knots, and by 11.30 were steaming down the Inner Sound between Raasey and the mainland, with the hills on either hand. Far away to starboard the snow-clad mountains of Skye shimmered silver-blue and gold, as if cast in solid ice. Through the Kyle of Loch Alsh and the narrows of Kyle Akin to Sleat Sound. Then on through a stretch of open water, past the islands of Rum and Eigg and Muck—delicious names—to Ardnamurchan Point.

At 2.30 we were abreast of Tobermory on our way down the Sound of Mull. At anchor inside the little harbour was a convoy of colliers, oilers, and storeships on their way up to the Grand Fleet, escorted by a couple of destroyers, with whom we exchanged signals. They had been ordered to wait, partly because of the gale, partly because many submarines, driven from the open sea by the weather, had been reported in the more sheltered waters of the Minches farther north.

The rest of our journey was practically uneventful, and by 9.30 in the evening we were passing Rathlin Island. Steaming down the Irish Sea was strange after the North Sea. All the shore lights and lightships were in full operation, and one by one they hove in sight over the horizon on both sides, winked at us in friendly fashion, and then, having served their purpose so far as we were concerned, faded away astern. It was quite like peace.

Soon after 11 p.m. we exchanged signals with a solitary destroyer, the *Racoon*, battling against the sea on her way back to Buncrana, Lough Swilly, while the next morning we were rounding Pembrokeshire on our way up the Bristol Channel to Avonmouth, where we arrived in the afternoon.

In the newspapers a few days later we read an Admiralty communiqué—"*Early in the morning of January 9th one of H.M.*

destroyers was wrecked off the north coast of Ireland. It is regretted there were no survivors. All the next of kin have been informed."

It was the *Racoon,* commanded by Lieutenant George L. M. Napier, the very ship we had passed and with whom we had exchanged signals. Little did we think when we saw her that within three hours every soul on board her would have perished.

In the pitch darkness and driving snow she struck the rocks within a few miles of the entrance to Lough Swilly. Nobody will ever know the exact circumstances of her loss. But the northerly gale was still raging, and one can imagine that little ship, reeling and lurching, groping her way towards the land in the midst of a blinding snow-squall, with the officers and men on her bridge endeavouring to see ahead. It was anxious work: but those on board were probably optimists, with little doubt in their minds that within one hour or two they would be safely at anchor and asleep in their bunks or hammocks.

Imagine the black shadow of a wall of rock suddenly looming up out of the darkness close ahead, and the fringe of leaping, whitened water surging around its base. An agonised scream from the men on the look-out, the clang of the engine-room telegraphs as they were rattled over to "Full astern" —for the last time. Too late.

A crashing, rending thud, which tore the bottom out of the ship as she drove ashore, lifted on a giant sea, and crashed again. Wave after wave breaking on board, to sweep men and deck fittings into the sea. Then a sickening lurch as she was lifted again and hurled broadside on to the rocks, to be battered to pieces, disintegrated.

We do not know the end of her officers and men, or of how, with their ship breaking up beneath their feet, they were torn one by one from their hand-holds to be drowned in the pitiless sea, or dashed to death among those cruel rocks. It is a mercy we do not.

GILBERT HACKFORTH-JONES

FIRST COMMAND

The night before his first day at sea in command of a submarine Baxter turned in early. He told himself that he wanted to be as fresh as possible for this day for which he had been working since he joined the Navy as a cadet thirteen long years before.

To command one's own ship, whether she be a monster whose tonnage is measured by the thousands, or whether she be your mother's washing-basket, is, or should be, the goal for which all sea-faring men strive. Rank or seniority do not count when a man is in command. He is the captain responsible for everything, all-powerful in his own little sphere, and with no-one to help him when in difficulties.

As he thought of the morrow Baxter felt a cold shiver run down his spine. It was not fear that he felt, but a form of "nerves" with which he had not been affected so badly since he joined his ship as a midshipman. That cold feeling in the pit of the stomach, that desperate desire to yawn, he had always experienced before any trial or test of his ability, and this was the biggest of them all. How he envied at that moment the specialist officers, the commanders who had risen gracefully to that rank without having this ordeal to go through.

"Captain, sir" (how he thrilled when he was thus addressed), "Captain, sir." It was his leading signalman who knocked at his cabin door.

"Yes, come in!" he called, and the rating entered.

"Signal, sir." He held out a pad.

Baxter took it and read: "Movements for tomorrow. Submarines H 60, 61, 62, and 63 to sea for exercises, returning harbour on completion." He returned the pad, and the signal-man vanished.

H 63, only a number, only a 400-ton and nearly obsolescent submarine of which there were twenty-four exactly similar ones still in existence, but this one was his. If only, he said to himself, if only I can do this one day, my first, at sea, and bring her back without having made any glaring mistake, then I know everything will be all right for ever after.

He got into his bed, switched out the light, and tried to sleep, but his brain was too active and he found himself retracing the events of the past three months.

He had joined the submarine headquarters at Gosport to do what is technically known in submarines as a periscope course. This course consisted almost entirely of instruction in the art of the submerged attack on surface ships. He had found it a difficult and perplexing business, this attacking; there were so many distracting influences at work. He remembered how in the special "teacher" in which instruction was given before the class was sent to sea to learn in a practical manner, it had all seemed so simple. But when he went out in a submarine it became a very different story. But he had mastered it sufficiently well to allow his instructional officer, known irreverently as Sinbad, to give him his ticket.

There had been five in his class, and all had passed, and they, too, he thought, must even now be shivering in their shoes at the prospect of taking their commands to sea for the first time. The thought comforted him, as had the remark of old Sinbad, who, in his uncanny way, had known what Baxter was thinking when they were seated in the smoking-room on either side of the fireplace; they had been the only two occupants of the Mess.

After a silence of thirty minutes or so he had put down his newspaper and said, apropos of nothing, "Comfort yourself, my dear Baxter, that there has never been a case of an accident befalling a first command. When you have been in command for ten years then you will have to watch your step. Beware, as the poet says, your latter end."

He had sighed, and Baxter remembered how a careless piece of navigation had written "*cul-de-sac*" across Sinbad's road to advancement. After ten years' service in command he had taken his ship the wrong side of a buoy, thereby "negligently performing his duty" and incidentally piling the vessel on a sand-bank. He had missed his promotion, hence his instructional job and these last remarks of his. He had been very kind and understanding during the "passing out examination", and had not allowed himself to be embittered by an event for which he had no reason to reproach himself. He had only made one mistake, but in the eyes of Their Lordships it was one too many.

After a while Baxter dozed off, but his sleep was troubled with dreams. He saw himself dashing across the bows of liners, colliding under water with dozens of other submarines, sticking on the mud at the entrance to the harbour and becoming inextricably entangled in the chains of the Portsmouth Harbour Floating Bridge. All that night he encountered disaster in every form, and it was with a genuine sense of relief that he awoke after a fitful slumber to find that it was morning and time to turn out.

He went to the window and looked out. He could just see the sea from one corner, and noted that it was calm. Well, so much the better, he thought, adding the rider—so long as it isn't foggy.

After a hasty toilet he made his way to the Mess for a breakfast that he felt far from eating. He seated himself alongside two of his former class-mates, both obviously as strung up as himself. They indulged in light badinage and tried to avoid the subject of which they were all thinking. Smith took a surreptitious look at his wrist-watch and yawned. His example was infectious. Baxter rose to his feet; he wasn't going to make an exhibition of himself. He went into the smoking-room, lit a cigarette, and picked up a paper. Then he buried himself in an arm-chair where he could see the clock. Twenty minutes to go.

The smoking-room began to fill with many submarine officers, old and young, talkative and silent, making plans for the evening and to-morrow. The twenty minutes seemed to be interminable. Baxter had resolved that he would imitate sedulously the example of the old hands who never went near their vessels until it was time to shove off, and so he compelled himself to remain seated until Smith rose and said in a slightly too unconcerned voice: "Coming along now?"

He rose, gathered his cap, raincoat and glasses, and made his way with his companion towards the jetty where the "H" class submarines were moored.

As the upper works of the submarines became visible a little knot of officers could be seen gathered at the corner of the wharf.

Smith grunted. "See those"—he pointed—"ruddy ghouls come to see the new C.O.s make a muck of it."

He was quite right. Blockhouse Creek is a nightmare to the inexperienced, a fact which all submarine captains find out to their cost. The old hands, having mastered the tides and eddies, were gathered to watch the beginners go through the hoop. Callous, but very human.

They parted at the gangway. "Good luck, old boy," said Baxter. "I shall need it," replied Smith gloomily. Baxter crossed the gang-plank and entered into his little kingdom.

His First Lieutenant saluted him as he stepped aboard and reported ready for sea. He longed to ask a thousand questions of his subordinate, but refrained and climbed stolidly on to the bridge. It seemed much larger than ever before, he could move about with freedom. Then he realized he could do everything with freedom on board this ship. He was in command.

He looked aft to see if the Creek was clear and gave his first order: "Let go!"

The berthing lines were slipped and he ordered both motors astern. The submarine began to slide quickly stern first towards the centre of Portsmouth Harbour.

He waited for what he had always been told would happen, a sudden desire on the part of his command to turn and shoot up stern first on to the mud-bank which bounded the other side of the Creek. The onlookers watched with interest, which turned to disgust as *H* 63 sailed out into the middle of the harbour without a hitch, stopped, went ahead, and presently glided out of sight towards the open sea in a manner which left room for no criticism. "Beginner's luck," said one old-timer. "Here's Smith; bet he mucks it."

Baxter was astonished at the ease of the manoeuvre. Already he felt better; now that he was "on the job" his old self-confidence was returning. He turned to ask permission to smoke, and remembered in time to say, "Carry on smoking". The lighting of the first cigarette out of harbour closed one chapter of his book. Anyhow, he was heading for the open and had not disgraced himself before the eyes of the experts. So far so good.

The channel ran parallel to Southsea beach for some little distance; as they neared the Castle, Baxter remembered his wife. She would be watching, she had said, and would he just give a little wave when he saw her. He soon picked her out with glasses; he lifted his hand, waved it decorously, and then, turning round to see if anyone on the bridge was laughing at him, was reassured to see that no-one was watching. He saw the flutter of something white in his wife's hand and then she turned and walked away rapidly. She never watched people out of sight, thought it unlucky. Then he applied himself afresh to the task in hand.

The Flotilla Commanding Officer in his wisdom had decreed a short and easy day's exercising for the "H" boats. He, too, had experienced the pangs of a first day at sea. They were each to go to an appointed position and dive; then the submarine tender *Attentive* would steam through the area and each submarine was to fire a torpedo at her as she passed. A simple enough practice in itself, but the waters of the English Channel south of the Isle of Wight are beset with many hazards. Strong tides sweep the unwary on to sandbanks and giant liners tear past on their way to Southampton at phenomenal speeds. So that the captain of a submarine using one eye only has many distractions to hinder his task of carrying out a successful torpedo attack.

As Southsea Castle was left astern Baxter was given a warm quarter of an hour. An enormous dredger towed by two tugs chose that moment to get out of control and almost block the deep waters of the Channel. Having wormed his way past with his heart in his mouth, Baxter was next compelled to go full speed astern for a small yacht which was interpreting the meaning of the Rule of the Road too literally. For the first time (but not the last) in his life the Captain of *H* 63 put a megaphone to his mouth and enjoyed the sensation of telling the sinners exactly what he thought of them. It gave him a sense of power as well as relieving his feelings. Thereafter they pursued their eight-knot way peacefully to the exercising area.

The First Lieutenant, having completed his duties below, came on the bridge and tried to engage his Captain in conversation. Baxter, on his dignity, was not overpleased with the faintly patronizing manner of this fellow who, because he had served nearly two years in *H* 63, was beginning to think that he owned her, especially as the previous captain had left hastily in unknown circumstances. He turned the conversation to "shop", and asked a few pertinent questions about the interior economy of the vessel. Number One replied with a tolerant smile, and then he in his turn asked a question.

"I suppose you won't be firing a practice salvo of water shots when the torpedo is fired, will you?" he volunteered.

Baxter had read his flotilla orders and knew that it was laid down therein that on all occasions of firing a single torpedo, water shots (*i.e.* compressed air charges) were to be released from the other tubes in order to practise the crew in the difficult task of holding the submarine steady at her depth when the bows had been so suddenly lightened. He had privately determined to disregard this order on this, his first time out, but something in the First Lieutenant's voice stung him.

"Why not?" he asked shortly.

"Well, I thought——" the voice trailed away, impossible for Number One to say out loud that he thought the Skipper was too green to try any fancy work.

Baxter allowed the pause to grow to a long silence and then went on with the subject.

"What method have you been using in this boat to keep her down?" he asked.

Number One began a long discourse on the various methods which had been tried out under his several commanding officers.

Baxter heard him patiently to the end, and then selected one to which he had become accustomed when some four years back he had been first lieutenant of an "H" boat. "Do it that way," he ordered.

"Ay, ay, sir."

Thank goodness Number One hadn't argued; if he had, thought Baxter, I should have lost my temper.

Presently the Nab Tower came abeam and course was altered to steer direct to the position in the vicinity of which the exercise was to be carried out. Looking astern, the Captain saw that the other "H" boats were not far away. So they've managed it too, he thought, and went on to think that his own problem did not lie in the handling of his command but in the instilling of a sense of inferiority into the mind of his First Lieutenant. He was determined to show who was the Captain of this submarine.

With this object in view he gave very little warning that he would be diving on arrival in their position, and then blackguarded his subordinate for not being ready. It was an old dodge that he had learnt from Sinbad, who gave much similar advice. "Don't be too reasonable," he had said; "a captain is expected to be difficult now and again." "Never apologise and never explain . . ." Someone else said that.

Having got Number One on the run he followed up his advantage by pressing the diving hooter button without any warning at all.

If he had foreseen the consequences of this action he would not have permitted himself to indulge in it. But he had himself been accustomed to diving without warning at all times, and thought nothing of it when he was first lieutenant. Apparently, however, Number One liked a post-card or warning telegram, he thought bitterly as, descending the conning-tower, he found a state of utter confusion in the control-room. It was all on account of A.B. Bloggs, who was absent from his place of duty at the wheel, which meant that the man who had to take his place was absent from his post, and so on. Some of the consequences of this lack of flexibility in the organization were that first, No. 2 main vent was not opened for at least a minute after it should have been; secondly, the voice-pipe cock was not closed until the arrival of the ocean straight down the helmsman's neck reminded him of his delinquency; and thirdly, the First Lieutenant, working on a last-minute policy, had omitted to open certain Kingston valves. The combined effects of these incidents, coupled with the more serious one that Baxter had omitted to screw down a certain watertight control box and salt water had affected all telegraph circuits, was to make the first dive a very sorry performance.

It was not for some little time and only after A.B. Bloggs, buttoning up his trousers and wearing an injured expression, had entered the control-room, that full control was restored. Baxter, reminding himself constantly that he must not on any account interfere with Number One's job, danced round the periscope endeavouring to keep his mouth shut and to have a look round, but this latter was almost impossible owing to the appalling depth-line kept by the Coxswain and his assistant.

When at last Number One had got the submarine in proper trim and it was possible to see through the periscope, Baxter was astonished to find that half an hour had elapsed since he had expressed his desire to dive.

He pressed his eye to the lens and searched inshore for the *Attentive*. There she was, flying two large flags denoting that torpedoes were to be fired at her. He fell to with a will to the business of manœuvring into a suitable position for delivering his death-dealing blow, but he found his vessel sadly lacking in performance. It was indeed lucky for him that Sinbad was on board the *Attentive*, and told her Captain not to zigzag. "My children," he had said, "just out of the box, all hot and

bothered—give 'em a straight run." And so *Attentive* ambled
past *H* 63 position at eleven knots, and Baxter was spared a
great deal. But not all. As his sights were coming on he ordered
the tubes to be brought to the ready, but he had not allowed
himself sufficient time and he was obliged to turn away from
the target ship to prolong the attack while forward in the torpedo compartment a fine old muddle was taking place. As a
last resort, he sent the First Lieutenant forward to deal with
the situation, and in a few seconds that worthy returned and
announced that all was now ready.

"Now don't forget what I told you about keeping down,"
Baxter said. "Up periscope!" He remembered the injunctions
of his teacher and had a good look round before firing in case a
third party might be in the way. All was clear. His sights came
slowly on. Nice close shot, he thought, as he spotted Sinbad
looking out on the other side of the *Attentive*, and he hasn't seen
me. "Stand by! Seventeen—sixteen—fifteen degrees—fourteen
—fire!"

Then things began to happen. Out sped the torpedo according to plan, then the bows of the submarine dipped very
swiftly, and the next moment the depth gauge began to show
that they were heading for the bottom. There was little time to
do anything, the water was very shallow. At fifty feet they hit
with a grinding of shingle on the pressure hull.

"Blow all tanks!" ordered Baxter, for he was alarmed by the
suddenness of the involuntary dive and thought that water
must be entering the boat. Then he sent Number One forward
at the run to see what had happened, and was reassured to hear
that as far as could be seen all was well.

It was some time before *H* 63 began to feel the effect of the
blowing of her tanks. Then she began to lift almost as quickly
as she had sunk. Baxter was determined not to surface like a
dolphin under the eyes of Sinbad, and so when the gauge
showed forty feet he ordered "Stop blowing!" and the vents to
be opened.

The result was instantaneous. Down she went again, harder
this time, bump-bump on the bottom. Something radically

wrong here, thought the Captain, and decided to pocket his pride. This time he blew her to the surface, and she jumped nearly out of the water. A quick look through the periscope showed that the *Attentive* was following up his torpedo. He scrambled up the conning-tower hatch, and, opening up, emerged into the bright sunshine and on to the dripping bridge, closely followed by the Leading Signalman with a signalling lantern. Already the *Attentive* was flashing. "Good— attack," sang out the signalman as he read the message; "exercise—completed—return to—harbour." Number One, who had arrived on the bridge just in time to catch the last part of the message, went to the voice-pipe, and was about to give an order.

"Not so fast," said Baxter in a cold fury. "Signalman, make a signal to *Attentive*. Request permission to carry out diving exercises before returning to harbour."

When approval was received, Baxter turned his submarine away from the *Attentive* and held an investigation into the numerous matters which had gone wrong. With patience, if not with good temper, he found the causes of everything. He blamed no-one and said little, but for two hours he dived his submarine, changing depth, firing water shots, and carrying out every possible manœuvre. It was only when the engine-room artificer announced that they were on the last "group" of compressed air that he stayed his hand and brought his command to the surface.

On the way back to harbour, Baxter sent for the First Lieutenant. There was little left of the patronizing manner now. "Well, Number One," said the Captain, "we've all learnt a great deal to-day—have a cigarette." Nothing more was said.

Baxter was feeling jubilant, but he remembered Sinbad's "Beware your latter end". The dreaded Creek was to be negotiated before his day's work was done. Slowly he brought *H* 63 into the narrows of the harbour and turned ninety degrees to port to enter the Creek. Twice he had to use full speed to prevent a particularly vicious eddy from turning his bows on to the mud, but he triumphed over these natural hazards and a few minutes later he slid up alongside *H* 61 and secured.

It was a different Baxter who stepped ashore that evening. He had been and he had conquered. He strolled grandly into the smoking-room and saw Smith with his usual gloomy face looking at him.

"How did you get on?" was his lugubrious question. Baxter's reply in his mind was: "Glorious, I've been out and come in, I've tamed the First Lieutenant and got my self-respect, and now I'm going ashore to tell my wife all about it." Instead of this he answered carelessly: "Not so dusty—and you?"

Smith groaned. "Lousy," he said: "my bloody First Lieutenant let me down."

T. WOODROOFFE

THE SAILING OF THE IVY

Though it was not her real name, she was always referred to as the "Old Ivy" because, in the words of the song, she "clung to the wall". Her life had started on a slip on the Tyne where she was built for the Italians and the Mediterranean passenger trade; at the outbreak of war she had happened to be refitting at her builder's yard, and along with many others was at once snapped up by the Admiralty. She began proudly as a "Despatch vessel", but was later converted into a depôt ship for destroyers. They painted her outside a dirty grey—her innards were largely removed and rearranged. In place of dining-saloons and *cabins de luxe*, there were now workshops full of whirring machinery, spacious store-rooms and crowded mess-decks; passages that had once heard the gentle pit-a-pat of dainty slippered feet were now defiled by the oily boots of burly stokers. No merchant ship, whatever she may have been in her peaceful days, is improved by being converted into a man-of-war; she can never shake off a faint air of masquerading in borrowed plumes. As she lay alongside the wall at a small coaling port on the East Coast she reminded one forcibly of another war-time expedient—of those elderly gentlemen, full of ardour, who enlisted for Home Defence and paraded self-consciously about with putties that always seemed to be on the point of coming down, and whose hopelessly ill-fitting tunics must have been a severe test of their patriotism.

For over a year now she had lain without moving at the same wharf, where she mothered a flotilla of destroyers—boats that ran continuously in the North Sea on the dull and uncomfortable jobs of Escort and Patrol. She did all their repairs and supplied them with stores; she paid them; did their washing;

cut their hair; gave them baths and cinema shows; her ward-room was a club where the officers of the flotilla could get civilized drinks and swap lies about their last patrol. In short she generally played the part of Lady Bountiful, and as is usually the case with that unfortunate class of persons, she got few thanks. As she never moved from her wharf and never accompanied her brood to sea (which would have been quite unnecessary, if not suicidal), her good offices were always forgotten and she was rewarded only with good-natured detraction.

The hawsers securing her to the wharf were grimy with lack of use. Their confused tangle looked like the lianas in a primeval jungle that have been there since the birth of time. The stone coping of the wharf was neatly whitewashed, while thriving evergreens in old rum-tubs flanked the shore end of her officer's gangway. She was such a permanent feature of the landscape that one felt that she would soon be shown as such on Admiralty charts of the place. Life on board her ran on ordered and peaceful lines, and the Fleet Surgeon and Fleet Paymaster, as they were known in those spacious days, never missed their little gamble with the "sticks" to decide who should pay for the first cocktail of the morning. The Captain got his golf regularly, and what with one thing and another the War was not so bad.

Early one morning one of her flock—the *Mongrel*—returned from patrol, and tied up with her stern under the *Ivy's* high overhanging counter. As Hostility Ordinary Seaman Mac-Gillivray wiped over the paint-work on the afterpart of the *Mongrel*, whistling some plaintive Highland air to himself, he little realized that he was soon to be the cause of one of the Events of the War. Having cleaned the after-gun platform, he started on the diminutive quarterdeck, and with a master's discerning eye decided he'd still have enough left to do when "stand easy" went to keep him gently employed until dinner, and at the same time not risk the rough edge of the tongue of that sceptical man, the Coxswain. As he wiped over the depth charges in their shutes over the stern he was quietly contented

with the contentment of a cow chewing the cud; the sun
warmed him pleasantly; he thought of dinnertime not too far
off. He paused every now and again to gaze at the signs of life
about him; tugs fussing up and down in the stream; boxes and
refuse floating by; the ship's cat treading delicately among the
cinders on the wharf on her way to pay a visit to her lover in the
Ivy; at the Dockyard Policeman doing nothing in a stately and
well-fed manner. He had got to the point in his meditations of
wondering whether he would spend the evening at the canteen or at the pictures in the *Ivy*, and was just deciding that
he'd visit both, when the quartermaster's pipe sounded shrill
and urgent "Staaand easy", and MacGillivray snatched up his
cleaning cloth with the first brisk movement he had made that
day. He knew there'd be a dish of tea for him on his mess-deck
if he didn't arrive last, and he had never yet been last. The
cloth caught up and he gave it a sharp tug—there was a swish,
a heavy plop, and some water splashed him in the face as he
goggled over the side. His rag had caught up in the releasing
gear of one of the depth charges and it had gone. Its shute
looked horribly naked and empty, and all he could see over the
stern were some bubbles slowly coming to the surface. Never
a quick mover, MacGillivray on this occasion broke all his
previous records. He had seen depth charges explode, sending
up a huge column of water like a lighthouse, and it dawned on
him that, when this one went up it would not be hundreds of
yards astern but only a foot or so. He was brought to a sudden
stop on the forecastle by the burly form of the Coxswain.

"Fer Gawd's sake! What's eatin' you, Macbeth?" asked that
astonished official. "I ain't the canteen."

"Ah've dropped yin dep' charrge, sirr."

"You done what?"

"Ay. A dep' charrge. Yonder over by stairn."

The Coxswain realized that something must have happened.
Not only was MacGillivray moving like a wounded rhino when
he'd butted into him, but he was on deck during the stand
easy. He ran aft and, sure enough, one of the depth charges was
missing. He was down the ladder to the ward-room in a second

and, hardly stopping to knock, pushed his head through the curtain.

"First Lootenant, sir, please," he blurted out. "Depth charge over the stern. One o' them 'orstile O.D.'s just released it."

The sub., who was also the navigator, was struggling with a mass of chart corrections that had arrived that morning; the ward-room steward was polishing up the brightwork; the First Lieutenant was stretched out in front of the stove with his feet up, deep in a magazine.

"I suppose it was set to 'safe'," he said without looking up.

The Coxswain gulped. It was one of his duties on entering harbour to set all depth charges to "safe", and at the same time put lashings round them in their cradles to prevent accidents like this one; he had gone round the charges, he remembered, but he had been in a hurry and had omitted to lash them. With duties that are purely mechanical and part of a routine, it is very hard to swear that they have been either done or left undone. He could not be sure. His doubt as to whether he had set them all to safe became almost a conviction that he had not.

"Well, yer see, sir, being a bit adrift like this mornin', I can't rightly say whether they wos to safe or not. As a matter o' fact, sir, I don't think they wos. Yer see, sir——"

But the ward-room was empty. And not surprisingly so because it was situated right in the stern—in fact it was practically over that cursed charge.

"See the others to safe and then get them forrard out of it," yelled the First Lieutenant from the quarterdeck, "and take a sounding aft", he added as he hurried down to his Captain.

Now depth charges *qua* weapons are simple but not precise engines of destruction. When dropped, they sink until a valve worked by the pressure of water explodes them, with disturbing results, it is hoped, to anything that may happen to be in the immediate vicinity. They can be set to go off at depths varying from 20 to 150 feet or more.

"What was she set at?" asked the Captain when he heard what had happened.

"Twenty-five feet, sir."

"What's the depth of water here?"

"I'm just getting a sounding. Here's the Cox'n, sir."

"Well?"

"Three and a half fathoms over the stern, sir," reported the Coxswain.

"Twenty-one feet. Safe for the present, but the tide's rising —Get me a tide-table. Quick!" shouted the Captain. "No. Local paper will do. It's easier than those damn tables." He grabbed the paper and tore it open.

"Here we are. High water, Lear Bridge, eleven forty-one," he read out, "and it's ten thirty-five now. By God, we'll have to hurry—the damn thing will go up any time after eleven. Now—tell the Chief to get steam as soon as he can and then stand by to slip."

And then he leant back with a roar of laughter as the full results of MacGillivray's haste suddenly dawned on him.

"The *Ivy*!" he shouted. "Don't you see? They'll have to dig her out. I'll dash over now and warn her what's coming."

That serene vessel was in her usual state of matutinal calm. The Fleet Surgeon and the Fleet Paymaster were just about to start on the "other half"—they were also by this time well into their everlasting argument as to whether Jenny Lind or Nellie Farren was the more attractive woman; and, as neither of the disputants had ever seen either of the ladies in question, the argument never got much further; they might just as well have argued as to who was the fastest bowler that ever lived. The Captain's steward was burnishing a set of golf clubs. On the upper deck a lounging throng in overalls were employing their time during the stand easy sucking Woodbines; a few Troglodytes—those pale-faced folk who worked and seemed to live for ever in holes miles below decks—had been tempted out of their lairs for a few moments by the spring sun.

Into this peaceful atmosphere the Captain of the *Mongrel* burst with shattering effect.

"Seems in a 'urry. Stunt on mos' likely," remarked the knowing ones among the Troglodytes, as they watched him dash up the gangway. They were right.

A few seconds after his meeting with the *Ivy's* Captain things started to happen. Bugles blared; boatswain's mates scurried round the decks piping the hands to fall in; the signal staff made frantic signals for tugs; the Town Ambulance and Fire Brigade were rung up; the Dockyard authorities warned. The War took on a more serious aspect when it got round that, if she wasn't out of it by eleven, the *Ivy* would ascend skywards.

Messmen and stewards suddenly realized that they had forgotten all their most important purchases in the market that morning and hurried to repair the omission; gangs of experts disconnected the shore telephones and electric supply and there was an ominous hush as the electric motors on board died down into silence; a hush, broken in the ward-room, by the indignant protests of the two controversialists when they found that the pantry bell would not work. Gangways were hauled up and parties started clearing some of the under-growth of the *Ivy's* hawsers; and wires which had lain undisturbed for months seemed to show their resentment by whipping this way and that out of the inexpert hands of her crew.

Tugs soon started arriving, and the Emergency Destroyer lay off. The *Mongrel* had cleared out by now and the decks of every ship in harbour were crowded by a delighted, gloating mob. It was almost believed by the irreverent, so often had they repeated the fable, that the *Ivy* couldn't move; she was firmly embedded on a foundation of empty bottles, and if she did slide off, her bottom would fall out and she would sink.

Breathlessly they watched the scene as the tugs ranged alongside and took her wires. They experienced a slight pang of disillusionment as she slowly moved away from the wharf and still floated, but a terrific cheer went up as she moved farther away and disclosed the empty jetty—empty except for the two small trees which had been left behind in the confusion and seemed to accentuate its bareness. The wit, never absent on these occasions, got his laugh by a cry of,

"Coo. She's left her blurry garden be'ind."

Ashore a cordon had been drawn up to keep unsuspecting persons from the wharf. It was at this moment that the chief Quartermaster of the *Ivy* earned that reputation for impetuous bravery which to this day provides him with free pints. Returning from shore leave he was horrified to see nothing left of his floating home but the two shrubs, which, together with gangways and fresh-water tanks, were under his charge. These two bushes were his especial pride and joy, and he spent most of his leisure time in working hours painting the tubs, watering and dusting the leaves, and looking with a fierce and hopeful eye for weeds. When he heard what was happening, he broke through the cordon and, heedless of bellowed orders to come out of it, you —— fool, dragged his embryo forest to a place of comparative safety. As told to-day in the parlour of the "Green Man" the tale is one of stirring heroism of the genus "How we saved the Guns".

Behind the cordon the ambulance and Fire Brigade were drawn up. No one quite knew what the latter were for as the infernal depth charge was already covered by too much water. Behind these again and well in the rear were high officials gazing earnestly at their watches.

Boom. Boom. The Town Hall clock broke the silence as it chimed the fatal hour. Everyone held his breath. The seconds ticked on. Lungs were near bursting-point and nothing happened. The *Ivy* was in midstream, her side black with people having a last look at her old resting-place. Still nothing happened. Conversation started haltingly as the seconds turned into minutes. The Fire Brigade and ambulance turned round and got ready to go. Some of the higher officials started slowly for their offices. Half an hour went by and still nothing happened.

At noon, the *Ivy* settled matters by sounding off "cooks" and everybody went to dinner.

That evening, at low water, a diver went down and retrieved the cause of all the trouble. It was gingerly removed to an isolated shed and examined by a band of intrepid experts. They found it still set to "safe".

There was always a decided coolness between the Ivys and the Mongrels after that. Her coxswain was treated with suspicion, treatment that he passed on with interest to MacGillivray. Though there was nothing to connect that gentleman with Helen of Troy, his position became somewhat similar to what hers doubtless became in her native town. Just as nautically minded citizens of her day must have nudged one another as they passed her in the street and said "Yes! That's her. She's the one that launched all those ships", so MacGillivray was for ever after admiringly pointed out in the canteen as the "bloke wot sent the old *Ivy* to sea".

T. A. POWELL

SHADI

Just how Shadi, the monkey, managed to join His Majesty's Ship *Circe* unobserved we were never able to discover.

The ship had been lying at Colombo, alongside a jetty, and her crew, with the sentimental abandon of their kind, had been buying tortoiseshell boxes, cheap jewellery, and other trash so much admired by their "loved ones far away", from the local bandits who had been allowed on board to trade during the dinner hour. In the ship's company was a certain Able Seaman Sloggett, a man with no female "commitments" at home, who was suffering from a long period of leave stoppage due to misdemeanours ashore. Owing to both the above reasons Sloggett was in a strong financial position, and it was rumoured that he had made arrangements with one of the Cingalee traders to smuggle on board in a basket "one monkey complete with collar and lead" for the sum of fifteen rupees.

The transaction must have taken place on the day that the ship left Colombo and started on her 900-mile trip to Bombay, for Shadi (the devil) was not a person to allow his presence to remain unfelt for more than a few hours. The officers certainly knew nothing about him till the first night at sea.

The First Lieutenant, duly complying with the King's Regulations, was inspecting the mess-decks and flats at 8.30 p.m., preceded by a boatswain's mate piping "attention for the rounds". He had just reached the seamen's mess-deck, when his keen eye noticed that the faces of the men, standing at attention by their mess-tables, bore, one and all, an expression of restrained amusement quite foreign to their usually placid countenances. He paused for a moment inside the watertight bulkhead, and in that moment his cap was gently removed by a small brown hand attached to a skinny arm stretched out over the ventilation trunk above his head.

Now the First Lieutenant was a brave man under ordinary circumstances, but there is something terrifying to the stoutest of hearts when the supernatural occurs as a man goes upon his lawful occasions. His jaw dropped, and a choked explosive titter went up from the seamen's mess. He looked up and saw Shadi, squatting on his haunches, carefully and with both hands trying on his cap; his face bore that rapt expression, oblivious of her surroundings, to be seen on a woman's countenance when trying on a new hat in front of a mirror. It was greatly to No. 1's credit that he did not give way to a paroxysm of wrath, which in some men always accompanies and, incidentally, adds to a sudden unexpected loss of dignity. He merely grinned and said quietly, "After you with my tile, old chap," then turning to the apologetic petty officer who, not without opposition, had retrieved the cap, he said, "Find out who brought that damned animal on board. I'll look into the case to-morrow."

Since the occasion when the ship's cat, a marvel of productivity, had last justified her existence, mammalian pets had been *verboten* aboard the *Circe*. The Captain was a man who liked animals well enough "in their proper place", as he expressed it, the proper place for a cat, in his opinion, being the bottom of a pool with half a brick secured to its neck. He may be excused, therefore, when he expressed resentment, after spending two days ashore at Aden, on discovering seven new-born blind kittens and a proud mamma-cat on his embroidered bed-cover. A few days previously he was paying a visit to the wardroom for his "sundowner", when the chameleon overbalanced in its efforts to secure a cockroach, fell into the electric fan, and was distributed all over the mess. He was thoroughly convinced that a small ship in the tropics is no place for pets, especially when long voyages have to be made.

Needless to say, at the inquiry next day, none of the crew had the slightest idea who had brought the monkey on board. The Regulating Petty Officer, who thought that he, if anybody, ought to make some suggestion, "surmised as the creature 'ad come aboard on its own, kind of stowaway as it might be," while the rank and file, true to type, very wisely offered no suggestion at all for fear of being tied up under expert cross-examination. The First Lieutenant, in a final hopeless attempt to discover the offender, adopted the policy of Solomon in judgment, and hinted darkly that the monkey was to be destroyed. Sloggett had overheard the remark, but he knew his man, and having witnessed the episode of the cap he felt that the worst No. 1 would do would be to send Shadi ashore at Bombay.

This was all very well; but there were the Captain's orders in black and white, "No animals are to be allowed on board as pets." The matter was discussed in the wardroom; and the doctor, who, to promote argument professed to believe in the transmigration of souls, said that Shadi was probably the spiritual embodiment of the late Maltese messman, whom, facially, he greatly resembled. Officer's steward, first class, Antonio Tabona must, he said, have died of a surfeit of garlic on arrival in his native island, and the monkey had been sent to haunt his late messmates, who had never fully appreciated his good points. In that case there was no question of any one having brought him on board; he had just been evolved out of nothing.

Now the Captain had spent three years off and on in the Persian Gulf, and had a liver like the proverbial Strassburg goose. No. 1 knew full well that the old man was quite un-approachable before eleven o'clock in the forenoon, but after that he was often as docile and sweet-tempered as one could wish. Allowing an extra half-hour for luck, No. 1 went along to the Captain to report the presence of the hated mammal. "Please, sir, I found a monkey on board last night. I don't know how it arrived. I think it must have come in over the brow before the ship shoved off yesterday."

"Found a *what?*" howled the Captain "*Monkey?* Wring its neck; d'you hear what I say?"

No. 1 certainly did, so did the wardroom officers through the bulkhead, and they listened attentively. No. 1, as I said before, was a brave man, and he stood his ground and said, "We'll be in Bombay on Wednesday, sir; could you give me leave to send it ashore then? It's a pity to kill it; besides, I think it's rather a rare kind of monkey."

"Pity be damned," said the Captain. "I don't care if it's as rare as Ben Jonson; I won't have my ship turned into a blinkin' menagerie for homeless, anthropoid, bally apes. The brute will be having a litter in my bunk like that infernal cat at Aden."

"It can't do that, sir," said No. 1 mildly; "it's a Tom-monkey. I'll see that he never comes near the quarter-deck."

The Skipper was a genial man by nature; besides he had enjoyed a really good bark. So Shadi's life was spared, but he was to be sent ashore at Bombay when the postman landed with the mails.

The next day was Sunday. The Captain was inspecting the seamen's division, pausing here and there to point out a small error in the cut of a jumper or the "sit" of a collar. The left-hand man of the front rank was almost hidden by the man on his right. It was Shadi, rigged in his best "No. 6" suit, correct in every minute detail demanded by the uniform regulations. He stood at attention, and if one could judge by the expression of his sad little phiz, he appreciated the gravity of the occasion, and that his fate hung in the balance. After this there was no question of his leaving the ship at Bombay. The Captain told No. 1 that as long as the monkey behaved properly and didn't disgrace his uniform, he could remain in the ship for the present.

In a small ship like the *Circe*, fate always provides a man who is specially gifted as an odd-job expert. Such an one was Able Seaman Sloggett. He carried out the duties of butcher, lamp-trimmer, painter, sail-maker, and sanitary engineer of that tiny unit of the Navy. When the ship was at sea or anchored at some deserted spot, he performed his varied "chores" with the greatest skill and thoroughness, though his knowledge had all come to him by light of nature. But when his ship arrived at a port where general leave was given, the effect on Sloggett was lamentable. Despite the most careful watching on the part of his devoted messmates, he would break away, and in less than an hour he would drink himself into a condition of complete paralysis, to be returned on board by a patrol or a squad of police. His invariable excuse at Captain's petty session, "I 'ad a couple of wets, sir, and don't remember no more," was probably a fairly accurate description of the debauch. Sometimes forty-eight hours would elapse before the "body" arrived on board, but he never missed the ship. His life was spent in long leave-stopped periods punctuated by the most frightful blinds, when the affairs of the ship would gang all a'gley.

When Shadi had become an accepted member of the ship's company, Sloggett constituted himself sea-daddy to the little beast. It was he who made the uniform and cut down a sennet-hat to fit Shadi's small round head. He even took upon himself to award or remove good conduct badges—blatant emblems of respectability which Sloggett had never been able to achieve for his own arm.

Shadi used to sleep in a wee navy-pattern hammock alongside his daddy. He was always ready to turn in at night, but, with the first grey light of dawn, a small black muzzle would appear over the edge of the canvas, and his twinkling, wide-awake, boot-button eyes would search the upper deck for something of interest. He knew that he was not allowed to turn out before the hands; if he attempted to do so, the boatswain's mate would point at him and say sternly, "'Ere, get back you. 'Oo said you could turn out?" and Shadi, chirruping pettishly, would snuggle down again into the depths of his flea-bag.

Several months had passed, and the old Captain had left the ship. The new officer, though holding extreme views on the subject of wine-bills and brass-work, had so far expressed no opinion, favourable or otherwise, about pets. To Shadi's great joy a gazelle and two wire-haired terrier puppies had been added to the *Circe's* complement. The ship was up the Persian Gulf, and the heat was intense. In the late afternoon, when the setting sun sank below the edge of the double awning, Shadi would stretch himself and glance over the edge of the wardroom hatchway-cover, where he had been having his siesta. His next move would be to collect the two puppies, and then go and hunt the gazelle. If that long-suffering beast refused to play, the monkey would jump on his back and pull his ears till he started off. Then would ensue the most delightful chivvy all round the upper deck, the two panting puppies, well in the rear, falling over themselves and squealing with excitement. When the gazelle considered that the pack had taken enough exercise, he would leap on to the after capstan and point his horns at Shadi, who would then round on the puppies and throw them into the sea. The pups enjoyed the whole affair enormously, though, in a tideway, it often meant that the quartermaster had to go away in a skiff to rescue them. They both finished the commission, though how they escaped a violent death was always a mystery.

When up the Tigris the *Circe* generally secured to the Bund with her starboard side open to midstream. Big unwieldy Arab boats would work their way down-river with the stream, and, having unloaded, warp their way slowly back against the current. When they came to any natural hazard, such as a vessel moored to the Bund, they had to pass in the tow and claw their way along with boat-hooks. The *Circe* was one of the most aggravating obstacles to their passage, and they often used to rest, half-way along her side, after passing a hook rope through one of her eye-bolts. The Arabs in these boats used to carry out a little mild pilfering through the *Circe's* scuttles, which were always left open to catch any stray puffs of fresh air which might be blowing about. To guard against this, the quartermaster used to have an ammunition dump of lumps of coal and odd pieces of wood with which to bombard the Arabs should they delay unduly. Shadi was on very bad terms with the Arabs, many of whom had never seen a monkey before, and were convinced that he was the Evil One—hence his name.

After a day or two secured to the Bund, the quartermaster found that he could safely leave the care of the Arab boats to Shadi, though he was almost too attentive to duty. As soon as a boat came within heaving distance the fun started; he didn't confine himself to coal—rope's ends, scrapers, boats' crutches, books, in fact anything he could lift would be slung at the wretched boat. He was a very good shot. Once when the officers had just finished breakfast on the upper deck, and before the table was cleared, Shadi was found in the forecastle bombarding a white-bearded old prophet in flowing robes, who was frantically trying to haul clear against a three-knot current. Two cups and a cruet had gone west before Sloggett appeared with collar and chain.

The wardroom messing was of that bully-beef and tinned-vegetable variety which is one of the drawbacks of a small ship in the tropics. Any change in diet was welcome. The doctor was a man with a cultivated and most discriminating palate—his eggs had to be boiled for three and three-quarter minutes, and he never ate the butt-ends of the tinned asparagus (3s. 6d. a tin) which he allowed himself on Sunday for supper. The bill of fare, to a man like him, was absolutely unspeakable—anything was worth trying as a change.

Now a Tigris salmon is a heavy slothful fish, with no good points about him either as sport or fodder. He swallows one's bait if he is clever enough to find it and is duly hauled on board, and when cooked he tastes like cotton wool stuffed with pins. The doctor disliked Tigris salmon as food, but he didn't hate it quite as much as he had come to loathe Maconachie rations.

One sultry evening he could have been seen sprawling in a deck-chair, a French novel in one hand and a fishing-line in the other. The evening steeplechase was over, and the puppies were shaking themselves after their swim. Shadi was looking round for some form of amusement when he spotted the doctor's fishing-line. With his head slightly on one side, he came slinking across the deck to the doctor, and gently tweaked the line to call attention to himself. He had seen a fish caught once, and though he had been rather frightened he thought he ought to be in at the death if it occurred again. Shadi noticed that there was a lump of dough for rebaiting the hook beside the doctor's chair, so, awaiting his opportunity, he snatched it up, stuffed it into his mouth, and shot up the fore-stay like a rocket. Then he ran along to the yard-arm, and squatted there gibbering at the doctor, who shook his fist at him and had to send down for more bait.

Shadi, though actually a member of the seamen's mess, used to dine in the wardroom twice a week as the doctor's guest. On the night of the bait incident he had quickly made friends with his host, and was sitting on a high stool between the doctor and the First Lieutenant. The desiccated soup course was over, and No. 1 had just been served with his tinned solids. Shadi watched him anxiously as, with a sigh, he doled himself out two spoonfuls of Heinz's beans to supply the lack of potatoes. Then, stealthily, the guest removed from the pouch in his cheek the lump of dough which had been there for three hours, and with his other hand he scooped up the beans from No. 1's plate. Then "plonk!" he flung down the dough on his messmate's plate and put the beans in his mouth. The First Lieutenant was, unfortunately, a man with an appetite which needed much coaxing, and he had to leave the table at the run. But it was impossible to be angry with Shadi, he had effected the exchange so deftly and with such scrupulous fairness.

The *Circe* had been ordered to China, and was on passage to Bombay for docking and a small refit. Opinions differed on the subject of the monkey. Some said that he would not be able to stand the cold in the north of China, while others, headed by Sloggett, said that the ship wouldn't be able to get on without him, and in any case he'd like the change. They were all prepared to do what they could for his good. Shadi settled the matter in his own way.

The ship was about five hours' steaming from Bombay, and the "time of arrival" signal was being drafted and sent to the wireless office. Under the awning, abaft the mess-deck hatch, Able Seaman Sloggett sat on a packing-case opening up bully-beef for the ship's company's dinner. Shadi, though a vegetarian himself, was not rabid on the subject, and was scooping out small pieces of meat which remained in the tins, and throwing them to the two puppies, which were chained together to the foot of the bridge ladder. This was not very exciting, so he strolled across to the other side of the deck, and started pulling to pieces a coir mat outside the wardroom hatch. While he was engaged on this pastime, he remembered that he had left some treasures up in the "crow's nest". He bounded into the rigging and raced up to the masthead. While he was grubbing about amongst the dates and banana skins he found a ball of spun-yarn, which he didn't particularly want, and which would make a good missile. Seeing the puppies underneath him, half-hidden by the awning, he walked along the yard to get a clearer shot. Holding on to the stay with his left hand, and standing with one foot on the yard and the other on the high-tension aerial, he was about to throw the ball of yarn when, down below in the wireless office, the operator started to make the signal.

Sloggett had just finished his job, and was about to throw the empty tins over the side, when he heard a thud on the other side of the deck. He looked round a corner of the hatch, and there, in a pathetic little heap, lay Shadi. He was just moving, but obviously wouldn't live long. A seaman carrying a bucket came up the ladder from the mess-deck. Sloggett handed him a broomstick, and pointing at Shadi, said, "'Ere, Bill, finish off the poor little bounder; *I* can't touch 'im."

At 1.30 that afternoon a group of sad-faced men were standing by the ensign staff at the after end of the *Circe's* quarter-deck. In their midst stood Sloggett carrying Shadi's hammock, sewn up and weighted with a 3-pounder shot. The bugler boy sounded the last post, and Shadi's body was lowered into the sea.

THE DAY'S WORK

Sub-Lieutenant Andrew Carr crouched in the basket of the kite-balloon, his numbed fingers gripping the telephone receiver—the microphone of which he pressed against his ear. With the other hand he clutched the edge of the gyrating gondola, as squalls of icy wind swooped down on the balloon.

"Blazes!" he muttered, glancing first at the snow-laden wrack in the north-western sky, then down at the deck of the kite-balloon depot-ship some thousand feet below him. "Blazes!" he repeated, "when *are* they going to give the signal 'Haul Down'?"

A feeling of exasperated impotence filled his soul. Up here he could see the urgency: down there they were fussing with the depot-ship's boats. Oh, he knew there was a blizzard threatening—more than threatening; for its first icy messengers were then screaming through the wickerwork of the basket and drumming through the gondola-stays. Above his head—though he dared not glance up too frequently, for it made him giddy—the balloon was swooping and pitching in a manner he did not care to see.

"Boats!" he stormed suddenly, as he stamped deadened feet on the frail platform. "Boats! why worry about boats? Why not get the damned balloon down to its night stowage before this blasted storm really breaks?" He dropped the telephone suddenly and grabbed at a stay, for a terrific gust had lifted the balloon-envelope and thrown it bodily to one side: with a frightening jerk the basket was yanked sideways so that for a moment the platform was angled at forty-five degrees. Cold fear gripped Andrew Carr as the stay in his right hand grew suddenly slack. The gondola began to droop at one end. In-stinctively he shuffled up to the higher end. "Gosh!" he mut-tered, his eyes full of fear, "the port for'ard stay's been torn out of its basket joint—there are only three more—oh, why *don't* they give the order for 'Haul Down'?"

He grabbed the telephone-receiver again and shouted down the mouthpiece. "Depot-ship! Depot-ship! Below there: why'n hell don't you haul me down? One of the basket-stays has parted: it's blowing like stink up here—oh, get a move on, why the . . ."

Andrew broke off. For the first time in his young life, panic threatened to obliterate every sense he had. Although he was numbed to the core, sweat beaded on his face, trickling down his nose, falling from under his woollen helmet and freezing on cheeks and lips. He felt, somehow, abandoned, lost, inhumanly forgotten: none of those devils down there, mucking about with boats, seemed to care a hoot what happened to him. Frenziedly he struggled against the waves of panic. He was only nineteen years old: a sense of unfairness assailed him. "Mucking about with boats!" he muttered bitterly—and, suddenly reckless, he leant far out over the side of the wildly swaying basket, holding his balance only because he had a knee jammed under a pro-jection. Through the darkness of the gathering night he peered down at the deck of the depot-ship below. Unconsciously, he noted the angle of the bar-taut steel wire that led downwards from the balloon to the winch of the ship. He had never realized before how frail it looked. But his eyes were concentrating through the gloom on the half-submerged picket-boat and the running figures of the seamen below moving about like ants at some desperate work.

"Something's gone wrong," he muttered, and, taking another grip with his knee, he focused with one hand his binoculars on the scene. In and out of his constricted field of vision there ap-peared now, when he managed to steady the glasses, a magni-fied view of the picket-boat as she dipped and jumped wildly alongside. Her funnel was stowed, and the stoker petty officer and two seamen-crew staggered and swung about her reeling deck in their attempts to hook the heavy ring of her slings on to the vast steel hook of the main-derrick hoist.

"Gosh!" said Andrew suddenly, as a sea broke over the boat's bows and the figures were hidden in whirling spray. "Gosh! if they don't get a move on, she'll founder alongside before they get her hoisted!" He could sympathize with that sweating, struggling crew; he had been midshipman of a boat himself when she bucked and cavorted and strong men were thrown about by a huge leaden ball just above the main derrick hook.

A new high note in the humming wind attracted Andrew's attention. He withdrew his straining eyes from the glasses and took a wider look at the vast harbour below. The sea was a medley of spume and scud, the smoky grey waves marbled into a seething white cauldron by the shrieking squall. In a moment, Andrew saw, it would reach the depot-ship, between which and the nor'-western shore of the low-lying islands everything was now blurred. Away beyond the depot-ship, plumes and eddies of smoke flew horizontally to leeward from the waking titans whose bulk loomed dim and monstrous—line after line. Battleships, cruisers, destroyers—the fleet was raising steam. The worst gale of the worst year's weather was breaking over the harbour.

Numbed, almost deafened, his frozen feet, hands and face leaden and blue, Andrew Carr crouched in his flimsy basket and peered through watery, narrowed eyes at the desolation below. His momentary panic had gone. Something of the majesty and sheer elemental destructiveness of the great gale that boomed and roared round his eyrie and blotted out distance and landmarks aroused an answering pæan in his heart. The great frozen wind spoke with the certainty of a mighty organ prelude, with a force and a passion that tore through the flimsy sense of civilized convention like a mastodon in full and resistless stride. Dimly, Andrew felt nerved up for great events. The brotherhood and support of countless generations of seamen seemed suddenly to close around him. Almost, in the hum and screech of the wind, he heard their strong deep voices over-riding the roar of the gale. Andrew braced his young body, and the lines of his mouth grew taut and hard, as a kind of nervous exultation gripped him. If only he could get down, he felt, and find some time to think: to sit in a comfortable chair in front of the wardroom stove, and be able to say with the airiness of nineteen years, slowly, gravely, "Yes, it *was* a bit thick . . . damn it all, they might have hauled me down before . . . I mean . . ." and knowing all the while in his inmost mind that he had been scared to death, had been feeling panic-stricken, and cold and miserable. It would be an experience to hug to himself with a kind of relish, somehow, and the implications and reactions of which—with a mystery all their own—could be explored tentatively and truthfully, but with a certain caution, in the five minutes as he lay in his bunk at night before switching off the cabin-light.

A loud crack, startling, unexpected, galvanized Andrew into sudden life, so that he gripped the edge of the basket and peered fearfully upwards. But the underside of the rolling, plunging balloon-envelope was in dark shadow, where night seemed already to have fallen. Though he looked up and thought he could see a waving end of thick wire, he could not be sure—only the suspicion lingered that something else in the rigging had parted.

As if remembering, he leant over the edge of the basket again and peered down at his floating home. The squall had shrieked on down harbour, and a huge rising sea had gathered in its wake. Big hummocks, razor-edged and grey-white, and deep hollows loomed significantly.

Andrew focused his glasses on the depot-ship and, tense for a moment, stared unbelievingly down. The picket-boat had gone. Moving the glasses frantically he caught at last a passing but steady look at the boat's empty crutches on the depot-ship's high deck.

His face paled.

"Gone!" he whispered—and as if in reply his own sense of dependability vanished. That chair in front of the wardroom fire; that snug little cabin housing warm changes of clothing:

all suddenly seemed to fade; they grew evanescent as hope itself. No longer could he depend on them. The depot-ship, that solid ten-thousand-ton vessel, their parent-ship, was not so certain, not so solid after all. She could not even guarantee the safety of her own picket-boat alongside. What chance, then, for him? In this tremendous storm she might drag her anchors . . . she might . . . the wardroom fire seemed all at once a picture from the past: that cabin a strange memory; in neither had he a confident stake now.

Andrew slumped down on the slanting platform and stared with unseeing eyes at the bearing indicator within a foot of his head. Then, dully, he noticed that its tarpaulin cover had gone, blown to shreds by the roaring gusts that still whistled over the edge and through the wickerwork of the basket.

As he crouched in a lethargy, almost comatose, the telephone-bell rang shrilly, urgently, through the basket—its pitiful little tinkle whipped away by the wind almost as soon as it sounded.

But Andrew had heard it. Kneeling low in the basket, he held the receiver against his frozen ear and shouted down the mouthpiece—

"Hullo! Hullo! At last! What the . . ."

But he broke off and listened to the urgent voice the other end.

"Carr, Carr; are you all right? Listen: we've had several kinds of trouble. Lost the picket-boat . . . swamped being hoisted in, and the coxswain's . . . no, we couldn't lower a boat; wouldn't have lived a moment in the sea that's running . . ."

"Yes, yes; that's all very well," Andrew's voice broke in. "But d'you realize this perishing basket I'm in's only hanging by a thread. Yes, one of the stays has gone. What . . ." Andrew burst into profanity. "Hell, man; I've been roaring down this blasted mouthpiece till I'm blue in the face . . .!"

"That'll do, Carr . . ." Andrew grinned as he listened. "This is 'on service'. Because we're friends, no reason why you should fly off the handle like this. I've been pretty busy down here. Now, listen, old man: take this in. Can you hear?"

Andrew spoke soothingly. "All right, old boy: I'm listening."

The voice of twenty-one spoke again crisply, authoritatively—

"We may have to let the balloon go—to get *you*, see? We're ready—double-banked this end—only chance's to heave down quick and steady—so once we start, hold tight, and look out—and remember these instructions—if a red light's flashed continuously from the winch aft—keep your eye on it, for heaven's sake—that's a signal to pull the rip-cord and scupper the balloon. Remember, after that, you've got about sixty seconds to get aboard. If you have to sink her—it may be your only chance—nip over the side and come down the wire hand over hand: we'll have a net ready for you, and . . . well, we'll be ready anyhow . . ."

Andrew Carr shivered. The emergency escape! The last resort of the kite-balloonists! Gosh, he thought, things must be bad if old Jimmy considered it was the only chance—and his balloons were the apple of his eye. A harsh jerk, like a badly-started lift, threw him in a heap on the bottom of the car. Bruised, he scrambled to his feet and glanced downwards at the wire. It was pulsing and vibrating. The winch had begun to heave-in.

The new strain on the wire and the downward motion somewhat steadied the gondola, though above his head Andrew heard with uneasy ears the rasping of the rigging and the straining fabric.

But the kite-balloon was coming in fast. Jimmy was taking the chance of heaving-in full speed. Andrew glanced at the dial. 900 feet . . . 850—800—750—700 . . . yes, he was coming down fast. Under his feet, the depot-ship was growing bigger and bigger. He could now recognize expressions on the features of the white faces peering up at him from the decks below: they seemed anxious. The men in oilskins round the winch looked now and again over their shoulders. Andrew shifted his position and threw a glance that way too. As he did so, his eyes widened, and, unconsciously, his hands took a fresh, convulsive grip of the gondola-edge. Another squall was sweeping towards the depot-ship: not half a mile away, the sea vanished in a smoking smother of rain and whitened water that eddied and boiled.

Andrew glanced at the height-indicator. 500 feet now. It seemed the last straw; when he was so near safety.

With a moaning hiss, the squall burst over the depot-ship —the sub-lieutenant catching a last look at the white faces below. He saw Jimmy, his C.O., frantically urging the last ounce out of the winchman; then, with a scream, the wind struck the balloon. The stays and rigging hummed: the basket seemed to jerk sideways and upwards with a wild, horrifying motion that struck intense fear into Andrew's heart. Peering out through the driving rain, he could not see any envelope above as the squall roared past. There came a sudden jarring crack, and Andrew groaned. At once, he sensed the free, lifting motion as if he were soaring skywards on a mighty swing. His chest and stomach all at once appeared to have been left hundreds of feet below him. Wedged in the corner of the careening basket he threw a horrified look downwards. The depot-ship had disappeared—lost in the welter of the squall. But he had seen enough. His face grew grey, as the realization came that he was utterly lost now, with no possibility, even, of trying out the emergency plan outlined by his C.O.

Below the basket, the parted winch-wire whipped and snaked and vibrated as if exulting in its utter freedom, while the wind, as if screaming its final triumph, howled as it battered the reeling torpedo-shaped envelope—howled and died away. Dazed, Andrew crouched below the edge of the car. The motion was worse than anything he had ever experienced. The awesome swoops and sickening side-plunges of the driven balloon made him feel as if he were tethered to the tail of a playful comet that gambolled in quarter-mile circles. But the atmosphere round the soaring car grew lighter, though the swiftness of his motion still made him gasp. Soon, with one frantic eye, he pierced the gloom below. The untethered kite-balloon had risen a thousand feet. A mile away to the nor'-west'ard, he saw the depot-ship.

"First the picket-boat, now me," yelled Andrew, anger

choking him. "What a ship!" But his fury was short-lived. He
noted the rapid, urgent flash of her masthead signalling light
—and he realized that in ten minutes it would be dark. His
thoughts cleared. With quick, practised eye, he took a snap-
bearing of the fast-vanishing depot-ship, then drew out from its
locker the powerful electric signalling lamp. But before using
it, he fired six charges downwards, from the brass Very
pistol, and the sight of their trailing, red lights cutting
brilliantly through the darkness towards the fleet brought a
badly-needed comfort to his young heart. Then he trained the
lamp over the edge and followed the Verey emergency signals
with a crisp morse message, repeated over and over again:

"Adrift. Course south-east. Speed sixty knots. Balloon
damaged. Am going to use rip-cord middle harbour. S O S
S O S."

Andrew was putting the signal-lamp away in the locker, his
eye already on the rip-cord, when a cross-current of wind
swooped down like an eddy of the gale. The balloon-envelope
lurched away to the south-west—the gondola jerked off to
the east. Andrew's feet were swung away off the platform: his
balance lost, he fell in a heap on the edge of the car. For a
moment, the wind knocked out of him, he trembled in the
balance, then slumped down into the basket. Winded, he fell
heavily, and his head met the solid bearing-indicator. In the
bottom of the basket he lay still; from under the woollen helmet
a trickle of blood slowly spread. . . .

On the bare, wet deck of the duty destroyer, a big man in
oilskins struggled aft. Arriving at the wardroom hatch, he
panted for breath, then clattered down the iron ladder. As he
twitched the curtain of the door aside, the captain glanced up
sharply. "What is it, torpedo cox'n?" he asked.

"Kite-balloon adrift, sir—half-way across the harbour.
There's—" the torpedo cox'n took another breath, "there's
somebody aloft in her, sir."

The tall, hook-nosed lieutenant-commander was already on
his feet, struggling into the oilskin lying handy on a near-by

chair. He was rather expecting something like this. As he settled the scarf round his neck, the yeoman of signals came down the ladder with a signal. "Priority, sir!" he reported, holding out the pad.

"Very good." The captain read it swiftly, then put it in his pocket. "Cox'n," he ordered. "My compliments to the first lieutenant on the bridge. Stand-by to slip at once—cable and all—at the first shackle, yes. We can retrieve it later. Chief"— the captain turned to another figure—"we're at five minutes' notice I know, but—I want to slip in a minute and a half from now. Sub!"

"Sir!" The young sub-lieutenant was making fast a length of spunyarn round the waist of his oilskins. "Sir?"

"Chart of the harbour—and the Pentland Firth—to start with. Up on the bridge with you. See if you can pick up the kite-balloon. If you find her—hold her. Get bearings, and check up on her course. Yeoman, make a signal: 'Am slipping at once in accordance with instructions received.'"

A rumbling noise came from forward. The first lieutenant had slipped the cable. The captain nodded his head appreciatively and ran for the ladder to the upper-deck. He had two hundred feet to travel to the bridge, and, in the weather prevailing, he knew the wire slip-rope would not last long.

On the bridge the special sea-dutymen stood by at their stations. The captain leant over the compass and took a quick glance round—a glance almost perfunctory, for all the salient points of the anchorage had long since been deeply etched in memory.

Figures loomed on the long, wet forecastle from which hoarse voices sounded, their insistent tones seeming to swirl disembodied, errant, without ownership, in the blast of the wind, now appearing close up, and with something of urgency, against the bridge-screens, then fading away, lost, in the darkness—as if they had been projected into the night-murk and surrendered to the overpowering, enveloping voice of the gale.

The captain, his shoulders hunched up, leant over the rails. "Slip!" he roared through a megaphone, and, like a faint echo, the order came back from the forecastle-head: "Slip, sir! All gone for'ard, sir!"

"Hard-a-port: half ahead port, slow astern starboard." The captain's order came just one minute and twenty-five seconds after he had jumped to his feet in the wardroom.

The long, scarce-distinguishable shape of the destroyer shuddered gently, then, like a vibrating wraith, she moved, mysterious, responsive, slowly at first, then faster. "Ten knots," the captain ordered, his eye piercing the gloom aft, his mind cognisant of the exact position of the invisible poop to which led the twin strips of gleaming corticine decks on either side of the funnels. At the wheel, the torpedo cox'n slanted a look at the yeoman of signals. "We're going to get wet soon," he muttered.

The man holding the telescope made an impatient movement by way of reply. He was looking round the harbour for relevant signals in the swift, instinctive exercise of his craft, his flitting eye reading, rejecting, selecting, the twinkling morse messages as a post-office sorter deals with a multitude of letters. As the destroyer swung round, he moved continually across the bridge in the background, appearing suddenly alongside the port look-out one moment only to materialize the next at the sub-lieutenant's elbow. In his ceaseless, restless search for vantage points, where visibility was good, he had the air of an oil-skinned jack-o'-lantern. The torpedo cox'n's remark was relegated to a corner of his mind whence it could be extracted when things were less pressing.

The destroyer was swinging fast now—seeming to spin round the hub of her bows, and the gusts of wind swirled through the bridge. Forcibly, at that moment, pitted against the blast of the wind and the assault of steep-pitched waves, the long dark boat seemed to present in her swift responsive obedience, eager, satisfying, the crystallization of some long-thought-out purpose of her distant designer—to entrust to the trained seamen who stood on her bridge, in control, a vastly powerful, yet delicate, engine of tremendous potentialities: a racing, lithe ship crammed full of mechanical perfection of detail, with the speed of a racehorse and the bite of a tarantula.

As if her lean shape were peculiarly adapted to crowded anchorages and constricted waters, the destroyer snaked her way easily, at fifteen knots, through the narrow channel. "Yes," replied the yeoman at last as he paused by the torpedo cox'n, "you're right; we're going to get wet." Out of the corner of his eye the cox'n caught a gleam of light and heard the sharp snap as the telescope extension was shot home. Though he did not see it, he knew the yeoman had tucked the instrument under his arm. He always did when they reached that part of the channel.

More than spray was coming over the flared bows now; for the fierce, steep waves had travelled over seven miles across the wide harbour before they broke heavily against the destroyer's questing stem. In the angle of the bridge, just forward of the ready-use chart-table, the captain stood jammed into his favourite corner. "You'd better get out of that," the first lieutenant had warned a new sub-lieutenant; "that's the owner's pet nook." And so it had always remained. Near by, the sub. kept an eye on the ship's course—more as a matter of routine than of necessity, for the torpedo cox'n was eminently dependable. The shrouded glow from the binnacle light shone upwards, lending a meretricious air of snugness to the enclosed bridge. As the cox'n moved the spokes of the wheel with sensitive, firm hands, the telemotor-gear sounded faintly, like a low-pitched chatter of protest, against the whistle of the wind and the drumming of spray on the bridge-screens.

The captain, without taking his eyes off the darkness ahead, held a muttered conversation with the sub.

"I know him," the latter said. "Yes, sir; you could just see the balloon through glasses . . . about the middle of the Firth, and going, well, just like the wind. Wonder why'n earth he didn't rip her and come down here?"

"May have got damaged." The captain spoke tersely, frowning into the night. "Has the answer to that signal come yet, yeoman?"

"Just coming through now, sir."

The captain grunted. "Just as well; I never did like the idea of charging a boom in a gale—and three of 'em. . . ."

Night had fallen completely as the duty destroyer bore down on the first of the booms. The gate-ship's lights shone out brightly, but they wallowed and plunged in the rising sea. The kite-balloon had disappeared into the south-east'ard.

"Golly, sir," the sub. breathed, looking ahead with wide-opened eyes, "there'll be some sea running in Pentland Firth."

The captain nodded. "It'll be a following sea, fortunately. I wouldn't care to try the Old Man of Hoy to-night—not after seeing what he can do to a full-blown battleship."

The sub.'s features grew suddenly grave, and a little disquieted, for he also had seen the spectacle alluded to: a grey, battered ship slowly steaming into harbour with her upper-works and superstructure looking as if she had been in action —as indeed she had, but the opponent in this case had been Nature, whose onslaughts are more terrifying than anything yet invented by the puny hand of mankind.

"It was a kind of wall of water, wasn't it, sir?" suggested the sub. in subdued tones.

The captain waved a hand at a dim figure on the tiny bridge of the gate-ship.

"Yes," he replied. "When you get a ten-knot current piling up against a contrary gale of wind with an uneven sea-bed in a constricted channel—well, curious things in waves result. You may run suddenly into a hole in the sea—and on the other side of the hole maybe there's a vertical wave of water sixty feet high waiting to welcome you. . . ."

The sub. shuddered, glad they were bound east'ard, not westward.

The destroyer slipped through the third boom gate. She cleared the narrow channel and came out into the Firth. The captain eased her away from the islands and watched the white-flecked mountains that rolled up in disarray ahead. His lips tightened and he gripped the rails as he gave the order "starboard ten". The cox'n was frowning with concentration at the wheel, his legs wide-straddled on the grating, his hands gripping the spokes more firmly. He muttered to himself as the fierce current took the boat in its swirling stride. The captain glanced quickly at the compass and looked out through his glasses. "Steady her head three points to port," he ordered as the boat lurched up on the shoulder of a huge following sea and yawed points away off her course.

"Ay, ay, sir," the cox'n replied. "Steady she is, sir, course south-east."

The sub. staggered to the chart-table, and lifting the canvas flap disappeared, as to the upper half of his body, into the gloomy recess. Switching on the tiny lamp, he entered up time and alteration of course in the navigator's notebook. As he leant there, temporarily cut off from the whistling hum of the wind, he muttered to himself fervently, "I'll be glad when the old hooker's out of this damned spot"; then, as he kept his feet with difficulty, an urgent need for human companionship gripped him, so that he struggled backwards out of the canvas flap and reeled to a friendly rail. After a moment, he noticed a new figure looming near. "What a night, No. 1!" he bawled. The newcomer nodded his sou'wester vigorously. "Be glad . . . when we . . . get out of the Firth."

The sub., glancing at the captain, wondered suddenly what that sphinx-like figure was thinking of so deeply. Then he saw that the torpedo cox'n was keeping his feet only with considerable difficulty. The wind roared after the reeling destroyer as if in a malicious frenzy that she was escaping: black clouds of smoke, greasy, pungent with the heavy smell of oil, swept forward from the squat funnels and enveloped the bridge; for the "Chief" was hotting-up his boilers, ready for any call for increased speed.

Aft, out of the welter of foam and driving spray, enormous heavy seas roared up, carrying in their mountainous bulk a strange impression every now and again of perpetual motion, so that the observer is persuaded they are only half-way on their thunderous journey round the world, immutable, permanent, and, as long as the ship can keep ahead of them, on a more or less fixed course, not particularly hostile.

Something of this impression came to the first lieutenant as he peered aft through narrowed eyes—though he was not looking so much at the vast following sea as at the clean-swept decks, and double-lashed gear, for which he was responsible. Then out of the murk astern his eye caught sight suddenly of a dark-looming mountain of a height so incredible that he jumped across the bridge and caught the captain's arm. At the head of the bridge-ladder, together, a few seconds later, they gripped the after-rails and looked out astern where the low poop, wet, wave-swept, and glistening, appeared all at once to be supremely and absurdly near the water and vulnerable. Rearing high above it, topped by ten feet of yellow roaring spume, the personification of implacable and dangerous threat, the vast wave dwarfed the destroyer so that the first lieutenant stared at it as with a sudden revelation. Never had he realized before how narrow was the beam, how low the freeboard, of his ship.

The captain whistled once through pursed lips, then jumped to the revolution-indicator. He revolved the latter until the whirring point of the handle seemed to coruscate in a glittering circle of light—like an enormous catherine-wheel. Years after, when the wind of a westerly gale drove spattering rain against the windows in winter, and the house shook with the shock of the gusts, the first lieutenant would suddenly remember that moment. He would see again the captain's tall figure bent in fierce concentration over the revolution-indicator, and the rotary motion of his hand—as if he were winding up a huge clockwork-machine with only ten vital seconds in which to do it. Then, with the roar and hum of the gale once more drumming round him, he saw the captain leap back to his side and point a steady finger aft where the vast wave seemed to be ready to engulf the ship, drawing inexorably nearer, growing steeper, with an implacable detachment more nerve-racking than outright anger because it was the personification of Nature at her wildest. It is at moments like this that men cluster together and the individual becomes part of the tribe banded in company, conjointly, unitedly, to face and repel the danger at the cave-door. And because the ocean is so vast, so universal, and her challenge so frequent and unmistakable, the phenomenon is more common at sea. There are no mutinies in a gale, no complaints, and the bad-hat of the mess-deck is first aloft and last down.

A curious idea came to the first lieutenant as he stood gripping the after-rails of the reeling bridge. He drew closer to his captain, who, as he noticed with surprise, was pointing aft and presumably speaking, for his lips were moving. The full force of the following gale caught at their bodies in that exposed position, tearing and flapping at their oilskins, snatching at their sou'westers. The first lieutenant bent nearer. He caught a few words before they were swept away, engulfed, by the wind.

"... Twenty knots ..." the captain was bellowing. "I think she'll stand it for a few moments ... this wave ... biggest I've ever seen ... passing over a ledge ... too near the Skerries ... must keep ahead as much as ... can ... If fall back, get pooped sure as eggs ... eggs ..."

The first lieutenant nodded vigorously, then suddenly clutched his sou'wester and swayed. Putting his mouth near the captain's ear he shouted back: "Huge ... father and mother of all waves, chasing us ... look! seems quite flat at the ridge, and high, high ..." He looked again at the wave, and there suddenly came to him an absurd fancy that in height and appearance it resembled strangely the long, clean-cut nave of a cathedral with a ten-foot line of snow left on the roof-ridge. He was about to convey his idea to the captain when he felt the ship under his feet writhe suddenly and shake. Simultaneously a hand gripped his arm.

"We're running ahead of it!" the captain was shouting in his ear. "Look! it's dropping back! Thank God! We're over that ledge ... passed it ... twenty knots ... risky—but done the trick ... must reduce soon ... though out of the Firth now."

Incredulously, the first lieutenant stared aft. The captain, he saw, was right: the huge mass of the wave appeared to be diminishing in size, its white, horizontal ridge was undoubtedly lower. The destroyer, as if exulting in her escape, was burrowing her way zealously along the floor of a deep, dark valley, and even as the first lieutenant glanced sharply for'ard over his shoulder he felt her bows rise. Out of the corner of his eye he noted that the captain was still looking fixedly aft, his gloved hands clenched on the rails, and in his whole appearance there was something irresistibly reminiscent of the victorious boxer who stands fixedly but watchfully while his opponent is counted out. Then, as if all at once tired, the captain let go his grasp, and turning, staggered forward to his usual place at the bridge-rails, where the sub., one arm hooked round a stanchion, legs widely straddled, peered out over the smoking bows through binoculars at the sea ahead. The first lieutenant, after a quick glance along the decks, followed.

"We'll have to ease her down again," the captain said, and No. 1 nodded. The latter bent nearer. "Fifteen?" he shouted. The captain made a gesture of assent.

The first lieutenant lurched to the revolution-indicator and rang down the revolutions to the equivalent of fifteen knots. His leather sea-boots appeared to be getting very heavy, his oilskin a burden. From his position at the rails, the captain was making signs which No. 1 easily interpreted. He touched the torpedo cox'n's arm. "All right, cox'n; turn over to the quartermaster now, then go below. On the way for'ard tell the P.O. of the watch to have a look at the gripes of the motorboat and whaler—and take in any slack. When we alter course to the east'ard, there'll be some heavy seas coming aboard in the waist."

The torpedo cox'n, having turned over to the quartermaster, saluted. "Ay, ay, sir," he said, and his voice sounded hoarse. He stepped down stiffly from the grating, and the lines of his gaunt face showed deep, grim, in the glow of the binnacle light.

Two hours later—watches forgotten—the captain, the first lieutenant, and the sub. still held the bridge. The destroyer's course had been altered to east; and her motion for an hour was frightful; heavy seas stormed her port quarter, breaking green on her low upper-deck and cascading through gun platforms and torpedo tubes. The three officers, except for an occasional remark, were silent. They found talking too difficult. Once the sub. had pointed aft and shouted into the first lieutenant's ear: "The wardroom hatch's gone again, No. 1!" and the latter had smiled grimly and replied: "More than that would have gone if that big one had pooped us—and, anyhow, we could do with a new hatch; we wanted one badly."

Now and again the skipper had struggled down to the charthouse and made rough calculations in regard to course and speed. He was keeping a close watch on the wind, for the direction of the wind—or its opposite—was the course that the unfortunate kite-balloon must perforce follow.

A curious phenomenon of those northern waters—of which the skipper was well aware—is that though a gale may be raging round the Orkneys and Shetlands, a placid calm may be holding only a hundred miles away in the North Sea. Therefore, the captain watched the wind, and at the end of two hours his scrutiny was rewarded; he was sure the wind was not only drawing aft, but also he began to suspect that there were signs the weather was about to moderate. On reaching this conclusion he raised his head and stared thoughtfully into the sky. The first lieutenant, observing him, came-to alongside.

"Backing a bit," the latter said, indicating the sea.

"Yes," the captain agreed, gripping No. 1's arm. "If it continues to draw round to the west'ard, that means our young friend aloft—who is ahead of us—will be blown first sou'east then east-sou'-east, and finally east. . . ." The wind swept away the last words, so that the first lieutenant drew closer. He saw, however, the trend of his captain's thought.

"Good thing, then, sir," he suggested. "We'll be able to cut off a bit of the corner?"

The captain nodded his head vigorously. "Yes."

The first lieutenant settled his sou'wester more firmly on his head and sent a thought after the unfortunate young officer in the balloon. Their own lot might not be so un-comfortable compared with his . . . driven helplessly before the gale away to the south-east over the open sea.

The first watch passed, and the captain was able to increase speed, for they were running out of the worst of the weather: the wind, which had backed to west, now blew in blustery squalls—those vicious blasts that often accompany the tail-end of a cyclone. The first lieutenant looked gloomily along the port side of the boat, noting the heavy damage she had sustained. As he stood gripping the bridge-rails, fragments of torn canvas, ripped from the dodgers, blew and pecked at his legs. Quite near and below him the remains of the whaler rattled eerily in the davits, round which the dim figures of the watch on deck moved cautiously. Every now and again voices reached him, and there was the intermittent sound of hammering. The first lieutenant sighed and turned away. She had been a good boat, and he had won a sailing race in her.

A signalman staggered up the bridge-ladders from the battered galley with a bowl of cocoa that he shielded from the swooping wind as if he were bearing the Crown Regalia. It was welcome: that thick ship's cocoa that no-one who has drunk it in a January gale in the North Sea will ever forget.

The middle watch dragged its stubborn hours through the night to the accompaniment of all sorts of new and strange groans and rattles from protesting beams and loosened cordage. The sub. had been sent down to the charthouse for a stand-easy, but the captain and the first lieutenant still stood leaden-footed on the bridge, the salt caking their faces, from which gleamed blood-shot eyes irritated by the greasy, pungent oil-fuel smoke; and neither was without painful bruises occasioned by sudden and violent contact with unyielding objects.

Dawn came at last to disclose a wide, yellow waste of waters, uneasy, sullen. The wind had dropped considerably, but it now blew in fitful gusts from the south. A long, hollow swell rolled up from the south-west. The destroyer looked bare as a flagstaff, her burnt funnels grey and dirty-white with caked salt. Aft, both wardroom and cabin-flat shelters had been swept away, and no-one but a seaman would have suspected that the few wisps of splintered wood on the port side had once been a whaler.

On the bridge anxious eyes searched the sea and horizon—but in vain: nothing was in sight. The skipper, moving one heavy sea-boot after the other with a kind of obdurate persistence, went down to the charthouse; came back.

"We'll alter course two points to starboard," he said. "Quartermaster, port ten."

"Port ten, sir—on, sir."

"Meet her; midships; steady!"

"Midships! Steady, sir!"

The bare, gleaming forecastle-head—visible at last—seemed to bore its powerful stem into the shoulder of a swell as the long, grey boat obediently swung to her new course; a lazy dollop of water, weighing perhaps five tons, came in over the starboard bow, brown, dirty-looking, and burst suddenly and surprisingly into a cataract of purest white and green that swirled aft and surrounded the forecastle gun until the latter looked like an island fortress—but the snap and power had gone out of its punch. Wildly flapping signal-halliards—unnoticed during the night—suddenly sounded unnaturally loud. At the rails the captain's brows drew together in a frown. He beckoned the first lieutenant.

A moment later a seaman made his way cautiously aloft, clinging with sure hands to the ratlines of the swaying Jacob's ladder that ascended to the foreyard. Arriving at the head of the ladder, he hooked one arm firmly, and stared out at the horizon. Suddenly he extended his hand, pointing, then looked down at the upturned faces on the bridge; his mouth opened, and the first lieutenant, glancing upwards with a strained attention to catch his message, noticed the flash of his teeth white against the black of his cowl-like sou'-wester. "Kite-balloon away to the south'ard!" the lookout man roared, and his stentorian hail fell upon the bridge with the urgent import of vital discovery. "Two points on the starboard bow—'bout four miles away!"

The captain gave a terse order; the bows of the destroyer bumped round to the point indicated; the revolution-indicator tinkled suddenly with a continuous whirr as accompaniment. In five minutes the derelict kite-balloon could be plainly seen. The captain's eyes narrowed as he observed her.

"She's down," he muttered; "probably been down for some time; otherwise . . . we shouldn't have overhauled her." The captain turned abruptly. "First lieutenant, see to the boat; get the crew all ready with lifebelts; warn the doctor to stand by, blankets, brandy—he'll know."

A sense of urgency descended on the occupants of the bridge, for the captain had increased speed as high as he dared—and more. The long, storm-battered ship seemed to the first lieutenant, as he felt the deep-seated throb under his feet enlarge, to grow more sonorous, to lay herself out like a lithe animal of the chase when the quarry is sighted. She stormed through the seas, propellers racing as the stern lifted over the yellow, rolling swell, sharp stem diving suddenly into the trough with a jarring thud, then, staggered, reeling forward with a violent roll while the flying spray rattled hard against the bridge-screens, stinging the tense faces peering out from above them. Soon they were quite close. The captain's hands gripped the rails with unconscious force, his grim-looking expression seeming to accentuate the prominent curve of the dominating hook-nose, and draw even deeper the two furrows that ran vertically from cheek to jaw. At half-speed, the commanding officer brought his boat round on the shoulder of a long, hollow roller; the engine-room telegraphs rang out suddenly, cleaving across the waste of yellow silence with an emphasis almost startling; at once the propellers thrashed madly astern, raising great boiling mounds of seething white water round the poop that piled up against the sheer of the stern. "Where is he?" the captain was muttering, taking hasty glances through his binoculars. There was no time to lose; the basket was awash, swept by waves, as the balloon careened drunkenly, precariously, on the surface of the sea. At one of his favourite vantage points the yeoman stood as if clamped in some extraordinary manner to the very texture of the ship's frame, so tense his concentration, so intent the whole of his being projected through the telescope in the effort of observation. The captain glanced sharply aft, and a gleam came to his bloodshot eyes; there was no time being wasted there. He saw the destroyer's dinghy take the water, one hand bailing as a confused sea broke over her. But she got away and pulled slowly over towards the balloon. The captain withdrew his gaze and turned round, for the yeoman had made a sudden exclamation as he stood leaning over the starboard rails, his hand stretched out, a flush of excitement rising in his sallow cheeks. "There! sir! There he is! Look! He's took to the basket-stays; fifteen feet above the for'ard end, almost hid; under that bulge!"

With a swift, instinctive movement, as if to lend corroboration to his report, the yeoman whipped up the telescope again and peered once more through it. But the captain was satisfied; he had seen that small huddle of clothing lashed to the upper end of one of the stays. For a fleeting moment a look of relief flashed across the weatherbeaten features. He looked again towards the destroyer's boat. There was, he saw at once, little time to lose. The balloon was growing more flabby; the storm and sea-battered envelope was failing there before his eyes; it had done well, the captain reflected, to last so long. Suddenly he drew in his breath: "Ah!" he muttered—and, as he opened his mouth, the yeoman closed up his telescope suddenly with a metallic snap. It was a symbolic movement, timed to the exact second—though the signalman was unaware of any relevancy in his action, for it was instinctive. The balloon, almost emptied of gas, had flopped on the water; like a dying fish, it moved spasmodically; then spread slowly. Somewhere under its convoluting, silvery folds was the basket.

The destroyer's boat was near now. In the sternsheets the cox'n, holding his balance by a miracle, was leaning forward, half on his feet, half crouched down. The oarsmen kept their eyes on his face. The latter was working strangely, the jaw convulsively chewing, the eyes gleaming. It seemed as if he were about to discharge at his crew some inspiriting message— but when, after what seemed a vast effort at self-expression, it came, it appeared strangely commonplace, for the cox'n, shifting his quid of tobacco, said simply and hoarsely: "What say now, lads, shall we shake her up?" The crew seemed to read into that simple message of exhortation a species of magic, however; for they "shook her up" to some effect, laying back on their oars and putting the whole weight of their strong bodies into their strokes. The cox'n, relapsing into his habitual taciturnity, regarded their efforts with an approving eye. It was only the second time in the whole of the commission that he had urged his crew to greater endeavour, and they, accordingly, judged rightly that the matter was pressing.

From the bridge of the destroyer the captain shouted through a megaphone: "Pull round the other side—get a move on! I'm coming closer."

The destroyer got too close. The greater part of the envelope was now floating, deflated, on the surface. Swept across by the southerly set, the forward end of the envelope drifted under the ship's hull. The skipper jumped to the engine-room 'phone and rang down a warning. "Right under the ship!" he muttered to the first lieutenant, who had returned to the bridge. "If we don't look out, we'll get the condenser-inlets scuppered— and full of the fabric."

In the boat, which had now reached the balloon, the bow-man was frantically pulling away the debris to get at the basket, and beyond that, the stays. The cox'n let go his tiller and came forward to help. He was up to his knees in water as he went. "Bail—and keep on bailing," he grunted to the crew. The bowman was holding on like grim death to what he had. With the cox'n's help he hauled in more. The small boat was listing madly, riding drunkenly over the long, hollow swells—almost awash. From under a ten-foot high tuck in the balloon-envelope the gondola suddenly surged out into the open; beyond it, and only two feet above the surface, appeared a huddle of clothing. The bowman caught sight of it. "There he is!" he cried. "He's there!"

"Heave now!" the cox'n grunted, his sinews creaking. "One, two—six!"

With a sudden swirl the basket came aft along the gunwale. The cox'n hauled in on the stay with one hand; produced, like a conjurer, a knife with the other. With sure, deft slashes, he cut adrift the rough lashing with which Andrew Carr had buttressed his failing strength as the balloon came down. The entire boat's crew swarmed round and drew the unconscious figure safely over the gunwale.

"Trim the boat—or you'll be swamped!" the captain's peremptory hail echoed over the water. The latter stood at the bridge-rails, condenser-inlets temporarily forgotten, his haggard face lightening. He turned to the first lieutenant, who had just arrived on the bridge. "I want to get away as soon as possible, No. 1," he said. "Put him in my day-cabin; get the boat hoisted; meanwhile, I want a volunteer to go over the side and examine and clear the condenser-inlets."

"Ay, ay, sir." The first lieutenant saluted and turned, brushing past the chief engineer on his way and giving the latter a commiserating grin as he noted his despondent face.

Five minutes later the first lieutenant was standing in the waist of the ship regarding with a certain concern the figure of the torpedo cox'n as that tall, hatchet-faced individual secured round his waist a length of lifeline. "Trained as a diver," the latter had said, putting forward his claim to do the work required. "Can hold my breath if I get foul of anything, for the best part of two minutes, sir . . ."

"Yes," the captain had said briefly, "let him try, No. 1." And so the first lieutenant stood doubtfully, because if anything happened to him . . . well, it would be unfortunate, to say the least of it—he was the best man in the ship.

The saturnine features of the torpedo cox'n, however, expressed no kind of doubt about the work in hand as he joked with the men around. The only concession he had accorded was in the laying aside of his heavy sea-boots. "Get a better grip with me stockinged feet, sir," he had remarked tersely. The first lieutenant, on his part, had rove a line right under the hull and secured it taut at each end, so that the man over the side would not be hopelessly inconvenienced by the heavy roll of the ship.

Thus, while Andrew Carr was being safely and snugly tucked up in blankets by the young doc., the torpedo cox'n took his chance and slithered down an angled slimy hull, with a long, dangerous-looking knife, like a pirate of old, clenched in his teeth.

With his heart in his mouth, and soaked to the skin, the first lieutenant gripped the rails and leant over them, directing the work. It was perilous enough on account of the confused sea, which had made it difficult to afford the man a good lee in which to work. But with the aid of the close-rove endless line round the hull the torpedo cox'n was enabled to cling close, like a gigantic fly, to the side of the ship. Once a big yellow roller, coming in suddenly, completely immersed him, and the first lieutenant heaved a sigh of relief when it rolled away to disclose a half-drowned cox'n still on the job. On his second trip he took with him a sharp hook on the end of another length of rope. When he had secured this firmly as low down as he could place it, the men on deck hauled away, and ripped bodily out of the condenser-inlet a great mass of crumpled and torn balloon fabric. For the best part of twenty minutes, off and on, coming inboard for a breather occasionally, the man over the side carried on, stoically and doggedly, with the job for which he had volunteered. He came inboard for the last time, and the first lieutenant clapped him on the back, glancing anxiously at the drawn and lined features, at the torn fingers. "Go aft at once, cox'n," he ordered, "before the chill penetrates any farther; get a tot of brandy from the wardroom steward."

"It wasn't so cold," said the tall man, panting, "the sea's warmer than the air, maybe." He grinned suddenly, and fingered the fabric, bits of which had got mixed up with his oilskins. "Make a good baccy pouch, sir," he said diffidently.

The first lieutenant laughed, and in his voice there sounded a note of relief. "Time to think of that, cox'n, when we get home again, and you've had that brandy and a darned good rub down."

As the duty destroyer turned and shaped her course homewards, the chief engineer paused at the engine-room hatch and cast a long look at the scarce distinguishable remains of the fast-sinking kite-balloon. The glance was not approving. "I should like", he muttered vindictively, "to have a word with the blasted cove who invented them . . . just a quiet word, in some quiet place. . . ."

It was late afternoon and dusk was gathering round the gate-ships as the skipper jerked a thumb at the long, grey ship that slipped through the boom defences at fifteen knots. With puckered-up, experienced eyes the old trawlerman cast a slow, grave look along her decks. "She's had a dusting and all," he said to his assistant. "Wireless gone, whaler smashed up, both after-hatch shelters gone. Ay, she's been through it . . ."

"I wonder," said the mate. "I wonder if—here she comes now; she may give us a hail." The speaker put a vast mahogany fist against his ear. He held on with the other as the gate-ship rolled.

Across the water, distinct above the roar of the forced draught and the swish of the bow-wave, came the destroyer's hail: "Many thanks; good night; weather poor, but fishing excellent!"

The gate-ship skipper grinned and dug his mate in the ribs with a calloused elbow. He was only an onlooker. He watched battleships, cruisers, destroyers, and all manner of craft through his gate, but his own job was far from a sinecure. In bad weather—and in fog—especially fog—his crew, and himself often, stood in imminent danger of total and sudden extinction. But like many onlookers, he saw much of the game—and more of the players. "Excellent fishing," he repeated and grinned again. "Then they got him all right."

Night was falling as the duty destroyer retrieved her shackle of cable at the buoy and moored up again. Andrew Carr was

146

safely in the hospital ship, his young mind clearing gradually from what seemed a nightmare of recollection. On the bridge the captain rang down "Finished with engines", and walked stiffly to the bridge-ladder, where he paused. "Make up the log, sub.; put away your charts and gear, then meet me in the wardroom."

The young figure engaged in casting off a length of spun-yarn from its middle, straightened up, and saluted. "Ay, ay, sir."

On the now silent bridge the yeoman of signals paused near the wheel, which the torpedo cox'n was just leaving. "Well, we got wet, mate, as we thought, but—you got wetter than usual; find it cold taking a dip over the side?"

The torpedo cox'n stepped down from the grating and smiled. "I been warm", he said in a hoarse whisper, "ever since. You had ought to've seen the tot of brandy I gets served out with. Good?" The speaker smacked his lips and smiled again. "It would ha' give a battleship a kick."

The yeoman made a sudden dive for the side, his telescope flashing up to inspect a distant winking light. "Here, mate," he grunted, "take this down, quick. 'Commodore F——'," he started to read.

In the wardroom, aft, there was an air of snug restfulness. The steward had brought a tray of drinks. A card-table stood ready for a game of bridge. Overhead there came a sound of sea-boots, and down the iron ladder clattered the yeoman of signals. The captain glanced up with an apprehensive eye. "What now?" he muttered, taking the proffered pad. Slowly his expression turned to one of pleased surprise. The signal was from Commodore of Flotillas, and the captain read it aloud. "Congratulations. Revert to eight hours' notice for steam. Report on board at 10 a.m. to-morrow."

The captain handed back the pad. "Thank you, yeoman. Have a copy put up on the mess-deck notice-boards."

"Ay, ay, sir." The yeoman withdrew. Just outside the door he encountered the steward. "Congratulated by Commodore F——," he hissed into the other's ear. "Oh, we're a tiddly boat all right——" The speaker hurried on, leaving a puzzled steward scratching his head doubtfully. He was not sure what "tiddly" meant, but finally came to the conclusion it was complimentary.

Inside the mess the captain yawned and stretched luxuriously in his chair. "A bath," he murmured; "a red-hot bath, then a game of bridge, and a spot of dinner—*and* a whole night in." The speaker looked reflectively at the roaring stove, and noticed that the dull corner of brightwork had been cleaned up, as directed after the previous Sunday's inspection. His glance travelled on, resting in turn on his grimy, unshaven officers, then stopped at the clock secured to the white-painted bulkhead. "Twenty-three hours," the captain murmured, and raised his glass. "The Day's Work," he added the words slowly, thoughtfully, then got stiffly to his feet, putting down the glass with an air of finality that had in it a vague suggestion that the captain found cause neither for regret nor for pleasure in the previous twenty-three hours, but only a species of mild satisfaction which was unimportant. He looked round the mess. "Now for that bath. See you in half an hour for that rubber— and mind you're not late, sub."

G. R. COLVIN

SEPTEMBER AFTERNOON

At about two o'clock in the afternoon of Sunday the sixth of September 1931, one of His Majesty's more modern cruisers was steaming down the Yangtse River from Hankow to the sea. Being about midway between Kiukiang and Anking she was following the north-easterly trend of the river: and those on board, after a stifling month as guard ship at Hankow, counted themselves lucky to have a strong breeze against them.

Down in the gunroom, which was situated abreast and above the engine-room on the port side, the midshipmen were taking full advantage of the head wind. With a windscoop in each of the three scuttles, the skylight wide open and the door shut, they were able to keep a current of air flowing through the compartment, and at the same time they were free of the horrible oily heat which is apt to rise in waves from the engine-room and make life unbearable in the spaces above.

The ship had a complement of twelve midshipmen, of whom two were then on duty; one, as midshipman of the watch, was leaning against an awning stanchion in the after starboard corner of the bridge listening to the Admiralty Pilot yarning with the Captain. He was still lazily trying to decide whether it was better to keep watch on a Sunday afternoon or on a week-day afternoon. Sunday was so very peaceful, no routine, everyone sleeping, nothing to worry about except "quarters" at four o'clock; but on week-days, in spite of the extra routine, there was always the chance of being called away for two hours of school—a blessed relief.

Tanky, the other midshipman on duty, after an anxious forenoon spent hovering at the beck and call of his lord and master
the Navigator, was now in the chart-house correcting the Light
Lists from the latest batch of Admiralty "Notices to Mariners".

"They're the finest boatmen, river boatmen, in the world,"
said the Admiralty Pilot. "Who else would get those dam' unwieldy great river junks and sampans up the gorges of the
Upper Yangtse with the river running like a mill-race?" And
he glared around him fiercely. The midshipman of the watch
had heard this said so often that he felt a little angry. If the
Chinese were the finest boatmen in the world, why did they
build such absurd craft? Great brutes of boats that could not
sail within seven points of the wind!

"And the finest fishermen," continued the Admiralty Pilot
complacently. "Why, I remember the time when a gunboat
(port twenty—port twenty, I said, quartermaster) when a gunboat anchored in the Poyang hu Lagoon near Nanchang.
Hadn't been there half an hour when a junk comes up and
makes (amidships—amidships, I said, quartermaster) and
makes to anchor ahead. Number One of the gunboat gets their
Chinese boy to sing out to the junk to keep clear of the gunboat's anchor. (Steady as you go, quartermaster.) Tells them
that their hook is lying four shackles out on the port bow."

The Admiralty Pilot chuckled into his short white beard and
looked around him. There he was, perched on his chair on a
little platform specially made for him (for he was a short man)
just abaft the gyro compass. He was the oracle. The Captain
was obviously deeply interested in his constant flow of anecdote;
the Chief Yeoman had edged nearer; the officer of the watch
was grinning broadly; the midshipman of the watch was all ears.

"So the junk anchors ahead of the gunboat and well clear,
and the First Lieutenant goes below with his mind at rest and
sleeps to morning. (Starboard ten, quartermaster.) Next morning the junk weighs at about breakfast-time and comes up close
alongside the quarterdeck. 'Velly nice morning,' says their
skipper to the First Lieutenant, 'and would the Blitish ship
like some velly good, velly flesh fish?' Number One is sick to

death of Chinese river fish, and recommends them to go (amidships—amidships, quartermaster) and recommends them to go to hell.

"'Would Blitish offisah like to buy nice anchor left Hwangchow by a steamer in flood time and found at low river?' Number One of the gunboat keeps quiet. 'Velly good, velly cheap anchor, new sort.'

"Number One tells them that the gunboat has two very fine anchors and recommends them (steady as you go, quartermaster) and recommends them to drop the anchor in the tomb of their ancestors. 'All light, offisah!' and off goes the junk."

The Admiralty Pilot cleared his throat. "Next day the gunboat weighs, but lo an' behold, no anchor on the end of their nice studded cable. That junk had dropped astern in the night, dived for the anchor, picked it up, hoisted it in, unshackled the cable and dumped the end overboard. Next morning they had tried to sell it back to the gunboat. Yes, sir. The finest boatmen in the world, and the finest fishermen!"

The midshipman of the watch smiled happily. That yarn, he reflected, would go down well in the gunroom later. Lucky blighters, he thought, probably all asleep now. He could imagine the scene. A deep peace pervading the gunroom. A chair placed at one end of the settee, which runs nearly the whole length of the room against the ship's side, lengthening it sufficiently to allow four midshipmen, slightly overlapping at head and feet, to sleep in comparative comfort. Both of the armchairs occupied by a midshipman, sleeping heavily, while the remaining six chairs would be divided into two groups of three, which, by careful arrangement, provided two more reasonably safe couches. In most cases the pillow would be a uniform cap, usually the sleeper's own, for it is annoying to be suddenly awoken when the rightful owner of your pillow rudely claims his property.

The midshipman smiled again. Suddenly a fiery wave of pain, little needle-points of agony, thousands of them, from his shoulders to his waist, assailed him, and with a stifled groan he moved across to a position where the breeze was stronger.

Once his back got cooler, he reflected, this accursed prickly heat would perhaps stop, and a short time in the cool paradise of Wei-hai-wei would cure it completely. His mind wandered off again, lazily. Another day, he thought, of following wind would have driven him mad: the damnable heat, steamy, damp heat, lying in waves over the river valley. And the smell of the corpses, ghastly, swollen, putrid corpses, floating past and floating past.

And then he thought of the floods. The biggest floods in Chinese history, which means the biggest in the world. All the Middle and Lower Yangtse valley flooded. The loveliest, the richest, the most densely populated part of China flooded: all those villages swept away: all the little walled towns with their tiled roofs and little temples destroyed: the beautiful rice crops all gone: the rice-fields which had gone on and on, two crops a year, for two thousand odd years, four thousand crops—the fields which had been carefully tended by generation after generation of cunning peasants, men, women and children, now obliterated under the cloak of yellow water. And the peasants, their fields and landmarks effaced, their rice destroyed, the seed for planting swept away, their cattle dead and their few poor implements lost, how could they survive it? The Chinese peasantry, who had survived fire and famine, taxation, oppression and slaughter, drought and plague for thousands of years, how could they survive this last most terrible disaster?

And he thought of the conditions at Hankow and its two suburbs, Hanyang and Wuchang, with their total population of little under a million people, the water from five to ten feet deep in the streets, and three hundred and fifty thousand refugees in and around the city. He remembered the sampans paddling through the streets with their terrible cargoes of the drowned, travelling their last voyage to the hills where there was dry land to bury them.

And that embankment on the south side of the river, which had stood fast for so long protecting many square miles of beautiful fields lying fifteen feet below the surface of the flood water: the Chinese had taken their customary stroll every evening up and down this embankment, and had smoked their evening pipes and had watched the river rise, watched gravely and sadly and hopelessly as it lapped higher and higher. It was on Wednesday, August the nineteenth, he remembered, that the river had lapped over the embankment at one spot, and had then lifted a fraction and poured over, becoming a muddy torrent, until the bank crumbled into ruin and the water burst triumphantly through to flood the land to the foothills.

He thought of the Chinese running before the water and the women tottering so gracefully on their little bound feet, swaying so charmingly on their little bound feet, little willows swaying, until the water caught them and swept them over and over. And the sun beat down on their bodies floating down the river, and they rotted and became swollen, and their clothes fell away, and the bound feet were no longer graceful, no longer charming, no longer did men laugh softly and tenderly at their little lotus feet. He thought of corpses and shuddered.

"Thieves mostly," said the Admiralty Pilot. "They'd brick 'em up in a little brick tower with a pointed roof, so small that they couldn't turn round or even bend their knees. One man in each tower." He chuckled grimly. "A little hole opposite the face and a soldier on guard to prevent anyone interfering. (Nothing to port, quartermaster.)"

"Are any of those little towers still standing?" asked the Captain.

"Lord, yes! There's one on a bridge over a creek, right in the middle of the bridge, just to the east of Nanking—I'll point it out to you when we go past. When the man dies they fill in the hole opposite his face and leave him there."

"Why the hole for his face anyway?" said the Captain slowly, "and why build the thing in the middle of a bridge?"

"Oh!" said the Pilot, surprised, "I thought that was obvious. It was so that all the passers-by could see the poor fellow—he'd lose face so much before he died. The more people that saw him miserably dying the more face he would lose."

"Really!" exclaimed the Captain. "Really! How very curious. I must tell my wife that next time I write to her."

With an effort the midshipman turned his musings to more pleasant subjects, and, his back now quite free from the irritation of the prickly heat, he returned to his favourite corner of the bridge, where he could lean against the awning stanchion.

It was now exactly forty days since he had last been ashore; at Hankow, with the Race Club flooded, the tennis courts under ten feet of water, the golf course under fifteen, there had been little chance and less inducement. But in four or five days he would be able to land at Wei-hai-wei for walks and golf and for bathing in the clean sea, for climbing the hills on the mainland and for snipe shooting in the Third Lagoon. He decided to get up a party of four, and they might hire a sampan and, by starting early, get over to the Fourth Lagoon for a shot at the duck.

It would now be cool at Wei-hai-wei and the seabathing would be glorious. He thought sleepily of Hankow and the sweat; sitting at dinner in the evening, with the sweat pouring in a little stream down the centre of your chest under your stiff shirt. Sweat trickling down your shins. Sleeping on the settee and sweating; the horrible wet patches of sweat left on the cushion-covers. Sweating at divisions, standing still at prayers and furtively shaking your head to shake the drops from your forehead. Everyone sweating. . . .

The Chief Yeoman suddenly stiffened and, putting his telescope to his eye, stared down the river for a few seconds. Still staring he spoke rapidly to the Captain.

"Stop both," said the Captain, and, to the Pilot, "Can we turn her in this stretch?"

"Not here," said the Pilot without a second's hesitation. He knew the whole lower river from Hankow to Wusung, six hundred miles of it, every shoal and bank, every eddy and current, the depths and the widths and the distance. "Not here," answered the Pilot. "But two miles on round that bluff you can turn her if you want to."

"Full astern both," said the Captain.

The officer of the watch sprang to the voice-pipe and repeated the order; in the wheel-house the quartermaster nodded to the telegraph men; in the engine-room the telegraph bells rang sharply. An engineer officer making a slow tour of the lubricating oil pressure gauges was galvanised into feverish activity, and the two great main-steam throttle-wheels were swung steadily round. The shrill high scream of the turbines faltered and fell away; the telegraph bells rang again and the noise of the turbines dwindled to nothing and then grew again, becoming louder and louder on a harsher note, while vibration shook the stern of the ship.

"Man the port sea-boat," ordered the Captain, and he turned to the midshipman of the watch. "Whose boat is it?"

"Mine, sir."

"You can go."

For a fraction of a second the midshipman stood there motionless; dressed in a white shirt, open at the neck, and a pair of white shorts, he seemed more like a schoolboy on holiday than an officer on duty; then he turned and, in a flash, was scrambling perilously down the ladder to the port waist, catching a fleeting glimpse as he did so of an overturned sampan with some Chinese clinging desperately to the stern as it drifted rapidly past. He reached the cutter a little before the officer of the watch, who had followed him down from the bridge to lower the boat, and, clambering on to the guard-rail with a steadying hand on the davit, he jumped into the stern-sheets.

Taking his place beside the tiller, grasping it in his right hand, the midshipman took stock of his crew; they were all busy adjusting their stretchers, putting on their life-jackets, getting their oars ready. The starboard bowman leant forward and twisted the pin of the slipping gear of the forward falls. The officer of the watch could be heard giving orders and the boat started to descend, with a creaking of rope and blocks, quickly and jerkily to the water.

"Out pins. Stand by."

The coxswain crouched over the cleat, holding the slack of the fore and after rope in one muscular hand. There was a pause.

"Slip."

With a single lightning movement of his wrist the coxswain flung off the last turn of the rope. The boat fell with a crash, leaving the falls swinging idly overhead, and a bucketful of yellow river water splashing up soaked the midshipman to the skin.

"Back port. Give way starboard." The sampan must be miles astern by now, thought the midshipman furiously, and would she never come round in this beastly lop.

"Give way together."

Now they were close to the overturned boat and the midshipman could make out a group of four or five Chinese clustered round the stern; they were clinging to the only handhold offered by the smooth flat-bottomed hull—that of the rudder. Almost every wave appeared to pass over them. The right bank of the river, perhaps two hundred yards away, was shown by a line of reeds above the surface, while half a mile farther inland a low range of hills rose from the yellow floods. The left bank, almost twice as far away as the right, was merely hinted at by a few ravaged trees which marked the end of the disturbed waters of the river and the beginning of a great expanse of shallower, calmer water which reached as far as he could see.

As they neared the sampan the midshipman could hear low wailing cries from the terrified Chinese. He measured the distance anxiously, and realised that he would have to accept the risk of crushing them between the cutter and the sampan.

Afterwards he could only remember how sickeningly his cutter had rolled in the trough of the waves, and how he had, in a fever of anxiety, expected to hear at any moment the scream of a man crushed between the two boats.

When the boat was clear of the sampan the midshipman had leisure to look about him. The cruiser, he noted, had gone on about two miles and was now turning preparatory to coming back to pick them up. Moreover, she was almost hidden behind a bluff where the hills came down to the river's edge.

"Pull easy," he ordered, giving himself and the boat's crew the opportunity of inspecting their catch.

As he looked at them the midshipman reflected that nothing could be more woebegone than a half-drowned Chinese. In the bows crouched an old man with grey hair, his face quite impassive, showing not the slightest signs of interest in his surroundings. In the stern-sheets was a young man, lying curled up on the floor-boards, who, as the midshipman looked at him, was quietly sick without moving his head.

Sitting on the stern bench beside the coxswain was a boy of about seven, the only one of the rescued who appeared grateful; he was grinning broadly at the stroke oars, who were addressing him with odd phrases and words of pidgin-English and with Chinese swear words. Huddled up almost at the feet of the midshipman sat a woman moaning and crying; her clothes of blue coolie-cloth hung wetly to her body, and her hair fell across her shoulders. She seemed to be chanting some plaint, some dirge, and all the time she rocked her body from side to side, clutching a baby in her arms.

Suddenly the woman turned, and, looking up at the midshipman, she burst into a torrent of words, screaming and sobbing and pointing up the river. The midshipman regarded her gravely, trying to guess at the meaning of her speech. It was obvious that one or more of the occupants of the sampan had been drowned before he arrived, and he remembered with horror how overcrowded the sampans usually were and how little there had been to hold on to. He shook his head to indicate that he did not understand.

Suddenly the fit passed and she turned again to her baby; she unbuttoned her jacket and held the baby to her breast, but the little creature, more dead than alive, refused nourishment, and the woman resumed her rocking and wailing.

The midshipman, rather embarrassed by the proximity of this display of maternal affection, became suddenly aware that the crew were highly amused at his embarrassment. Raising his head he saw that the cruiser was now heading towards them and would soon be in a position to hoist the cutter.

"Give way properly there," he ordered sternly.

It was nearly four o'clock when, his cutter hoisted and secured and the Chinese safely in the sick bay being ministered to by the Surgeon Commander, the midshipman was free once more. As he was walking rather stiffly aft he encountered his divisional officer. "Snotty," said the lieutenant, using a form of address hallowed by tradition but loathed by all midshipmen, "you'd better put on a dry shirt at once." He paused and looked at his watch. "Shan't require you at quarters," he said, and passed on.

The bugler was just sounding off "Evening Quarters" as the midshipman entered the gun-room, and, in a few moments, everyone else had left. Mechanically he crossed over to the settee and lay down in the best place—the forward end where there was an electric fan just overhead.

No good ringing for tea, the midshipman decided, it would just make him sweat and bring on that prickly heat again. He felt strangely tired. It was that "Hankow dog"—a mild form of dysentery—which had kept him as hollow as a drum for the last ten days. That, and the heat. He was as weak as a kitten; he only seemed to be able to sleep and sweat.

He felt like weeping for no particular reason. It was, he thought, his nerves—all wrong. So tired he was, and as thin as a lath now. The woman, crouched in the stern, how she had screamed and sobbed! Would he ever get it out of his mind? He sighed profoundly.

When the rest of the midshipmen returned after quarters he was sleeping heavily, a sleep which continued until the steward came in to lay the table for supper and was only disturbed by the nervous twitchings of his face and limbs.

IAN SCOTT

FLOTSAM

Among the curious habits and customs of the Chinese on the sea coasts and great rivers is one which thrives as strongly to-day as ever it did in the past.

The Chinese will never rescue, or take the slightest trouble to assist in the rescue of, a drowning man; and the authorities appear to acquiesce in this; for rarely is an inquiry held on any aquatic disaster, although many thousands are drowned annually.

This is due to a strange belief or superstition that in every part of the sea and in every great river there dwell water-dragons, whose function it is to swallow and keep in captivity the spirits of those who have died by drowning. As the capacity of the dragon is limited, he has, when gorged to completion, to release the spirit of the departed he has held longest, to make room for the next candidate.

The Chinese consider that this spirit, joyfully anticipating his freedom, will, when he finds his captivity prolonged by the unwarranted interference of some person who has prevented the new spirit from arriving, take the necessary steps to punish this mortal when he finally does escape. In other words, it is the worst kind of joss.

To discourage the would-be rescuer still further, it is an unwritten law that a man saved from drowning or the peril of great waters, becomes the responsibility of the rescuer for the rest of his life; and in a country where the feeding of an extra mouth is always a grave problem there is little chance of a life being saved under these conditions. Even to-day, in times of famine, female babies are sometimes thrown to the dogs by their own parents.

Most people will remember the wreck of the *Hong Moh* on

159

the Lammocks Rocks off Swatau, and the magnificent rescue work by Captain Evans (now Admiral Sir Edward Evans) of the *Carlisle*. The *Hong Moh* was repatriating a vast number of coolies after their three-year period of service in the tin mines and plantations of Malaya, and each man carried with him his hard-won savings.

Before the arrival of the *Carlisle* on the scene, the numerous fishing sampans and junks had gathered round the wreck like sharks round a stranded whale.

In their panic and frenzy, hundreds of coolies had jumped overboard, hoping to be picked up by their own kinsmen. Picked up they certainly were, but after their money-belts had been ripped off they were thrown back into the raging sea to drown.

Evans had to use force to make the survivors jump into the sea; for they had already witnessed their late shipmates' unsuccessful attempt to break an age-long superstition.

Once, while walking along the Hong Kong bund, I saw a crowd of Chinese laughing and chattering, with a few Sikh policemen controlling them roughly. Knowing the strange sense of humour of this happy race, I thrust my way through the mob expecting to find a man riddled with bullets or suffering from a compound fracture. Instead, I saw an old woman splashing weakly in deep water only a few feet off the bund; beside her in the water was her shopping-bag, and in it two live ducks were struggling to free themselves. The crowd roared with laughter; but I was furious; for I had on a new shantung silk suit, and further, I had an important date at the Hong Kong Hotel. *My* suit would be ruined, but it was Hobson's choice; for if I had disrobed I should have lost my possessions and my clothes.

The old woman fought fiercely, much to the added amusement of the crowd; but I managed to get her to Murray Pier, where willing European hands hauled us out. I am glad to say the policemen were "dipped a badge"; for, although they had no belief in water-dragons, they were afraid of losing the henna from their beards and their "face" before the Chinese.

Up in Wei-hai-wei the submarine flotilla was busy working through the long programme of summer exercises in weather which, like a glorious English summer, was perfect.

After a long day at sea of torpedo attacks we were hard at work re-embarking the torpedoes we had fired and re-charging our deplenished batteries. The blazing sun struck down fiercely on the steel hull, and I am sure all hands thought longingly of cold beer ashore in the shadow of the canteen trees. I had just decided to go ashore myself for a bathe and a game of bowls to stretch my limbs, when Captain S. appeared through one of the long windows of his day cabin almost abreast my bridge. I was surprised to see that he was still on board, and in uniform.

"Come up to my cabin," he shouted across. "I want a word with you."

In his cabin it was refreshingly cool, and a gentle breeze, augmented by electric fans, drove athwart-ships.

Captain S. motioned me to a seat, and I noticed the captain of *L 15* was also present, looking a shade depressed.

"Cocktail or beer?" S. inquired cheerfully. "Cigarettes beside you."

"Beer for me, sir," I answered, wiping my forehead with an already damp handkerchief.

The boy brought in the drinks silently, and as silently disappeared again.

"Got a job for you two," S. said without preamble. "The consul at Cheefoo reports considerable amount of plague there. The Chinese authorities have banished all the known and suspected cases to the off-lying islands, but the consul reports that they are returning to the mainland at night by sampan. *L 15* and *L 2* will patrol the islands for the next two nights to prevent this. You will sail at daybreak. I will give you no written orders (he rarely did), but don't be too drastic. You, Scott, will be under the orders of Digby. Any questions?"

I was in my first command in Chinese waters and I was therefore delighted to encounter anything out of the ordinary flotilla routine. Digby, on the other hand, was distinctly annoyed; for his wife and children had only just arrived on the station and had reached Wei-hai-wei that day; luckily I had no such entanglements.

Roland, my first lieutenant, was as pleased as I was. "I'll have a chance to paint out the torpedo-room," he said gaily, "before Captain S.'s inspection. I was beginning to think we would never be able to do it."

Bukes, my navigator, got out the large-scale chart of Cheefoo, and we studied the harbour closely.

Cheefoo is a small but important port at the entrance to the Gulf of Pechihli. For years the American submarines used it as a base, much as we use Wei-hai-wei, but at this time of the year they were still in the Philippines.

To the northward, about two miles off the town, lies a long low island right across the points of the bay and forming a natural breakwater. On this island the plague contacts had been landed.

Digby and I worked out a plan of campaign. During daylight hours one submarine would patrol to seaward of the island, while the other remained inside. At night we would cruise off the ends of the island, checking up on any fishing sampans coming into the harbour and watching the entire shore side of the island to intercept any boat leaving or landing there.

We had no searchlights; only the short-range Aldis lamps, but we discovered we would enjoy a period of nearly full moon all the time.

On the whole the job looked simple enough. There was to be no contact with the mainland or the island, in case of infection, and we were to remain on patrol till relieved by other submarines.

Day was breaking as we cast off from the depot ship, and the sharp-pointed hills of the mainland took on a rosy tint above the pale-blue dawn mists lying sleepily in the valleys. A light breeze stirred gently the calm surface of the harbour.

As we passed Port Edward we could hear the creak of windlass and the groan of heavy blocks as some junks slowly warped out of the crowded anchorage to take advantage of this slight air.

L 15 hoisted the signal "Single line ahead—12 knots!" and our Diesel exhausts greeted the fairness of the morning with a black cloud of smoke as the cold engines coughed and roared with the increasing revolutions. Our thin bow wave climbed up the stem in sparkling spray and the creaming wash came splashing aft over the saddle-tanks as we gathered way.

A small Antung Bay trading junk appeared round the shoulder of Outer Island; the battened lugsails goose-winged as she entered the channel through the sinister fringe of black rocks.

Suddenly I was aware of *L 15* swinging rapidly to port. She had made no signal. Was she going to take the short-cut through the reef? I used it myself, but only when I was alone, for there was little room to manœuvre.

The "disregard" flag ran swiftly up *L 15's* halyards, and I realized his steering motor must have blown a fuse. Gosh! He was going to hit that junk!

I saw the engine-exhaust fade away to be followed by the white cascade of foam as his motors were put full speed astern.

Relentlessly the two vessels approached each other as if drawn together by some strangely powerful magnetism. A thin shout and a piercing wail came from the junk, then a grinding, splintering crash as the knife-edged hydroplane guard tore through the port side of the junk, leaving a gaping underwater wound.

By this time my engines were stopped and I had brought my boat to the fringe of the wreckage.

"Man overboard!" I bawled down the voice-pipe.

L 15 had broken clear of the junk, and even as I watched, the latter listed heavily to port, to roll over on her beam-ends and sink, her masts appearing upright again for a few seconds as she went down.

The calm sea was littered with struggling Chinese and floating debris.

FLOTSAM

As I drew closer *L 15* was already at rescue work, and almost half my crew were sporting in the water, seizing this unexpected opportunity of "hands to bathe". (There are many sharks in these waters, though, strangely enough, Wei-hai-wei has a clean record, but for this reason I encouraged large numbers to bathe together when outside the harbour, for a shark will not attack a crowd.)

In a very few minutes every soul had been picked up, my crew noisily collecting three men whom they escorted back to the boat, where they were hauled on to the saddle-tanks to lie gasping.

My cox'n, displaying his usual initiative, had taken a small bottle of rum down on to the casing, and I saw him offer it to the three Chinese in turn, but in each case the offer was refused. The cox'n, nothing daunted by this spurned hospitality, took a long swig himself and wiped his mouth with the back of his hand. Looking up, he caught my disapproving eye, and his contented smile disappeared.

"Take the wheel, cox'n," I told him; "I'm going alongside *L 15* to drop these passengers."

Digby greeted me unhappily; for the rescued laodah of the junk was still screaming at him shrilly.

"I'll have to go back and land these blokes at Port Edward and report to S. You carry on to Cheefoo, for I'll only be about an hour adrift. That junk *had* to be full of brick from Dairen, that's why she went down so damn fast."

"Well," I said thoughtfully, "there seems to be something in this 'olo China' custom of letting the blighters drown, for it would save you a Court of Inquiry and the Admiralty a lot of money; besides, in theory, you have got to maintain these blokes for the rest of their lives."

"On your way, blast you!" Digby cried, slightly peeved, "or I'll make *you* take the perishers back."

Accompanied by the steady vibrations of the engines we cut swiftly through the still, blue waters as we ran up the coast. Long stretches of sandy beaches between rocky promontories, with here and there a fishing hamlet set in the shadow of green trees, made a foreground for the distant blue mountains of Shantung. Fishing sampans and an occasional junk drifted on the calm surface, which was disturbed solely by a few flying-fish and the fins of slow-moving sharks.

Arriving off Cheefoo in the afternoon, I circled the islands to give myself some impression of their lay-out. It seemed to me there was rather a larger area to guard than I had gathered from the chart, and I felt that, if the moon for any reason failed us, our task would be almost impossible. Shortly after I had completed my tour *L 15* arrived and closed me.

Digby shouted to me across the narrow strip of water, "That laodah swore he had ten thousand dollars in silver aboard the junk!"

"You are lucky he was so modest!" I answered. "But it all goes to prove that Chinese custom is sound. We should adopt the slogan 'Sink without trace'!"

We parted company to carry out our daylight patrol as previously arranged, taking up, as darkness fell, our positions for the dark hour patrol.

Digby was taking the western end of the island, while I cruised slowly on one engine off the eastern end. The night was very still and one could plainly hear the barking of dogs ashore. As the moon rose the sky filled with a clear grey light and a million stars shone valiantly. To us, the sea became a silver carpet leading to the dark silhouette of the mainland.

Soon a small sampan under sail was descried beating out in the light airs towards the island.

Although we were cruising without lights we must be plainly visible in the bright moonglow. Even if the local inhabitants had not noted our arrival, this sampan must surely realize what we were there for. Nevertheless, as she came on steadily I estimated she would pass close to me, and when she came within range of my megaphone I bellowed across the glittering water, "Boat ahoy!" There was no response. Again I shouted, with the same result, although I felt sure my voice could be heard a mile off.

Loading a Very pistol, I fired a green light high over the

approaching boat, and it fell in a graceful curve lighting up the boat and the surrounding waters with a sickly hue. Still the sampan came on without reply.

"To hell with them!" I exclaimed. "Bukes, give them a burst of Lewis gun across their bows!"

The stillness of the night was broken by the staccato rattle of the gun, and I saw a sheet of silver spray rise suddenly ahead of the sampan. Immediately she luffed, her sail flapping darkly against the stars, and an angry howl arose from those on board. With her sail lowered she came alongside under uloes.

"What the hell do you think you are doing?" came a furious voice from below me, and looking down I saw a stout figure actually quivering with anger.

"I don't know who you are," I replied calmly, "but you asked for it. Why couldn't you answer our challenge?"

"I am the British consul!" he cried importantly.

"Gosh," I thought, "that's torn it! The man must be the worst kind of fool, for he knows exactly why we are here."

I went down on the casing to meet him, where he was being helped aboard by Roland.

"Sorry about your reception, but we could hardly expect a visit at this time. The senior officer is in *L 15* at the other end of the harbour if you want to see him." Observing he was still almost speechless with rage, I continued, "Come below and have a drink."

He followed me below without speaking, and Bukes poured him out a man-sized drink.

Surprisingly he piped down. "I'm afraid I was a bit hasty, for you were only carrying out your job," he said. "I came off to tell you that the plague suspects on the island and the boatmen ashore have all been warned that they may be fired on if they approach or leave the island. They will realize *now* it is not an empty threat."

He left in a much more pleasant frame of mind than when he came aboard, and I promised to pass on his message to *L 15* right away.

L 15, however, called us up first.

"What were you firing at?" he signalled.

"Only saluting the Consul," I replied.

The next day *L 2* patrolled the inside of the island, and in the forenoon three sampans came racing out to us from the town. As they closed us we could hear the plaintive wail arising from all three, "Stlawbellies. Stlawbellies."

I had not only heard of the Cheefoo strawberries, but had also sampled them in the Wei-hai-wei Club, and there was no doubt that they were very good. However, we had agreed to have no communication with the shore, and as fresh fruit is a potential germ-carrier I sadly waved the sampans clear.

"No can do, John!" I sang out. "No wanchee stlawbellies."

"Have got egg! Have got chicken!" they choroused, holding up their wares to display them to the best advantage.

The position was rather absurd; for these provisions were brought to Wei-hai-wei by junk from Cheefoo when the fleet was in, and, furthermore, everybody aboard had been inoculated against plague. But "orders is orders", and I drove them off, the Chinese smiling good-naturedly in spite of their long futile trip from the shore. I felt rather sorry for them as I climbed down the conning-tower.

Sitting down to dinner that night I found a beautifully written menu which made me think a little, for it read—

> CHICKEN MARYLAND,
> STRAWBERRIES AND CREAM,
> RUM OMELETTE.

Perhaps the ingredients had come from Wei-hai-wei. I did not propose to inquire, for it was a darn good dinner, anyway.

A light tapping on my bunk rescued me from a losing battle with water-dragons which I found it impossible to torpedo; perhaps it had been the rum omelette.

"From the officer of the watch, sir," the messenger reported. "It's coming on very thick."

"What's the time?" I inquired.

"Three thirty-four, sir."

"All right. Tell the officer of the watch I'll be right up."

As I climbed on to the bridge I was enveloped in a damp and clinging sea mist. It advanced upon us silently like a cold grey ghost, shutting out the sea and sky, the stars and the moon.

"When did you lose the light on Cheefoo Bluff?" I asked.

"I got a snap fix as it faded out, sir," Bukes replied; "here is our position two minutes ago."

Looking at the chart I noticed we were well clear of the traffic route of both steamers and junks, and decided to anchor till the weather cleared.

"Anchor stations!" I ordered. "Put her on 067° and we will run one mile and anchor in eight fathoms."

To Roland, who had arrived on the bridge, I added, "Three shackles, No. 1, port anchor; and put a leadsman in the chains."

We moved slowly through the cloying mist, silently but for the faint rustle of our wash and the deep voice of the leadsman calling the depth.

"By the mark, ten! By the deep, eight! By the deep, eight!"

"Stop both!" I said, and shouted forward, "Let go!"

The cable rattled out noisily, and from for'ard I caught the faint light of No. 1's torch as he counted the shackles.

Silence settled on us once more as if this blanket of sea-fog were a sound-proof curtain.

I sat on the bridge smoking and yarning with Bukes, while our bell rang sonorously through the fog to give warning of our presence.

A hail from the look-out for'ard brought us to our feet.

"Sampan drifting down on us from ahead, sir!"

With the Aldis lamp we picked up a small sampan drifting down on the gentle current. It had floated off the beach, I thought, or broken away from a junk unnoticed in the darkness.

"My God, sir!" cried Bukes, "there's someone in it. Look at the stern-sheets."

In the beam of the Aldis light I saw a flash of vivid red and green, and realized it probably meant women (for these are their favourite colours in North China); but there was no sign of life.

"Get a grapnel and a long boat-hook and haul her alongside," I ordered, "and we'll investigate."

As it happened, the sampan came alongside of her own volition, almost as if she had been handled by some unseen helmsman. Looking down into the boat I could make out three women, all lying quite motionless. I did not like it a bit.

Were they plague casualties? Should I let them drift on? No, I could not do that unless I was quite sure they were all dead.

"Give me a pair of rubber gloves," I told Bukes. "I'm going to see if they are alive or not."

I slid into the sampan and stepped aft to examine the two women in the stern-sheets. I saw they were middle-aged women with greying hair beneath the conventional bandeaux, and I noticed they had bound feet. I felt their hearts and pulses, but, looking at them closely, I knew they had been dead for some time. They were quite cold.

"Both dead," I exclaimed, turning to go for'ard.

In the bows, sitting propped up against a thwart, was the third. I discovered, with a strange pang of pity, that she was just a child. At a glance I could see she was of a different class to the other women. Her dark clothes were of better cut and quality, and her feet were unbound. I put her age between twelve and fourteen, and she, like the others, had no visible signs of plague about her.

I took off my gloves the better to feel her pulse; for to me she looked more natural than the others.

She was quite warm!

"Lend me a hand, Bukes!" I cried. "This kid's alive."

On the casing we massaged her heart, her hands, and her feet, forcing some spirits between her lips, and were at last rewarded by a flickering of her eyelids.

"Cut that sampan adrift before she comes to," I said.

The child was terribly thin, and I was coming to the conclusion that it was hunger or thirst that she was suffering from and not plague.

FLOTSAM

At the same time I could not afford to take chances.

"Bukes," I told him quietly, "we'll have to put this kid through the sheep-dip when she's a little stronger. Get up a hip-bath filled with warm water and disinfectant, and bring up a flannel shirt and some pants from my drawer."

The girl appeared weak and slightly dazed, but she managed to swallow an egg-nogg, and a faint tinge of colour returned to her cheeks.

I had expected a little opposition to my plans, but she submitted quietly enough when I threw her clothes over the side and gave her a sound scrubbing. Actually it seemed to refresh her, for she climbed into her new outfit of clothing with little help.

I bundled her down the forehatch and placed her in my bunk and in a few minutes this strange child was asleep as peacefully as if she were in her own bed.

"Don't wake that kid!" I warned them. "Let her sleep it out."

With the dawn the rising sun dispersed the thickness of the mist till only distant patches remained on the calm surface of the sea.

Weighing, we continued to patrol, and I wirelessed to *L15* now on the other side of the island—

"Have picked up Chinese girl, only survivor from drifting sampan. Request instructions."

"Rejoin me," he replied. "Relief submarines in sight."

We were soon in company again, and closing *L15* I shouted over to Digby—

"What shall I do with this girl? Shall I turn her over to the Consul here or take her back to Wei-hai-wei?"

"She's your property now!" he laughed. "A cheap way of collecting a wash and sew-sew amah. Bring her back with you. The P.M.O. had better have a look at her, and then we can turn her over to the Commissioner."

Already I began to regret that I had broadcast the rescue of this girl; for now the whole depot ship and flotilla must be laughing at the idea of a submarine on patrol with a female aboard. My ears tingled.

I went below before noon to find our passenger awake, and it surprised me to find the matter-of-fact way in which she accepted her fantastic surroundings and these strange foreign men.

"Good morning, Mèi Mèi," I greeted her cheerfully; "had a good sleep?"

She smiled shyly, nodding her head as if she understood.

"Come on," I said, "I'll help you down from that bunk. Are you hungry?" I called my boy along to interpret, which he managed to do nervously and with very few words.

"Missi say, 'Thank you; velly hungly'."

I have come across many different pets in submarines, but Mèi Mèi (little sister) was a hit on sight. All went out of their way to be of some assistance to her: she was placed in a deck-chair on the casing; extra guard-rails fitted to prevent her falling over the side; a rug and scarf were given to her; and the crew brought her enough fruit to choke her. Someone had over-heard me calling her Mèi Mèi, and on the run to Wei-hai-wei she was Mamie to the ship's company. She accepted all this devotion as a right, and never for a moment lost her self-possession.

I did not propose to worry her for her story; that could wait till the Commissioner saw her; he had lived in North China for nearly forty years and understood both the language and the people thoroughly.

Arriving at Wei-hai-wei in the evening we were lucky to find most of the flotilla ashore, and there were few 'goofers' to em-barrass us as we climbed inboard. I took her up to Captain S.'s cabin, and the P.M.O. vetted her in the night cabin.

"You picked up a beauty," said S., smiling. "Weren't the others up to standard?"

"They were very dead, sir," I remarked, somewhat incensed, "but I feel certain they did not come off the island. My guess is that they drifted out to sea from somewhere down the coast."

The P.M.O. entered with his arm on the girl's shoulder. "Clean bill of health, sir," he said to S. "I think she has been near starvation; all she wants is rest and building up."

"Well, what are we going to do with her now?" S. asked plaintively. "I suggest that, late as it is, you take her over to the Commissioner in my motor-boat and I'll give you a chit for him explaining the circumstances."

Mèi Mèi, wrapped in a gaudy sweater and a naval scarf, sat up in the stern-sheets of the motor-boat, revelling in the cool rush of air as the boat sped swiftly across the harbour to the mainland.

At the pier she looked round with interest as if confirming the fact that she was safely ashore at last, and in rickshas we made for the Residency.

I gave the No. 1 boy the chit, and in a few minutes the Commissioner himself appeared at the door.

"Come in, come in," he exclaimed, and looked closely at my companion. "This is a strange business, for you have got no village or junk woman there. You sit down here and have a drink while I get the girl's story from her. I won't be long." He turned to the girl, talking to her gently, and I saw her rare smile as she looked back at me.

I waved my hand as she disappeared through the doorway, and downed my well-earned drink.

I had hardly done so when the Commissioner came striding into the room.

"Do you realize you picked up the daughter of an old friend of mine? It appears to be a long story and I haven't got it all myself yet." He seemed more stirred than I had ever seen him before. "I know you want to get back to the island now, so come over to-morrow forenoon if you can and I will have the whole story for you then. The child will be well looked after by myself and my wife."

"I'm glad she's fallen on her feet, sir," I said, "for my crew will want a very good reason for surrendering their new-found joss-piece. You might tell her perhaps what she probably well knows, that we are all at her service."

Back in the depot ship I was met by Roland and Bukes.

"What have you done with our *chisai*, sir?" they chorused.

"She's been locked up as a vagrant in the local cooler," I

replied, backing to a more favourable position for defence. "We suspected she was a spy from a great naval power sent to find out how submarines obtain fresh strawberries after two days at sea!"

My cox'n, on behalf of the crew, also inquired after the fate of our passenger, saying that they would like to subscribe a sum of money to help her on her way.

I was glad to tell him that she was with friends, and that I would probably be able to tell him more the next day.

I ran over to the mainland the next forenoon, taking with me an enormous box of chocolates tied with an *L2* cap ribbon and inscribed—

"To 'Mamie', from the Ship's Company of H.M. Submarine *L2* with all good wishes."

The Commissioner took me into his library and placed a long drink at my elbow, and, lighting a cigarette, he began to talk.

"It really is a strange coincidence that you should pick up this child and bring her to me; for as I told you last night I know her father well and can remember her as a tiny bundle. I have already cabled him and await a reply. He is the head of a very old family in Peking, and owing to the trouble there he thought his only daughter would be safer with an aunt in Tsinan-Fu. As the railway between Tientsin and Tsinan-Fu is in the hands of bandits, he sent her by junk to Tsingtao to complete the journey from there by train. Why on earth he did not make use of the steamer service I can't imagine, unless he mistrusts it on account of piracy. Anyway, his daughter, with her two amahs, set off on this long-drawn-out passage. This was her first journey away from home and her first voyage at sea. As day succeeded day she grew more homesick and frightened, thinking she would never see her father again as the junk put more and more miles of sea-water between them.

"Gradually she developed the idea of escape, and easily persuaded her amahs to accompany her. She has seen so many junks going north; surely, she thought, one of them would take her home—for she had plenty of money with her."

FLOTSAM

The Commissioner paused to refill our glasses, and smiled at me.

"By the way, you left all her worldly goods in that sampan!"

"I'm sorry——" I began.

He held up his hand to silence me, and continued: "They got into the sampan, which was towing astern, only taking with them some water and their valuables, and cast off in the darkness. They were influenced by the fact that land was in sight the evening before (probably the nor'-west corner of the Promontory), and thought they could make land if they failed to pick up a north-bound junk.

"It was the most hare-brained scheme; for they had no sail, the amahs could not uloe, and they had no knowledge of the old superstition which would have prevented any junk picking them up unless they were close enough to see the colour of their money.

"I have lectured her on her foolishness and filial dis-obedience, pointing out to her the extraordinary luck which drifted the boat alongside your submarine, and she is now going to continue her journey to Tsinan-Fu this afternoon. She wants to thank you and say good-bye."

As I entered the drawing-room where Mèi Mèi was sitting with the Commissioner's wife I was still clutching the box of chocolates, and I felt an overwhelming sense of shame as if I had come to a favourite god-child's birthday party and for-gotten to bring a present. Dash it all! I had nothing with me except a cigarette-case, and it was scarcely a suitable present.

I gave her the box and explained it was a present from the crew. She in her turn held my hands and was apparently thanking me for picking her up, but I laughed at her and told her never to be a naughty girl again.

"I must be off, sir." I said in sudden embarrassment. "I've got a boat waiting for me."

I slipped off my signet ring and thrust it at Mèi Mèi. "Just a keepsake to remember us by," I told her. "Good-bye." As I left her she was gaily trying it on her fingers.

I was to suffer a lot on her behalf for the rest of the year; for somehow it got out that I had given her a ring, and my leg was pulled hard and often.

For some extraordinary reason, sea rescues seem to stick to certain individuals, and all the time I have been at sea I appear to have been mixed up in them. Even during the war my submarine picked up two Norwegian crews in the North Sea. In China, as I said before, where millions live on the sea and the great waters, there are always people to be saved every minute of the day.

It was only a few months later that *L2* again featured in another such scene.

We were returning to Hong Kong from the Philippines, when out of the ether we caught a fragile message from amidst the perpetual crackle of atmospherics. We were labouring in the worst of the monsoon under a low-roofed sky, with the wind whistling across the flat-blown wave-tops and driving the flying spindrift fiercely on to the plunging bridge. It was an S O S from a Dutch ship aground on one of the rocky Lem Islands, a few miles ahead of us.

The visibility was very poor and we were forced to grope round the rocky ledges looking for her, and it was two hours before we sighted her about seven miles from her reported position. I broadcast the correct position; for I knew the duty destroyer and tugs would already be on their way to the scene from Hong Kong.

The vessel was firmly wedged on a reef and would obviously become a total loss; for the heavy seas were sweeping over her. As we drew closer, I saw she was crowded with coolies, and realized that the task had become a thousand times more difficult.

A steep cliff beyond the reef made shore rescue an impossibility, and the heavy surf and backwash made it too dangerous to go alongside with my half-inch hull.

One heavy lifeboat, overcrowded with frantic Chinese, was lowered into the boiling surf. The job was well done and the boat got clear of the ship's side, only to turn turtle as she came broadside to the waves.

Closing in as near as I dared we picked up most of them, but at least half a dozen were drowned, in spite of the utmost gallantry of the crew. No. 1 alone brought three men aboard, till I gave orders forbidding anyone else to go over the side. Many of the crew had been badly hurt against the hull, and one man had broken an arm.

I signalled to the Dutchman to wait till the destroyer and tugs arrived, because they could probably go alongside and at least had boats.

When the destroyer at long last arrived, I flooded the sea with oil fuel, and the skipper, handling her magnificently, took her alongside. Even through the noises of the elements I could hear the ominous grinding as the two ships worked together, and I knew the destroyer could not stay there long.

We watched the men pouring aboard the destroyer and being driven aft to keep the fo'c'sle clear. Suddenly she came astern at full speed, the sea pooping the unfortunate Chinese on the quarterdeck; but she was clear at last.

When we left the wreck the tugs were approaching, but I was certain the task of salvage would be beyond them; however, they intended to wait for the weather to moderate before deciding the matter.

The destroyer (H.M.S. *Scout*), with some three hundred coolies on her upper deck, had to proceed at slow speed to avoid washing them overboard. We were able for this reason to keep fairly close astern of her, and it was rather fortunate that we were there; for we saw a heavy wave wash over the *Scout's* quarterdeck and two black heads appeared in her swirling wake.

"Man overboard!" How often had we heard this cry. I manœuvred the boat to windward of the two struggling bodies, letting the wind blow us down on them while the submarine acted as a breakwater.

"No. 1," I shouted, "only two men to go over the side and on life-lines. Take one each. Spare hands haul them in, and smack it about!"

No. 1, of course, had to be one; for he was a regular water-baby. The conditions were far from pleasant; the boat was rolling and pitching erratically, and the casing for'ard was continuously under water. In spite of this we had both victims on board within a few minutes of their falling overboard; and, although badly frightened, they were none the worse for it. No. 1, in his third change of clothing, came up on the bridge, his great moon of a face creased with a happy smile.

"We've done it again, sir. Another blinking girl!"

"This one's yours, Roland," I said firmly; "I have had all I want, of female passengers. Keep an eye on her till we get in. I expect the Hong Kong Government will have to keep this whole party for weeks till another 'slave-ship' arrives."

I'm afraid we changed the sex of this girl in our report of proceedings, and considered it justifiable if it could save us from earning the doubtful reputation of chasing girls even at sea!

It is strange, but true, that all the weeks these unfortunate refugees awaited another steamer no relief funds or gifts were given to them by Chinese!

That, I thought, was carrying a superstition too far. However, the chief thing was that no one discovered we had picked up another Chinese girl from the sea, and that was all we really worried about.

Back on the China Station some years later, Roland (now in command of his own submarine) and I decided that a trip to Peking would do us a lot of good. Catching the weekly steamer as it passed through Wei-hai-wei, we booked as far as Tientsin. The little steamer had only a few passengers on board, with whom we were soon at home, and the voyage passed quickly.

The ship was held up at the Taku Bar for an hour waiting for enough water while we swung at anchor in a jaundiced world; for the yellow sea was hung with a thin yellow mist, and vast brown junks and small fishing sampans blended their orange and amber matsails into the hazy panorama.

At last we were moving up the muddy Peiho River between low-lying banks where mud-walled villages broke the monotony of flat stretches of cultivated land and paddy-fields. Coolies could be seen at regular intervals working the treadmills that supplied this huge acreage with river water.

We arrived at Tombs Corner, so called from a number of bee-hive graves in the vicinity, to find an awkward turn to navigate. A large U-bend, too small for the turning circle of the ship, was made even more difficult by the action of the current.

The captain tackled it in a novel but seamanlike manner. He ran the ship's nose into the mud of the bund and allowed the current to swing his stern into the bank, then going astern when the ship had turned sufficiently to take the corner, he broke clear and went ahead up the other leg of the bund. Beside the large V-shaped mark I noticed a coolie planting cabbages, and he had paid not the slightest attention to the ship crashing into the bank a few feet away from him. As the river grew narrower the traffic appeared to grow even thicker with junks, sampans, and other river craft. Perilously we skimmed past them to secure alongside the bund at Tientsin, in the heart of the Concessions, as the long evening shadows fell across the city.

We agreed to spend the night at the Astor House and to move on to Peking in the morning. Out at the Country Club, we were told there was trouble brewing amongst the Northern factions and warned that travelling would probably be uncomfortable. Roland and I paid scanty attention to this till we actually boarded the train, and found it crowded with troops armed to the teeth and looking a shade truculent. It is strange what a difference firearms can bestow on the Chinese character; the lowly farm coolie, when given a rifle, will affect the pugnacity of a Japanese.

These fellows appeared to own the Pullman car, deliberately crowding the Europeans and expectorating promiscuously. It was *not* a comfortable trip.

Roland and I both knew our way round Peking and liked it enormously, but this time we were not eager to poodlefake, a thing it is always difficult to avoid in Peking.

From the Club in Rue Marco Polo we were drawn into a dance party at the Peking Hotel, and I think it was then that we finally decided to go farther afield in search of something different.

My hostess, the acknowledged belle of Peking, was a little hurt at our casualness. Neither Roland nor I had asked her to dance; for we were formulating our plans over some excellent whisky and had quite forgotten our surroundings.

"I don't believe you two like dancing at all," she said aggrievedly. "Aren't the girls pretty enough?"

"I'm sorry," I began half-heartedly, but Roland put his foot completely in it by remarking—

"Well, there *is* a really pretty girl," indicating a Chinese girl in native costume dancing gracefully.

Involuntarily I backed him up. "She's exquisite! Looks, figure, clothes, and dancing. The most beautiful Chinese girl I have ever seen."

Our hostess took this shattering bombardment rather well, but I fancied we would never again be asked to dance with her.

"You had better be careful whom you call Chinese in Peking," she said with some asperity. "That is the Princess Dji Shi-Yuan, a Manchu. You ought to be able to tell that by her face and dress."

Riding back in rickshas through the dusty streets to the Wagon-Lits Hotel under a high cloudless sky, we made up our minds.

We had gone into the details that afternoon, but everyone had warned us that under existing conditions the very idea was madness. We proposed to go by car to Kalgan and Inner Mongolia. We could make the return trip for 150 dollars Mex., providing our own food and drink.

We had been told that even under good conditions it was a devastating trip. There was always the risk of bandits and the roads and going were beyond description; now, to add to this, there was trouble between two powerful war lords, and the factions were fighting it out somewhere along this very road.

I must admit we did have periods of trepidation after buying our tickets; for we had leave only as far as Peking and we could not afford a breakdown. As for being held up by troops or bandits—well, we just did not consider it. The thought of capture and ransom never crossed our minds.

Of all the crazy things Roland and I had attempted this was about the silliest. We had come croppers in the past, but on the whole we had always managed to get away with our more outrageous crimes, and we held a high opinion of our ability to get out of difficulties.

I am not likely to forget that trip in a rocking, hard-driven car piled high with cargo, petrol, and provisions.

We were lucky to be the only passengers apart from the driver and guard, and even so we could only alter our positions slightly from time to time, so cramped were our quarters.

Once into the hills, the winding, climbing road was a nightmare corkscrew of loose stones, rocky ruts, and huge boulders. When the car was stopped to refill the steaming radiator we staggered stiffly to our feet to ease our cramps and bruises.

By the time we arrived at the Great Wall we had had more than enough; but some strange pig-headedness drove us on. The blazing heat of day was followed by bitter cold at night. For hours we drove through a perpetual sand-storm and cursed through dry tongues and gritty teeth the very name of Gobi.

We passed only long lines of heavily laden camels, herds of sheep, and strings of Mongolian ponies, all making for Peking. It was hard to see in these shaggy griffons the sleek and polished polo ponies and racers of the Treaty ports and Hong Kong. They were escorted by Mongolians, in their blue quilted coats, mounted on the lasso-ponies with which they had captured their merchandise.

Bouncing and twisting up a rocky defile, behind a radiator cap which flaunted a white plume of steam, we gazed heavy-eyed at the grim expanse of naked rock. I was getting a bit tired of this scenery.

"Roland," I grunted, "believe it or not, I would rather be balancing a cup of tea on my knee and politely discussing the weather at this very moment than bumping about in this blasted tin can."

Roland gave up his attempt to swallow beer from the bottle neck.

"My oath!" he cried, "it's not nearly as bad as that. We're bound to get some fun out of this jaunt."

Crack! A rifle bullet flew over the car, to go whanging off the rock face. We snugged hastily down behind the luggage, drawing and cocking our .38 Colts.

Peering over a bale of silk I saw a man brandishing a long rifle some way up the hillside; he was shouting in a high-pitched voice.

I had taken two quick snap shots at him when the guard turned an agonized face towards me.

"No shoot! No shoot! He belong flend."

He stood up in the bucking car and threw four live duck into the road.

Cumshaw! It flashed upon me that this must be the usual toll at this particular point. The unfortunate duck, lashed together by the legs, were soon left, protesting noisily, in our wake.

"Gosh!" I exclaimed to Roland, "they should have warned us. We might easily have spoilt this matey entente."

I had a feeling that we had already covered the most boring part of the trip. Travelling with this stormy petrel, Roland, I had never previously failed to get into trouble, and as we slumped in the back of the car, drowsily listless under that strangely blue sky, something warned me that trouble was again about due.

Crack! Crack! A young salvo of rifle-fire brought the car to a grinding halt.

I wondered indifferently what the fee would be for passing this party, but I noticed the driver and guard sitting motionless as if paralysed with fear.

Roland and I climbed out of the car eager to take this opportunity of stretching our legs.

"Holy Mike!" Roland cried, "we've bought it this time!"

I walked round the back of the car to see a whole platoon of troops, well drilled and well dressed, advancing upon us. The sun caught their bright bayonets, throwing back on us its reflected fire; but in spite of the sun it seemed of a sudden to be bitterly cold.

"Roland," I cautioned, "we've got to go mighty slow: no skylarking with this bunch. Must be Feng's troops, since we're about half-way between Paognan and Suan-wha. Softly, softly, catchee monkey!"

An officer appeared from behind his men and approached us, a heavy Mauser swinging in his hand.

"*Hoo jow! Hoo jow!*" he ejaculated throatily, and once again, more aggressively, "*Hoo jow!*"

Roland, smiling sweetly, advanced on him with his arm outstretched.

"How joo doo!" he said politely.

The officer, however, did not appreciate the effort, and waved him off angrily with his pistol.

"*Hoo jow!*" he said again, and at last it penetrated my senses. *Hù-djoa* meant a pass or a passport, surely.

"No have got," I answered him, "belong British officers."

With the help of the guard, who had a smattering of pidgin-English, we made the officer understand roughly what we were. He, together with four of his men, piled into the car with us, and we proceeded on our course in even greater discomfort than before.

I realized that our luck had at last deserted us and we were about to reap our deserts. Imprisonment, torture perhaps, detention certainly. I knew only too well how long it took to free prisoners, and beyond that was the obvious fact that we had not the slightest right to be there at all.

"Blast it! Roland," I said bitterly, "we're in the soup properly. These blighters will hold us up for weeks!"

Roland, unmoved as usual, replied, "Well, I could do with a few weeks' rest after this ruddy car."

Within a mile we pulled up at a ruined temple, around

which had been pitched some Mongol tents. I gathered we were about to meet the "Man Higher Up", and racked my brains for some words of Chinese.

While we waited outside for the officer to make his report, we handed round cigarettes and smoked cheerfully enough with our guards.

At length we were hustled into the dim precincts of the temple, where I could make out a youthful officer, wearing the badges of a colonel, sitting at a rough table.

His uniform was immaculate and his leather gear highly polished; he gave me the impression of intellectuality and efficiency. At a glance I knew he was not the type one could bluff or threaten. I determined to get my word in first.

"Colonel," I said firmly, "this is not very hospitable treatment for officers of a friendly Power. We are British naval officers from the China Fleet."

"So?" he said quietly. "From where?"

"We are the captains of two submarines stationed at Wei-hai-wei," I told him, "and we have to return there within the week."

"Submarine officers?" he echoed, staring at us as if we were some strange exhibit.

"Do you perhaps know," he went on slowly, "of an officer in submarines called Scott?"

What the devil was he driving at? I wondered. How could a Chinese officer beyond the Great Wall have heard of me? Grudgingly, and perhaps a little nervously, I admitted that I answered to that name.

The effect was electrical. The man pushed back his chair and darted round the table to seize my hands and fasten his eyes on my signet ring.

"*Ni Kàn!* (look)" he cried loudly. "*Lào-ying!* (the falcon)"

The startled guards closed in on us, grasping their weapons more fiercely.

Roland, unmoved as ever, grinned broadly. "I always thought you'd pinched that ring."

The young colonel ordered the guards from the room and regarded us with an attractive, an almost boyish, smile.

"I must apologize," he said sincerely. "Please forgive, but I could not know who you were. Please be seated."

He offered us his cigarette-case while he searched for words to enlighten our bewilderment.

Roland took the opportunity to mutter, *sotto voce*, "By Gosh! You Scots certainly are clannish!"

I hacked him neatly on the shin; for this was definitely a time when Roland must be suppressed.

"My name is Dji," the colonel began, "which can mean nothing to you; but some years ago a British submarine saved a little girl from the sea. The captain gave her a ring to remember him by. You were that man and the little girl is now my wife; so you see I will always be in your debt."

He had pulled, as he talked, a locket on a gold chain from his tunic. It contained an exquisite miniature.

"You remember her?" he inquired, handing it to me.

Roland gazed over my shoulder.

Simultaneously we realized that Mèi Mèi had grown into the beauty we had seen at the Peking Hotel!

Ahead of us the Great Wall stretched indefinitely, dipping into valleys and climbing the steep hillsides till it faded from human sight on the far horizons. Something of its grey strength and timeless patience was borne to me like the warmth of a fire, bringing with it a strange sense of comfort. Under the tall blue cloudless dome the world seemed very still, and I realized that we were extremely lucky to be reaching haven.

Roland apparently was thinking along the same lines. "Didn't some blighter," he asked, his brow creased with deep thought, "write about casting your bread upon the waters?"

L. LUARD

STRICTLY ACCORDING TO PLAN

I shall never forget the experience. It was vivid, exciting, almost bewildering in its sudden intensity. Doubtless the luck was with us—that good luck men earn and deserve when carefully planned tactics, accompanied by exactitude in detail, achieve success. And my friend, the commodore of the convoy, spoke of it afterwards as a naval occasion.

We were proceeding south down the North Sea. From the bridge of our ship, situated in the centre of the port wing, I had a faultless view of the convoy advancing, like an open phalanx, in columns disposed abeam. They were a strange collection, gathered, one would say, from the corners of the seven seas. They ranged in size from five hundred to three thousand tons. Some were in ballast, others deep loaded. Some held a curve and sheer that delighted the eye, others, squat and angular, with topsides straight as walls, were bereft of beauty. From all clouds of smoke rose intermittently, spreading like a pall above the calm placidity of the sea. The slim grey hulls of the escort vessels, sweeping wide arcs, formed etched symbols pregnant with hidden power.

It was difficult, at times, to believe we were at war, though the night, curtained by mist, had been trying. But dawn brought increasing visibility to a festal pour of sunshine, a sky of deep unstained blue that held no hint of hidden anger, with the line of the coast, limned against a diaphanous haze, a remote, impregnable bulwark.

"Do you believe in announcing the odds against a ship being sunk in convoy?" Bradshaw asked, averting his eyes from the eastern horizon.

"Perhaps it is tempting Fate," I said.

"It is," he returned. "One should never boast in war; the unexpected too often happens."

He leaned against the binnacle. Though he had been on the bridge all night, he showed no signs of fatigue. Five years ago he had retired from the Navy, with the rank of rear-admiral. Now, a commodore of the Royal Naval Reserve, responsible for over twenty merchant ships, he had found a new lease of life. "I had my work cut out to begin with," he would admit; "but they soon learnt. They keep station like the Navy. They swing into anti-submarine formation with the precision of a Guard's regiment. They're far greater than they know."

I watched him fill his pipe. He pressed the tobacco into the bowl slowly and deliberately, as though he were reviewing the course of events. His bronzed face, lined and seamed, held wisdom born of experience. "Yes," he continued; "the odds may be five hundred to one against being sunk by a submarine when in convoy."

"As high as that?"

He nodded. "I don't necessarily agree. And the same odds may hold good against bombing attacks, because, for some unknown reason, the Germans don't seem to press them home."

"And mines?" I questioned.

"Almost non-existent now. We're steaming down channels swept each day. But I'm not so sure they haven't other methods up their sleeves. Why not? Surprise is the essence of success. And conditions this morning are ideal."

I knew from his words that something was afoot. Bradshaw rarely discussed the war. He kept it segregated in one compartment of his mind. "Brooding on what may happen destroys efficiency," he often remarked. "Fear is our worst enemy—the fear of the unknown."

He pointed to one of the new war light floats broad on the port bow. "There's the result not of fear, but of insensate bombing. All to the good for us. The lantern burns for more than two months—unattended. In five years' time all lightships will receive their power from the ether, and one of the loneliest callings in the world will be abolished."

He straightened, glanced at his watch, then moved to the starboard side of the bridge and stared ahead. "Time they approached," he said.

I held my peace. A direct question would do no good. Something seemed in store. I attempted an assumed indifference.

Bradshaw grinned. "You're all eagerness," he said; "with luck you won't have long to wait. Mind you keep your eyes open. It will come and go so fast that you'll hardly realize what has happened."

He spoke into a voice-pipe. "Any signals through? None? Complete wireless silence? Right."

He began to pace the bridge. I noticed he was becoming anxious. Yet nothing seemed amiss. The ships were in station, steaming a steady nine knots; our dead reckoning was correct; and the white feather of a hostile periscope would be as easy to spot as the black specks of approaching bombers amid the unruffled serenity of sea and sky.

"I'm becoming impatient," Bradshaw said, half to himself. "Getting old. Getting nervy. Looking into things, despite my resolve. But it's too audacious. We're taking too big a risk. . . ."

He paused in his stride. "Were you listening?"

"I was," I said; "but for the life of me I can't understand your remarks."

A hail from the look-out interrupted his reply. He jumped to the starboard side of the bridge. "Good!" he exclaimed, "here they are."

I followed his gaze. Fine on the bow a long line of foam, like a miniature tidal wave, broke the calm surface of the sea. It came travelling towards us at an immense pace, gaining form and definition.

"Motor torpedo boats!" I cried.

Bradshaw lowered his binoculars. "Quite right. They're all out—making forty-five knots. Now the Germans can do their worst. Events are working strictly according to plan."

"According to plan?" I questioned. "Do you mean we may be attacked by German M.T.B.s?"

A slow smile spread over his rugged features. "I'm not suggesting anything. I'm leaving it to our Intelligence Service. They know best; they've got the information. The Operations Division has done the rest. A big risk—no doubt; but it's been planned to the last detail—timed to a minute."

I held my breath. It seemed difficult to believe. Their craft had nearly three hundred miles to travel. Doubtless well over double this distance was within their radius of action if they proceeded outward bound at economical speed. But they would have to run the gauntlet of our surface and air patrols— no easy matter.

"Conditions seem ideal for us," I pursued.

Bradshaw gripped the bridge rail. "They are now. But don't forget there was fog last night and no moon. An attacking force of mosquito craft would leave at dusk, and have every chance of eluding our patrols. And I don't believe they'll be accompanied by aircraft."

"I'm no tactician," I said, "but aircraft scouting ahead seem essential. They would be the eyes of the flotilla; they would deliver a simultaneous attack. Surely the chances of success would be more than doubled?"

He shook his head. "Not if visibility remained poor. The German M.T.B.s carry two torpedoes apiece. They would stake everything on complete surprise. If we first sighted them at two miles—four thousand yards—their torpedoes, slightly spread, would play havoc before we could turn away."

"Yes," I returned. "You may be right; but, as a landsman, I would still deliver an attack in conjunction with aircraft, even if they came in afterwards. Besides, conditions are no longer ideal for them. Visibility is good. We should sight them five miles away. Even now our M.T.B.s are only just closing home."

"Watch them," Bradshaw returned, "and remember the Germans always work and hold to a preconceived plan. Conditions were ideal last night, I repeat. If they're out, they won't return until they've attempted something. That's where they fall down. They can't adapt themselves to sudden changes— in this case meteorological."

Our craft, roaring over the water in line abreast, approached within two cables. Then, without warning, the high-pitched drone of the motors fell, the misted upflung bow waves merged into flecks of white. Turning into line ahead, they steadied on a parallel course—dispersed, each taking station on the starboard beam of one of the convoy.

"We form a perfect screen," Bradshaw murmured. "Do you see what they are carrying aft?"

I studied the M.T.B. steaming on a parallel course fifty yards away. Her squat hull, with its torpedo tubes, its small tripod mast, its anti-aircraft pom-pom, looked diminutive, insignificant. Then I concentrated on the heaped mounds near her stern.

"Nets!" I exclaimed.

"Quite right. Nets. Have you guessed what we're hoping to achieve?" He raised a megaphone. "M.T.B. ahoy! A red flag at the yard arm is your signal."

"Ay, ay, sir," a youthful voice returned. "The sooner you hoist it the better. We're ready and waiting. We've been practising for weeks."

"Senior officer of twenty ships," Bradshaw commented with a touch of envy. "I don't suppose he has many more years to his credit. No wonder they call them the 'Death or Glory Flotilla'."

I ran over the sequence of events, attempting to elucidate matters. Convoys had been attacked by submarines and bombers, with small measure of success. The magnetic mine which had, at first, claimed many victims, was no longer a serious menace, most ships being fitted with the antidote. I glanced at the live cable, lagged like a steam pipe, running round our scuppers, and marvelled that the current was neutralizing the permanent magnetism of the hull. We could steam safely, without attracting the sensitive needle that closed the detonating circuit. There remained, then, this problem of a massed torpedo attack by German M.T.B.s. It could take several forms. Aided by poor visibility, which favoured the element of surprise, it might well succeed, especially if some of the craft were fitted with floating contact mines, which could be dropped ahead of our course.

"Well, have you guessed?" Bradshaw repeated.

"I think so; but I'd rather see a flight of fighters and bombers overhead."

Bradshaw smiled. "Maybe you will. They're ready to take off—only a few minutes distant in time. Haven't you forgotten that craft travelling over forty-five knots are more difficult to hit than stationary targets?"

I saw a signalman climbing the bridge ladder. Bradshaw glanced at the pad. "Thanks," he said. He wrote rapidly. "Code and get this off."

He turned to me. "An outer flight patrol has reported them. I've just sent a signal to the necessary R.A.F. Coastal Command. Relaying for safety. Don't know what we'd do without wireless. They're twenty miles away. We ought to sight them any minute. Watch for the executive."

I watched, right enough. A few seconds later I saw the red flag break from the yardarm of every ship. Instantly our M.T.B.s moved ahead. They increased to full speed. Covered in flying belts of spray, they formed into single line, turned eight points; and again a long trail of foam rolled, like a miniature tidal wave across the calm surface of the sea.

"Good luck to them," Bradshaw said. "Now we'll play our part by steaming steadily ahead. We shan't even zigzag. If things go awry, we shall disperse like a frightened flock of sheep. Every skipper has his orders, and knows exactly what to do."

He thrust his hands deep in the pockets of his reefer jacket and searched the sky. "Good," he said. "There she is—the M.T.B. guide. She'll pilot them to the best position. The heavy brigade won't be far behind."

I saw a black speck mirrored aloft—a Spitfire fighter. The line of foam, rapidly diminishing in size, curved slightly to the southward.

Suddenly a hail from the look-out set my heart pounding. "Hostile craft on the port bow, sir!"

Bradshaw swung up his binoculars. "Ay, ay." He slipped

the strap over his head and passed them to me. "Can you see them? Streaming in line abreast. Thirty or forty. Now watch our fellows." He laughed like a schoolboy. "Sorry I'm giving you the dud glasses; but you'll appreciate I want the best ones myself."

The next few minutes seemed interminable; but I realized Bradshaw had found the other pair of binoculars and was standing by my side, speaking in a rapid undertone. "Look, our craft have started to swing south. Beautifully timed. They're putting up a smoke screen. The greyish white curtain's spreading rapidly—no; it's not poison gas. We're not starting that game. Now they're turning in succession. They'll be steaming north in a brace of shakes. They *are* steaming north. Can you follow——?"

"Yes," I said, every nerve tense and taut.

"Over they go!" he exclaimed. "The special nets are going overboard. A mile, two, three miles of them, dead behind the smoke screen. We're working up to the climax."

Suddenly I saw light. "By heavens! The Germans will hit them at full speed and foul their propellers."

"Quite right. And then we'll settle with them in our own sweet time."

He glanced at the compass, at the lines of ships steaming steadily ahead, at the escorts still in station on bow and quarter. "The convoy maintains its course and speed," he murmured. Straightening, he stood very still, his features set and resolute. For him, for all of us, the next few minutes were momentous, and I experienced a deepening feeling of awe and expectation. "What a lovely summer's day," he said suddenly. "Who would believe vials of wrath are winging through sea and sky?"

I could find no answer: but I saw our M.T.B.s making towards us in full retreat; I heard far away a droning whirr that swelled rapidly to a full-throated roar. The planes—Blenheim bombers—swooped over our mastheads, making for the long grey barrier of smoke suspended, like a sinister miasma, over the distant sea.

"Excellent!" Bradshaw commented. "They're flying low to avoid detection. They should be invisible to the German look-outs. We don't want to frighten our quarry."

Then the hostile craft broke through the smoke screen, like speeding black arrows. I began to count—ten, fifteen, thirty, travelling in line abreast at tremendous speed, fifteen thousand yards distant.

For a moment I felt our plan, despite its amazing precision, had failed, and I shuddered to think of the consequences.

Bradshaw pressed a button. I heard the action gongs sound through the ship. Men manned the four-inch gun aft, and two flags fluttered to our yard-arm. "Nothing to worry about," he announced. "I'm only sending the convoy to action stations. A necessary precaution; but it won't be needed."

I held my breath. The suspense became intolerable. Suddenly the advancing line wavered, broke, came to a dead halt, as though every engine had been disabled by esoteric magic.

"Snared!" Bradshaw exulted.

A minute later the bombers were over them. They had a sitting target. The dull roar of distant explosions resounded. Columns of water, pierced by yellow flashes of flame and smoke, rose and fell. Our M.T.B.s, turning, pressed home, ready to torpedo the helpless craft.

Bradshaw lowered his glasses. "Poor devils!" he said. "Not one will return. The German Admiralty will be kept guessing again; but I hope we'll find some survivors. It's a naval occasion, right enough—one that worked strictly according to plan."

HUGH POPHAM

MALTA CONVOY

June slipped away; and then, at the end of the first week of July, we rejoined the ship. No one had the faintest idea what we were going to do next; or if they did, they kept it to themselves. We turned south, paused briefly at Durban, and even more briefly at the Cape.

Obviously we were on our way home. So said the more optimistic, and the Commander was lost under requests for permission to "continue shaving"—to remove, i.e., the innumerable beards that had sprouted during our nine months away, the friezes of fair fur, the Player's advertisements, the fringes of black that seemed to put their owners' faces into mourning, the red whiskers that thrust straight out, and the brown ones that curled like the Assyrian's.

Conflicting with this pleasant rumour, there grew slowly, but with increasing assurance, another. This one maintained that we were circling Africa in order to escort the next convoy to Malta. The more we thought about it, the more plausible it sounded. The Malta run was about the hottest in the book, hotter (in every sense) than the long-fought and disastrous convoys to Kola Inlet and Murmansk; and, apart from *Victorious*, we were the most experienced carrier afloat. If there was to be a Malta convoy, it was a reasonable deduction that we should be in on it.

In something under a month we swept round Africa from Mombasa to the Canaries; and when, at last, the skipper, Captain T. H. Troubridge, R.N. (known to the wardroom simply as "Tom", and a heroic figure as he stood beaming on the bridge, a tiny pair of binoculars balanced somewhere on his massive chest)—when the skipper announced with calm relish that the rumour was indeed a true bill, it hardly came as a surprise. It still had power to shock, nevertheless. No precise image formed in one's mind; only a visceral acknowledgment that the months of make-believe were over and that now, after nearly a year's roving commission, we were going in at last among the real enemy. The Germans, we knew, were in Sicily and Sardinia in strength; we should be operating within range of shore-based fighters; and a large fraction of the Luftwaffe would be taking considerable pains to see that the convoy did not get through. Whatever else it turned out to be, this was not going to be a mere solemn prank at the expense of the unhappy French. We needed no briefing to know that.

The evening after the skipper's announcement, we picked up the convoy of fourteen fast merchant ships, and the fleet that was to accompany them, outside the Straits of Gibraltar and well beyond sight of land. They made a formidable array as we took up our station among them. *Rodney* and *Nelson* with that lean, powerful profile; *Victorious*, *Eagle* and ourselves as fighting carriers, with *Argus* in reserve and *Furious* with a load of Spitfires to be flown off to Malta; seven cruisers and thirty-two destroyers: perhaps the most impressive show of British naval power ever assembled during the war so far. From it could be judged the importance with which Malta was regarded, and the scale of the opposition we might expect.

That afternoon before passing the Pillars of Hercules, the carriers put all their Hurricanes into the air, and we flew in formation over the ships as if to show them they would be well looked after. Then we landed-on; and, as dusk drew in, the great concourse of ships turned to the eastward.

Everyone knew what to expect, and the suspense had a stillness at the heart of it. Everyone knew what to expect; but no one knew what special demands would be made on him in the inevitable battle, what particular contingencies he was going to have to meet. The tension of those open factors, that personal anxiety, was discernible in people's eyes, in the

wariness or the excessive casualness of their voices and movements. Excitement, fear, suspense, were a physical thing,
tickling the skin, and danger something to be made light of.
The mood on board was cheerful, resolute, and as taut as
wire.

On the bridge, the skipper was in the best of humours, the
substantial image of confidence. If he too was visited with
qualms like the rest of us, he showed no sign of it; with his
tremendous chest and profuse grey hair and invincible bon-
homie, he seemed to steady the very ship herself. Whatever
demands were made on him, he would meet them with the
same vast Olympian calm.

For him, as for everyone else, there was nothing to do but
make sure that everything was ready, and then wait.

During the night of August 9th, the convoy and its escorts
entered the Mediterranean. From first light the following
morning four fighters were kept at immediate readiness;
engines warmed up, pilots strapped in. The day broke fine and
clear; all round us the ships moved easily over the sea in a
profound and tranquil dream. From time to time, Albacores
took off on A/S patrol, others landed-on, and hardly disturbed the serenity. The aerials of the radar sets turned steadily
through their 360 degrees, sweeping the empty skies. Submerged beneath the surface inaction, men pored over their
sets, listened intently to the crackle of their headphones,
peered through their binoculars in the look-out positions,
with unblinking, rapt vigilance.

Sooner or later the peace would be shattered; and nerves,
jumping at every pipe, at every change in course or revs.
screamed out for it to happen and be done with.

All morning the ships steamed on in undisturbed calm.
Then, suddenly, in the afternoon watch, two Wildcats from
Victorious went tearing into the air. We moved nearer the
island, hoping for tit-bits of news. The Tannoy crackled. It
was the Commander: "*Victorious* has scrambled two fighters
after a suspected shadower. That's all for the moment."

We waited, nerves prickling. That was how it would start,

with a shadower picked up on the radar, lurking low down on the horizon or at a great height, and sending sighting reports back to base.

But not yet. This was not a shadower but a Vichy French flying-boat, probably about its lawful business, a routine trip from Toulon to Morocco. But Admiral Syfret was taking no chances. Without enthusiasm, it was shot into the sea. When it sighted our fighters, it would know that there was a fleet in the vicinity; its course would have taken it within sight of us; if it was left in peace, the news would be out. One day's less grace might make all the difference, to us, to the convoy, to Malta at the far end of the line, already on starvation rations and almost out of petrol for her fighters and ammunition for her guns.

That was the key. What happened to us, to the forty fighting ships deployed on this smooth sea, was unimportant so long as the little knot of merchantmen in the centre reached their destination. To ensure that, we were, if need be, expendable.

Dusk closed in. Peace had returned and continued all that night, the threatened, unreal peace of a dream. Many turned in fully dressed, sure that they would be at Action Stations before dawn. But the night was quiet.

We were on deck again at first light. The convoy was now south of Sardinia, and there was little chance that it would elude detection for more than an hour or two longer. Shadowers were certain, and the first standing fighter-patrols, four at a time, were sent up at dawn with instructions to keep R.T. silence unless, or until, something happened.

Nothing did. Steadily, in open formation, Brian and I circled the fleet as it forged steadily on its way in the slight early haze. Somewhere in the same sky, two more Hurricanes from *Eagle* were doing the same thing; waiting for the ship to break silence and send us off on a vector. There was no sound from her, and at the end of an hour and a half we landed-on again. Ten minutes later the first shadower was reported on the screen. The patrol in the air went after him, a Junkers 88 at 22,000 feet. Before they could get him, he put his nose down and made for home.

Now it was only a matter of time.

Readiness was stepped up. There were two in the air, two in their cockpits on deck; four standing by in the Ready Room; the remainder at immediate call. Later, in the early afternoon, it was my turn, with Brian, to fly again. *Furious* had started to fly off her Spitfires to Malta. There had still been no air attacks; but the fleet was under more or less permanent observation from snoopers. The dream was dissolving into the turbulence of waking.

The wind was chancy, and we were to be boosted off. I was in position on the catapult, engine running. The flight-deck engineer waggled the ailerons to draw my attention to something or other, and I looked out over the port side to see what he wanted. And, as I did so, I stared in shocked surprise beyond him to where *Eagle* was steaming level with us, half a mile away. For as I turned smoke and steam suddenly poured from her, she took on a heavy list to port, and the air shook with a series of muffled explosions.

Over the sound of the engine, I yelled: "*Eagle's* been hit!"

Listing to port, she swung outwards in a slow, agonised circle, and in seven minutes turned abruptly over. For a few seconds longer her bottom remained visible; and then the trapped air in her hull escaped, and with a last gust of steam and bubbles she vanished. All that remained was the troubled water, a spreading stain of oil, and the clustered black dots of her ship's company.

There had hardly been time to assimilate the fact that she had been hit before she had capsized and sunk; and when I took off a few minutes later, my mind was still numbed by what I had seen. It had come so completely without fore-warning. Our thoughts had been focused on the idea of air-attack; we had never dreamed that a U-boat would slip through the screen of destroyers to attack with such chilling precision. It was as if, at any moment, our own ship might stagger and lurch and list, and our aircraft go slithering down the deck into the sea.

In the air, we saw the whole fleet alter course, while the destroyers hounded back and forth, dropping depth-charges. The loss of *Eagle* had screwed up the tension by another full turn, and we flew our patrol with tingling nerves. And still the expected raids did not come.

The day wore on. At 2000 hours Brian and I were back on standby. The sky was gaudy with the first high colours of sunset. In an hour and a half it would be dark, and readiness would be over for the day. We hung about on the flight-deck, Mae Wests on, helmets round our necks, gloves in sticky hands.

"Another forty minutes," Brian said, "and I should think we can call it a day."

The Tannoy crackled. "Scramble the Hurricanes! Scramble the Hurricanes!"

The fitters in the cockpits pressed the starter-buttons, and the four Merlins opened up with a blast of sound and a gust of blue smoke. As we scrambled up the wings, the crews hopped out the other side, fixing our straps with urgent fingers. Connect R.T.; switch on. Ten degrees of flap. Trim. Quick cockpit check. The ship was under full helm, racing up into wind—and we were off and climbing at full boost on a northerly vector to 20,000 feet, heads swivelling. Down to 12,000; alter course; climb to 20,000 again. And there they were, a big formation of 88's below us. One after another we peeled off and went down after them. They broke formation as they saw us coming, and Brian and I picked one and went after him. He turned and dived away, and we stuffed the nose down, full bore, willing our aircraft to make up on him. At extreme range we gave him a long burst; bits came off and smoke poured out of one engine, and then he vanished into the thickening twilight. We hadn't a hope of catching him and making sure; already he had led us away from the convoy; and so, cursing our lack of speed, we re-formed, joined up with Steve and Paddy, the other members of the flight, and started to climb back to base.

The sight we saw took our breath away. The light was slowly dying, and the ships were no more than a pattern on the grey steel plate of the sea; but where we had left them sailing peaceably through the sunset, now they were enclosed in a sparkling net of tracer and bursting shells, a mesh of fire. Every gun in fleet and convoy was firing, and the darkling air was laced with threads and beads of flame.

For a time we hunted round the fringes of it, hoping to catch somebody coming out; but the light was going, and we were running short of petrol. We had already been in the air for an hour, most of it with the throttle wide open. There was no sign of the 88's which had started it all; and it was not clear at first what the ships were still firing at. Then we saw the tracer coming morsing up towards us, and one or two black puffs of smoke burst uncomfortably close. We moved round the fleet, and the bursts followed us; and the truth could no longer be disregarded. They were firing at anything that flew.

We pulled away out of range, and called up the ship and asked for instructions. Stewart Morris's voice was never calmer or more sweetly reasonable than at that moment.

"Stand by, Yellow Flight. Will pancake you as soon as possible."

"If you'd stop shooting at us it would be a help," Brian said, without eliciting a reply.

We closed the convoy again, to test their mood, and provoked another hail of gunfire. We tried switching on navigation lights, which merely encouraged them to improve on their earlier efforts. Disheartened, we withdrew.

By now it was beginning to get dark, and in the gloom I lost the others. With the prospect of a night deck-landing at the end of it all, the situation was beginning to lose its attractions.

"Check fuel, Yellow Flight"; the urbanity of Stewart's voice gave one a sudden, sharp yearning to be back on the familiar deck. Worlds seemed to divide the dark cockpit and its glowing instruments from the dark Air Direction Room with its glowing screens, worlds of twilight sky and sea, as black now as well-water, and the spasmodic blurts of fire.

I tested the gauges of the three tanks, and found I had less than twenty gallons left, a bare half-hour's flying. On my own now, I throttled right back, cut the revs, went into fully weak mixture. It looked as if those eighteen gallons were going to have to last a long time.

Every now and then I approached the ships, still just visible below; and each time the guns opened up. At last, I dropped down to fifty feet, and ploughed slowly up and down between the screen and the convoy, waiting for a chance to find the ship, and hoping to find her into wind. From time to time one of the merchant ships on one side—they had thoughtfully been provided with four Bofors guns each against just such an opportunity—or the destroyers on the other side would spot me, and the red dots of their tracer would come drifting up at me. Once something bigger hit the water with a splash alongside, and I jerked away, frightened and angry. It was at about this point that my R.T. decided to pack up.

I was down to ten gallons, and began to go over in my mind the procedure for ditching, for if I wasn't shot down, and if I didn't find a deck to land on very soon, I should surely have to land in the sea. I jettisoned the hood and released my parachute harness and kept ducking the gusts of gunfire, and came, all at once, to the sudden, stabbing realisation that this might be the end of me. Up to that exact instant, flying up and down between the dark lanes of ships, I hadn't thought of it like that. Now it hit me, as blindly bruising as hatred, as confusing as a blow. I didn't know how I was going to get back aboard: now, for the first time, it seemed highly probable that I should not, and I understood the implications. I didn't wholly accept them; there was still a loop-hole or two through which the mind went bravely peering, past the dead-end of the inimical night.

Automatically I checked the tanks. Five gallons. The time had come for desperate measures unless I was going to accept without an effort my own approaching death. I flew in low over the convoy, disregarding the squalls of fire, in search of a ship to land on. It was now 2130 hours, and quite dark, and the first one I chose turned out to have a funnel amidships. I sheered off hurriedly, and just managed to make out what looked like a carrier astern of the convoy. I made for it, dropping hook, wheels and flaps on the way. It was difficult to see what she was doing: then I caught the glimmer of her wake, and began my approach. There wasn't a light showing; but I could see by the wake that she was under helm. Would she be into wind in time?

I steadied into the approach, and a pair of lighted bats materialised on her deck and began mechanically to wave me round. I checked my petrol for the last time. All the tanks were reading 0. There was a slight chance I might get down in one piece, even with the deck swinging: there was no chance of my getting round again. I continued my approach.

The batsman's signals were becoming a little feverish; but now I could just see the deck, swerving away to starboard under me. It was my last chance. I crammed the nose down, cut the throttle, and with the last bit of extra speed tried to kick the aircraft into a turn to match the ship's. She was swinging too fast. The wheels touched, and the skid wiped off the undercarriage and the aircraft hit the deck and went slithering and screeching up towards the island on its belly. I hung on and waited. It stopped at last, just short of the island, on the centre-line—what was left of it.

For a fraction of a second I was too relieved to move. And then, out of the corner of my eye, I saw a tongue of blue flame flicker across the bottom of the cockpit, and I yanked the pin out of the straps and was over the side. An instant later the wreck went up in a haze of flame.

It seemed excessively ignorant to have to ask which ship I was in; and so I waited in the doorway into the island while the fire-crews doused the blaze, and Jumbo the crane lurched up and removed the bits.

"Did anyone see the pilot?" I heard close beside me.

"No. Did you?"

"I haven't seen him. Wasn't still in the cockpit, was he?"

"No."

"Well, either he must have made a ruddy quick getaway, or the kite must have landed-on by itself."

I didn't feel particularly like advertising myself, but I had to settle this.

"It's all right," I said diffidently. "I was the pilot."

They both looked at me.

"Crikey!" said one of them after a moment. "Nice work!"

"Are you all right?" asked the other.

"Fine," I said. "Only I could do with a drink."

"I'll bet. I'll take you down in a minute. The skipper wants to see you, though, first."

"I supposed he would," I said, and made my way up to the compass platform.

The Captain, when I reported to him, was very put out. "What do you mean by crashing your aircraft on my deck against a wave-off. Eh?"

"Very sorry, sir. No petrol." At least I knew now which ship I was in—the wrong one.

The Captain glared at me in the dim blue light. "Oh. I see. Very well."

Dismissed, I was guided down to the wardroom where, although the bar was shut, a bottle of gin had been left out by someone's thoughtful provision. I had two stiff ones, and felt better. The deck trembled under my feet as the ship altered course, and I suddenly remembered the remote urbanity of Stewart's voice, the moment when I had appreciated with such exactness that I might never feel a deck tremble under my feet again; and for a second or two I felt quite weak, the vivid past clashing with blurred present—a past that it was still difficult to realise hadn't happened after all.

The ship went to Action Stations before dawn next day. The braying of the bugle woke me and I jumped out of my bunk in sudden panic. Why hadn't I had a shake? I was late—and then, in the unfamiliar cabin, the memory of the previous night came back, sharp and detailed, and I felt lost and rather foolish. Somehow I must get back to *Indom*; and with the thought I remembered Butch and realised that for eighteen hours—less, for it was only 0500 now, but for the timeless period since the pipe "Scramble the Hurricanes" had sent us tearing into the air, I had forgotten all about him. It wasn't often in the past ten months that I had been out of the shadow of that ill-temper for so long. Now I must get back to the ship—but how would he take it?

I dressed hurriedly and went up and saw Commander Flying. Could they fly me over? Not a hope. Was there a spare aeroplane so that I could fly with the half-squadron of Hurricanes from *Victorious* herself? No again. *Vic*, like the other ships of her class, had lifts that were too small to take a Hurricane, and so all she had were half a dozen stowed on outriggers on the flight-deck. There were none to spare.

Disconsolately I went down the steel ladder, back on to the deck. I had lost my chance of flying on the one day that would be really busy. I was out of my own ship, cut off from the squadron, and consigned to the completely superfluous role of spectator. I had, I realised as I blinked across the glittering stretch of water at *Indom*, a ferocious headache. I was depressed and disappointed—and, some cowardly little voice insisted, rather relieved.

To be glad, against all one's resolution, that one was out of the battle, however little one had willed it: that was the shameful thing; like turning over a piece of meat and laying bare the maggots that bred and squirmed beneath. I had to try Commander Flying again, and badger the Squadron Commander, to obliterate that horror; they were adamant; and all day the disgusting maggot-life wriggled under the surface of my brain until I could no longer tell what was good and what was rotten.

From dawn, twelve fighters were in the air continuously, with the remainder at readiness. The first big raid came in soon after 0900, a bombing attack by Junkers 88's. Twelve of them were destroyed, and only one or two ever reached the convoy to drop their bombs, and they did no damage. On board, there was ceaseless activity: the A/S patrols and fighters—Hurricanes, Fulmars, Wildcats—for the next standing patrol to be ranged and flown off, and, immediately afterwards, while the ship was still into wind, others to be landed-on, refuelled, re-armed, patched and serviced and ranged aft again ready for the next emergency. In the A.D.R. the screens were never clear of enemy aircraft: a group of torpedo-bombers trying to sneak in low; Heinkel 111's dropping mines ahead of the fleet; another bombing raid to be intercepted, broken up; and then, as one or two succeeded in breaking through the ring of fighters and the massive ack-ack fire, the white gouts of water erupting among the lines of ships. And each time the anxious wait as the spray cleared; and each time the same undiminished numbers, plodding on over the calm sea.

Reports, rumours, tales: the air was full of them. Brian and the remainder of Yellow Flight had landed safely back on *Indom* the previous evening. Tom Troubridge, weighing the risks, had decided that a carrier with half its fighters missing was going to be of little use on the desperate third day, and so had turned into wind, put his deck lights on, and steamed on a dead straight course for an hour at twenty-six knots, far beyond the limits of the destroyer screen, and had landed-on nine-tenths of the aircraft in the air. It had been my mischance to have found *Victorious* and not *Indom* in that last critical ten minutes when the last of my petrol was running out.

Butch had returned to the ship with his flight in the thick twilight and flown slowly up the starboard side, wheels down, looking as much like a Hurricane as was possible, and had received a short sharp burst from the starboard after pom-poms. Incensed, he had landed-on, flung out of his aircraft almost before it had come to rest, and storming across to the offending guns, grabbed the wretched Lieutenant in charge by the throat and nearly throttled him.

"You bloody useless bastard," he had roared at him, shaking him like a door-mat. "You brainless oaf! Don't you know a Hurricane when you see one!"

In the early afternoon, during a lull in the attacks, two fighters came screaming down out of the sun and swooped low over *Victorious*. We watched them. "Silly twats," someone remarked, "beating up the fleet at a time like this. Serve 'em right if somebody fired at them."

But nobody did, and fortunately the two smallish bombs they dropped bounced off the armoured flight-deck and exploded harmlessly in the sea. The only casualty was a starter-trolley which got badly bent; but there were some red faces among the guns' crews and they had to stand a good ribbing for not being able to distinguish a Reggiane from a Hurricane.

The pilots snatched meals as they could and rushed back on deck to take their places on the revolving wheel of readiness. And in the hangar the maintenance crews worked like men possessed to make the aircraft serviceable as they were struck down. They were coming on now with battle-damage to be repaired as well as the normal troubles of oil-leaks, coolant leaks, sprained oleo-legs and what-not. The hangar itself was a shambles as aircraft were ranged, struck down, stowed, refuelled and re-armed at top speed; and the hangar-deck became more and more slippery with oil.

The attacks continued with varying intensity all the afternoon. At a quarter-to-five, one of the destroyers went after an asdic contact and dropped a pattern of depth-charges. As she turned after the attack, a submarine abruptly surfaced astern of her and in the full view of the whole convoy. There was a cheer and a volley of gunfire, and the submarine's crew abandoned ship smartly.

An hour later the radar screens began to pick up the largest formations of enemy aircraft of the day, and it was apparent that the attacks were reaching their climax. Every available fighter was flown off, and reports flowed in of interceptions of squadrons of Junkers 87's and 88's and

He 111's with heavy fighter protection. It was obviously an attempt to saturate the fleet's defences, and soon the ship's guns were opened up, the sky was pocked with bursting shells and smeared across with the smoke of burning aircraft, and the bombs began to fall. The raid had reached its peak when, suddenly, a squadron of twelve Stukas appeared, high in the sky over *Indom*. Fighters were after them, and a hurricane of flak went up from all sides, as one after another they peeled off at 12,000 feet and dived on to the ship. The thousand-pounders rained down in a concentrated onslaught, and in a moment she had vanished behind a dense geyser of spray. Two, three, were hit and plunged across the sky into the sea—but *Indom* was hit too. Smoke and steam billowed up above the wall of water; and for a quarter of a minute it seemed as if she could never re-appear except as a smoking hulk. Then, slowly, as the mass of water heaved up by the near-misses subsided, she emerged, listing, on fire fore and aft, nearly stopped, but still afloat.

From every ship men watched her anxiously; isolated from the disaster, yet sharing it, impotent to help yet suffering the wound as if it were to their own ship and their own friends. For twenty minutes she dragged in a slow circle, her deck heeling and the smoke pouring from her. Then she began to right, and the smoke that seemed to issue from her lifts lost its density and thinned to a wisp; a signal lamp blinked: "Situation in hand", and she steadied on course.

Force Z, consisting of the battleships, the carriers and their escorts, had already turned away to the westward. Our job was done. Spitfires from Malta were ready to give the convoy fighter cover; and in the golden afternoon we left the fourteen merchantmen—fourteen, still, though one had been damaged in the last attack—with their escorts, forging eastwards on the last leg of their voyage, the last and worst. Our thoughts, too deep for words, went with them. By the morning, how many would still be afloat? How many would ever reach any destination but the bottom of the sea?

Half *Indom's* fighters were in the air when she was damaged, and, as they returned from patrol, had to be landed on *Victorious*. They caused a scene of frantic confusion. The Hurricanes could not be struck down, and in any case all spare hangar space was soon occupied by visiting Fulmars; by the time the last aircraft had landed-on, the park was choked with them right back to the aftermost barrier, and it was obvious that if the enemy chose to attack again—and he well might so choose—we should not be able to put a fighter up against him. Only a certain number could be kept on deck if the ship was to use her power; and so, as the crews checked them over, any that were not fully serviceable or could not easily be made so were pushed aft and overboard.

This was more than one or two opportunists could bear to watch without a struggle; and as the condemned aircraft were wheeled aft, a fitter or rigger could be seen wrestling with the screws that held the clock on to the instrument panel. Gradually the aircraft gathered momentum; more frenzied became the efforts of the man in the cockpit; more anxious the glances he threw at the deck slipping past; until, six feet from the round-down, he would leap out and off the wing, empty-handed, just as the aeroplane went scraping over the rail into the ship's wake, to float for a minute or two belly upwards and then disappear for good.

It took more than an hour to sort things out; and then there were, at last, six Hurricanes, refuelled, re-armed, and ranged aft ready for take-off, with nothing in front of them. Several members of 880 were now on board, Dickie Cork—with six enemy aircraft shot down—among them, and I heard the day's tidings. Butch was dead. The rear-gunner of an He 111 had got him as he attacked from astern. Ironically, he had impressed on us over and over again that the stern-attack was fatal (to the attacker); but lack of superior speed, not disobedience of his own instructions, had been the cause of his death. Crooky was dead too, bounced by an Me 109 before anyone could save him. Brian had been shot down by the fleet's ack-ack, but had ditched successfully and been picked up by the last destroyer in the screen. Most of the others had one or two to their credit, and the day's score was impressive.

"The first thing Butch said this morning," Dickie told me, "was: 'Where the devil's that man, Popham?'" They hadn't heard till later that I was kicking my heels in *Victorious*; the rumour was that I'd bought it. "You'd better fly now, anyway," Dickie said. After the ceaseless strains and exertions of the day he was still as cool and calm as if he had merely been doing half an hour's camera-gun exercises.

I looked at the day. The sun was already well down; within an hour it would be growing dark.

I nodded. "More night-landings?" I said as lightly as I could. The thought of approaching the deck in the dark again in the face of the fleet's assembled anti-aircraft armament chilled my blood.

Dickie grinned. "No night-landings. You'll be all right."

The aircraft was strange and lacked a hood among other things, and I watched the sun drop below the horizon with sheer cold terror on me. It only needs a raid to come in now, I thought, and it'll be the same caper all over again. I pushed the fear away: if a raid did come in, I might at least be able to redeem the horrible day's inaction, to forget that for that bitter moment in the morning I had been glad to be out of it. But this was the unkindest trick of all; and as I feared it, so I longed for a vector from the Fighter Direction Officer that would send us off to intercept in the gathering twilight.

Below us as we circled, the diminished fleet steamed tranquilly on; and somewhere over the horizon to the east, the rest of them were looking into the shadows with a more constant, a more instant terror in their bowels. With the wind roaring round me in the open cockpit, I knew how they were feeling. This was the intense, personal centre of war, the secret colloquy the mind carried on behind the muscles' reflexes; the shape and detail of it bearing down like a great weight on the spirit, a taste in the mouth like iron.

The R.T. crackled. "Right. Going down now." We began

to lose height in a wide arc over the elephant-grey sea. The ship was turning into wind. The hooks went down. It was still light enough to see the detail of the deck as we flew past.

One more day of uneventful patrols, of restless picnicking in a strange ship, and then we were rounding the friendly, familiar hump of the Rock into the Bay of Algeciras. *Indom* went straight into dry-dock, for apart from the three direct hits she had received, she had been near-missed by several more bombs, and it was likely she had suffered underwater damage. From the air we had been able to gather a superficial idea of her punishment: it hardly prepared us for the savage disorder we found when we returned aboard. The main hits had been for'ard of the for'ard lift and aft of the after lift. The former had pierced the flight-deck and exploded in the mouth of the hangar, killing, or wounding with flash-burns, many of the ratings working on the aircraft. The force of the explosion raised the seventy-ton lift, which was up, two feet above flight-deck level, where it stuck jammed on its chains, like a cork half out of a bottle, and started a fire in the torpedo-store where, after a time, the torpedoes began to cook off. The latter also pierced the flight-deck, buckling the after lift, and laying waste the officers' cabin flats. A third thousand-pounder had struck the side of the ship just above the water-line where it had burst on impact, wrecked the wardroom anteroom, and killed the half-dozen officers—mostly off-duty pilots and observers of the Albacore squadrons, but including my cabin-mate, The Boy—who were there at the time. Considering the amount of damage and the weight of bombs, casualties had been fairly light, the worst being among our own squadron maintenance crews. But the ship herself was strange to us, the run of her that was as familiar as home broken and interrupted by the jagged rents in her plates, the charred and splintered woodwork, the great, flapping tarpaulin anchored across the missing bulkheads in the anteroom. The strangeness of it all was enhanced by the faces that were missing; their death, during our absence, cut them off from us, for no ghosts could live among these draughty ruins: was enhanced also by the break in normal squadron life. Our aircraft were in *Victorious*, so even the routine of servicing was at an end; there was little or nothing for us to do; above all, Butch, the thundercloud in any sky however clear, had been unaccountably dispersed. His absence, like the sudden, nagging absence of a familiar pain, severed the last link with the past and completed the sense of unreality. To be so free to swim in the cold, pebbly sea and drink Tio Pepe and gobble shrimps at the Capitol, or climb the Rock or wander with no object through the narrow streets of the town, to savour the sheer, voluptuousness of being alive—we did them all at first with an unquiet conscience. Shouldn't we be doing A.D.D.L.'s, in borrowed aeroplanes, on the concrete wilderness of North Front?

Before the ship was patched up and ready for the voyage home, we heard the first wild rumours of the fate of the convoy. That first night after we had left them they were attacked continuously by U-boats and E-boats until only half of the original fourteen were left afloat. At daylight these survivors were subjected to more massive air attacks, and at last only three (rumour said only one) entered Grand Harbour, Valletta, under their own steam. Two more—one of them the vital tanker *Ohio*, still afloat, but only just—were towed in next day. Five out of fourteen, but enough to keep the island alive for the next few vital months, and to fuel and arm not only the Spitfires that could blunt the edge of Kesselring's attack, but also the Fleet Air Arm Swordfish that ranged out night after night in search of Rommel's supply ships. At a cost of one aircraft-carrier sunk and one damaged, two cruisers sunk and one damaged, and a number of destroyers sunk and damaged, the object of Operation Pedestal had been achieved.

And then, in the last week of August, we were on our way home. Despite the thirty-foot hole ripped out her hull below the water-line which had been discovered in dock, *Indom* was still capable of twenty-six knots, and with our escort of destroyers we steamed in a wide circle out into the Atlantic on the last lap of a voyage that had covered 90,000 miles and half the oceans of the world. The after lift was still working, and such

Fulmars and Albacores as were still on board were ranged. The carpenters set to and built a ramp up to the rostrum of the for'ard lift. And as we steamed up the Irish Channel the aircraft were flown off.

As we entered the Mersey and the tugs came alongside to shepherd us into the King George V Graving-Dock, the ship's company fell in in a square round the damaged lifts, and the Marine Band played the bold rousing tunes ordained for ships on entering harbour, and the damp September wind, blowing the funnel-smoke to tatters, had a smell of rain and autumn in it, the driving, small and half-forgotten rain of home.

THE DITTYBOX

D uring the war, when light reading matter was hard to come by, the Admiralty started a magazine for sailors called the *Dittybox*. In a war few sailors see anything of what is going on because in any ship larger than a destroyer at Action or Cruising stations, practically everyone is down below. The bronzed sailor of fiction, then, gazing with fearless eyes out to the horizon, is in real life an individual in an overall suit open to the navel squatting uncomfortably in a stuffy compartment down below trying to read a paperback in a bad light. Towards the end of the war what he read was the *Dittybox*. He read it in the Arctic escorting supplies to Russia, on Malta convoys in the Mediterranean, he read it at the bottom of the Malacca Straits until the depth-charges put out the lights, and in the Pacific off Japanese-held islands. He read it on every ocean in the world. As editor of this little publication, I invited contributions from the Fleet, and I include here a few of the contributions I received. Two of these were by a Polish naval officer, one of those fine seamen who sailed with us from the very beginning to the (for them) bitter end. As I have remarked in the Preface, these aren't literature, but they were written by sailors for sailors and so deserve a place in a Naval Anthology.

Anyhow, in this one they are getting it.

BRUCE WAUGH

A CASE OF SHOCK

Able-Seaman Watt, carrying a small canvas bag, knocked softly on the door of the sick bay in H.M.S. *Topsides* and, without waiting for an answer, respectfully removed his cap and walked in. He glanced round apprehensively, smelling the chemical odours and the disinfectants with obvious distaste.

"What's your name?" asked an ill-nourished-looking Sick Berth Attendant, glancing down a list he had in his hand. "And why are you sniffing?" he added irritably.

"Sniffin'?" Able Seaman Watt laughed tentatively. "I don't like the smell in here," he said.

"Nor do I," replied the S.B.A. abruptly. "But I don't sniff. Wait in there."

Able Seaman Watt glanced up apprehensively, opened his mouth to speak, caught the stern look in the S.B.A.'s eye, wavered momentarily, and then walked into the examination room.

Ten minutes later the S.B.A. came in, loudly slamming the door behind him. "Doctor'll be here soon. Any complaints?"

"Why, no. None at all," Watt replied in surprise. "I came in——"

"All right. Get your clothes off."

"But I was sent here to——"

"I know all about it. You should have come yesterday."

Able Seaman Watt appeared genuinely astonished.

"And now you are here you'll do as I say and jump to it."

Able Seaman Watt slowly and wonderingly removed the clothing and stood, like a shorn lamb, shivering in his nakedness.

"Take your socks off," the S.B.A. ordered.

"They are off." Watt pointed to a pair of woollen socks on his pile of clothes.

"Why do you wear two pairs?"

Able Seaman Watt glanced down at his feet expectantly.

"Oh, that," he said. "I got my feet wet this morning. That's just dye from my socks."

"Then you'd better get 'em wet again now—and use some soap this time," the S.B.A. said peremptorily. "If the doctor sees your feet that colour he'll think you've got foot-and-mouth disease." Able Seaman Watt began to look frightened. "And do you know the treatment for that?" the S.B.A. asked menacingly.

"No," stammered the seaman.

"Slaughter! Then we pour petrol on the carcase and burn it!" the S.B.A. explained in a tone of relish.

"Where's the bath?" Able Seaman Watt asked, pulling on his clothes in agitated haste.

"First on the left."

Watt spent five minutes furiously scrubbing his feet. Then he replaced his socks and returned to the examination room.

The S.B.A. looked up from the mortar in which he was pounding some green crystals.

"Doctor's just sewing the last one up. He'll be ready to start on you in a couple of minutes."

Able Seaman Watt swallowed hard and gradually paled. He pulled out a greyish handkerchief and made a series of jerky dabs at his brow. His mouth felt like a dried river-bed and thwarted all his attempts to utter anything coherent. He sank down on a form, because his knees felt suddenly insecure.

The S.B.A. left the room and returned with a large blue bottle which he placed on the table. Watt's eyes followed every movement like a trapped animal, and finally settled on the bottle. He gasped, and his eyes protruded like the headlights of a lorry. He pointed weakly at the label and tried to frame a word.

"Arsenic?" he finally queried in horror.

But the S.B.A. seemed supremely unconscious of anything but the crystals, and continued his vigorous stirring.

"Doctor'll be here soon," he said, without looking up. "Better get undressed."

A gleam of renewed terror flashed in Able Seaman Watt's eyes, and he wiped the palms of his hands with his handkerchief.

"Hurry up!" urged the S.B.A. "You don't want to upset the doctor before he even *starts*, do you?"

Able Seaman Watt hastily rid himself once more of his clothing and waited, nervously watching the door.

The S.B.A. stopped his monotonous pounding and, looking round at the naked man, pointed with his pestle.

"Lor'!" he said. "Look at your feet!"

The wretched Watt glanced down at his offending extremities. The perspiration that was being so freely released had dyed his toes with another coating of blue from his socks.

He looked helplessly at the S.B.A.

"Remember what I said about the doctor when he sees blue feet?"

Able Seaman Watt remembered vividly and, with a desperate look, dived, naked, out of the door and into the bathroom.

"I think we'll make a start on you now," said the S.B.A., as Able Seaman Watt returned and sank limply on the wooden form. "Get on that couch." Watt shrank back against the wall.

"D-don't I have an anaesthetic?"

"Lor', no," replied the S.B.A. "This doctor doesn't believe in them."

Able Seaman Watt had to support himself against the table while he made a last effort to delay his coming ordeal.

"I'm not feeling very well," he stammered miserably.

"Not *feeling* very well?" said the S.B.A., as if it had never occurred to him before that a man in the sick bay would feel other than in the most robust condition. "It won't be long. The doctor'll soon finish with you."

"*Finish* with me?" echoed Able Seaman Watt feebly.

"He doesn't take long if he gets properly started. Lie down."

Watt lay down, clenched his hands, screwed up his eyes tightly and waited tensely for the first stab of pain.

"You can sit up," said the S.B.A. "I thought I heard the doctor, but it must have been the stretcher-party."

Able Seaman Watt obediently sat up and stared dully round the room. "Have you filled in a next-of-kin form?" the S.B.A. asked casually.

Watt wilted like the top of a burning matchstick, and a stifled moan escaped him.

"Yes," he whispered hoarsely.

Then the door suddenly opened.

"All ready, Sir," said the S.B.A. cheerily. The words shot through Able Seaman Watt like an electric current, and he bit his lip to stop his instinctive desire to make a run for it.

The S.B.A. handed the Medical Officer a card. "Examination for special draft, Sir."

The doctor, a mild-looking little Yorkshireman, approached the prostrate sailor.

"Sit up," he said. "Any pain?"

"Oh *no*, Sir. None at all, Sir," Watt emphatically assured him.

"Open your eyes. No, your eyes, not your mouth. Lie back. Does that hurt? Good. Bend forward. Breathe in. Count one, two, three. Breathe out. Bend your knee."

Able Seaman Watt did his best to cope with the Medical Officer's requirements.

"Why are you shivering?" the doctor asked.

"I'm c-cold, sir."

The doctor called the S.B.A. aside. "Get this man turned in. He's not fit to go on draft."

"Very good, Sir."

"And turn the electric fire on."

"I'm afraid it's still out of order, Sir."

The Medical Officer frowned impatiently.

"The Torpedo Officer promised to send someone along an hour ago."

"Torpedomen always take their time, Sir. I'll get in touch with them again."

The doctor, having given his instructions for suitable treatment, left the sick bay.

"When are you due to go on draft?" the S.B.A. asked the shivering sailor.

"I'm not," said Watt, aghast. "I only arrived four days ago."

"Aren't you P. Watt?"

"No, I'm B. Watt."

"Ah," said the S.B.A., rubbing out a tick he had placed against the name on his list.

"Well," he continued, "makes no odds. You're sick, anyway. Doctor says you've had a shock. Good job you decided to come in. Funny thing, shock. Anything been frightening you lately?"

"Nothing of importance," sighed Able Seaman Watt, resting his head wearily on the pillow. "Would you send that little canvas bag I brought in back to the Torpedo Office? Someone else will have to fix your fire now I'm sick."

Lt.-Cdr. JULIAN GINSBERT, P.N.

CONFORMING TO TRADITION

Britain is
A world by itself; and we will nothing pay
For wearing our own noses.

The above quotation is extremely just. Britain is a world unto herself. Lieutenant-Commander(E) Bemski, Polish Navy—Chief on board O.R.P. *Switez* (O.R.P. corresponds to British H.M.S. and means Ship of the Republic of Poland)—experienced it not without a certain amount of trouble.

The British world is traditionally conservative. That is why Mrs. McGregor travels every year from Scotland to London in July, booking her room six months in advance. When in the Blitz she was told to stay put (warning issued by the Home Office) she answered: "I have gone to London every summer for twenty-five years. Neither the Germans nor the Home Office can stop me."

The British world is traditionally conservative. That is why everybody in England is complaining about the cold and lack of fuel. But if a Continental imprudently proposes to construct a proper stove which would give real warmth and would use in a week the fuel which the open fire uses in a day, he is politely told: "Impossible." And the people of England continue to complain about 'flu and the cold, while its "Tiny Island" is being warmed by the heat which escapes in pure waste through the chimneys.

The British world cannot realise that on the Continent (a Briton says "on the Continent" as a Continental says "in South America" or "in the Far East"—despite the fact that

that funny Continent is only a few miles from "Merry England") anything could be different or better than in this country. That is why respectable Mrs. Smith, when hurt by a bus in Paris, exclaimed: "I cannot understand why those wretched buses are all running in the wrong direction." Certainly she could not realise there was a right-driving rule.

That is why Mr. Lewis, on business in Sweden, shocked everybody when lowering the window of a railway carriage in forty degrees of frost for the purpose of opening the door. Certainly he did not realise that carriage doors could be opened by a handle from inside.

In Lord Fisher's Memoirs one can find that in 1850 the Admiralty opposed the construction of iron-clads because "iron is heavier than wood and would sink". The same Admiralty in 1880 opposed the introduction of breech-loaded guns because "the cartridge may have a retrograde action and kill the gun-crew".

In 1943, Mr. X, a famous English collector of firearms, showed me a pistol: "French, and very old," he told me.

I looked at the pistol. It was marked "Manufacture d'Armes a Steyr—MDCCCLXXXV".

"Sorry," was my answer, "not French, but Austrian. And not so old, as it was manufactured in 1885—some seven years before I was born."

He looked at me with surprise and asked: "How do you know?"

"Well, I understand French, I know something about geography, and I can decipher Roman numbers."

"But if it is written in French and the numbers are Roman why should that pistol be Austrian?"

"My dear friend, the crest of the United Kingdom has two French mottoes, but notwithstanding it is British."

"Oh, you are pulling my leg!"

I showed him the United Kingdom crest in a dictionary, including the two proud mottoes: "Dieu et mon droit" and "Honi soit qui mal y pense".

And here I could understand the full strength of the British tradition. Because instead of being cross or offended, as every Continental would, my noble host started to laugh and concluded: "You know, we are a peculiar people."

This was true and conformed to tradition. And it is also true that the lack of inside door handles did not prevent the British Railways from being the fastest in the world; the Admiralty's conservatism did not stop the British Fleet from having first the Dreadnought or Radar; while Mrs. McGregor's journey to bombed London was nothing but a proof of British courage and tenacity.

Some foreigners are inclined to consider that British courage and ability to resist danger are nothing but lack of imagination. Well, even if it should be true, it is a big quality. If Mr. Johnson reads his newspaper calmly during an air attack, or Mr. Freeman (three times bombed out) puts in his shattered shop-window the poster "Business as Usual" in the sixth year of war—then it is clear that one can only bow to that supreme expression of "non-imagination".

And perhaps that lack of imagination, together with the above-mentioned conservatism, is responsible for the well-known fact that up to now Britain has never lost a war.

But let us go back to our story. It is that lack of imagination and surfeit of tradition even which led Lt.-Cdr.(E) Bemski, P.N., into trouble.

I think the best way is to let him tell his adventure himself to a charming lady:

"Well, to appreciate the story one must know some naval traditions and distinctions. This is very simple. In our Navy I am holding a rank which is called in Polish 'Kapitan' (Captain). The corresponding rank in the Royal Navy is not Captain, but Lieutenant-Commander. Lieutenant-Commander translated literally into Polish is a British full Commander. 'Kommandor' (Commander) in Polish means not Commander but Captain. And may I repeat that Captain in Polish is nothing but Lieutenant-Commander. Do you understand?

"Not at all. I am wearing, as a Lieutenant-Commander in the Polish Navy, these three broad gold stripes on my sleeve.

But in the Royal Navy these three stripes are the mark of a higher rank—a full Commander. And as the people in your country cannot realise that things elsewhere can be different from what they are in England, I am always taken for somebody I am not. Sometimes it pays, sometimes the opposite."

"And what does that red colour between your stripes mean?"

"That's a direct hit! You've guessed! It is the real cause of my adventure. . . . You see, in the Polish Navy 'Red' means an Engineer Officer. As you can easily realise, I am a very important man. If my engines do not turn, the best fire-eater on the bridge would be helpless. But the trouble is that in the Royal Navy 'Red' is reserved for Medical Officers or Surgeons."

"Oh!"

"And now, please listen to what happened. Last Sunday my ship was moored and I went ashore for a few hours. After thirty days of Atlantic Patrol it was a blessing. But in your country Sunday conforms to tradition—it is a day when one should rest and not look for amusement."

"Certainly."

"Well, I confess, I committed a sin. I was looking forward to a good time and I earned my punishment. I was just walking along a bombed-out street, where entire houses were as rare as virgins in Piccadilly, when suddenly I was stopped by two women followed by a dockyard worker. They asked me as a doctor to come immediately and help a woman who was giving birth to a child.

"'I am not a doctor or a midwife,' I told them, thinking, not without reason, that all the local doctors were probably enjoying their Sunday in the company of their lady friends while I was alone and lonely.

"'Don't tell us that you are not a doctor,' answered the dockyard man. 'I was in the Navy and know the distinction. Please come along. It's urgent.'

"'But the Polish Navy has different distinctions. I am telling you that I am not a doctor,' I nearly shouted.

223

"'Tell that to the marines!'

"'But . . .'

"I could not explain further, for the elderly woman started to harangue the crowd which massed around me.

"'Yes,' she shouted, 'we know these crazy Poles. They are just good to make love to our girls or get them into trouble, but to help them . . . No! All landlords and fascists . . .!'

"Some more dockyard workers arrived and the tallest approached me. 'You'd better go!' were his words and I realised that any resistance would be useless and even dangerous.

"Perhaps some M.P. would raise in Parliament the question of 'an undesirable Pole' refusing aid to a sick woman. . . . So I went.

"In an icy-cold room with the windows wide open in spite of the Channel mist (conforming to tradition), and with the radio set transmitting loudly a jazz tune, a young, pretty woman in bed cheerfully gazed at me. To my 'How do you do?' (conforming to tradition), she answered in a not less traditional manner: 'I am all right, and you?' To look at us both one would have thought that I was the patient.

"My brain worked painfully. I felt helpless, uncomfortable, stupid. . . . I should have preferred to enter the rotor of a high-pressure turbine or an Admiralty boiler. The situation was very awkward. If I did something wrong I was taking a great responsibility. If I did nothing—the responsibility still was mine. I think Hamlet's 'To be or not to be' was a childish problem in comparison.

"Then suddenly an inspiration entered my overworked brain. Yes . . . that's the solution. I have no instruments with me. I cannot be of use without them. I must go and find some . . . quickly.

"'I'll be back in fifteen minutes with some instruments. Keep quiet, you may have a cup of tea but nothing else. I shan't be long.'

"I ran down the steps. I entered the first telephone box. I rang for the ambulance. I waited until it came. I climbed the

stairs together with the ambulance-men. I gave orders—
'Careful!' 'Drive slowly!'

"Then I gave the father the excellent advice to come to a
pub and have a drink with me. I also gave him as much comfort as possible, but he did not seem anxious. Finally I got
rid of him.

"In the evening I rang the hospital. A nice young voice
inquired, 'Are you perhaps the Polish Surgeon-Commander?'

" 'Yes. Is there something wrong?' I asked, not without
anxiety.

" 'Everything is all right, sir, thank you.'

"I returned to the little house. I brought the good news to the
father and the whole family. They asked me if it was a son or
a daughter. I was stunned. . . . My lack of experience did not
permit me to act conforming to tradition. I was unable to
answer.

"Notwithstanding, they offered me a cup of tea and ten
shillings. I drank the first and refused the second. Then I
left, accompanied by the blessings of the entire family."

"Is that all?" asked the listening lady.

"No. There were some articles in the Press. In one, under
the headline: 'Gallant Polish Surgeon', appeared the following:

" ' Surgeon-Commander Bekbreski '—that must be me!—
'called suddenly when on leave to a confinement case, carried
out his task in spite of the fact that he had no instruments or
any professional help. He saved the life of both the mother
and child, who are now making good progress.

" ' Commander Bkdrvski '—hum!—'is a famous Polish doc-
tor(!). He studied medicine in the Russian(!) town of Lem-
berg(!). His wife was sent to Siberia(!) by the Germans(!). His
family has a royal title(!) but dispensed with it for political
reasons(!). His castle in the Sudeten(!) was burned by the
Finns(!). Commander Bkdski(!) sailed twice round the
world(!), has fought in the Battle of the Atlantic and ferried
himself from a Polish destroyer to a Canadian corvette, over
thirty miles in a gale(!). He wears the M.B.E. and the Polish

Order of the Golden Lamb(!). We congratulate the Royal(!) Polish Navy on possessing such a distinguished officer, and we hope that he will soon be back in Gydnia(!). ' "

(The true name is Gdynia but most Britons call it Gydnia.) "Excellent!"

"Well, another local paper wrote just the opposite!

" ' Polish Naval Surgeon Refuses Help.

" 'Called to help a Mrs. Y., the wife of a dockyard worker, a Polish Naval Surgeon refused his assistance. The neighbours called the ambulance which took Mrs. Y. to hospital, where she gave birth to a child. Both mother and baby are still in danger because of delayed medical treatment. The hospital staff fears complications.'

"And finally, conforming to tradition, there was also a Polish epilogue. I was informed by my authorities that I had usurped the rank of Commander and the function of a surgeon. I was told by some colleagues that I had committed a criminal operation on my own girl-friend. And—last but not least— I was told that the child born in hospital was my own!

"It resulted in a lot of fuss and trouble. When finally I was cleared, I swore to myself never to be a doctor, and I wrote a long petition to the Polish Admiralty proposing that the colour of the arm stripes should be changed to that of the Royal Navy in order to avoid further confusion.

"But this time the Polish tradition was as strong as the British. My petition was refused, I was reprimanded and told never to try again.

"Besides, I have forgotten to tell you that I was jilted by my own lady-friend, because of 'unfaithfulness'. But that—as Kipling said—is 'another story'."

JOHN DAVIES

AO DGHAISA

Paolo Giuseppi Saviour Angileri Chercuti, scion of the ancient and most honourable Chercuti family, heroic citizen of the most ancient and illustrious city of Senglea, in the proud island of Malta, lay back in his dghaisa and scratched himself.

Life, decided Paolo, was good. In spite of the privations which still remained even now that victory had been won, life was very good indeed. It was good to lie in the sun. And in a little while he, Paolo Chercuti, prince of dghaisamen, would untie his *Santa Maddelena* and take her round to the creek where the sadly inferior vessels of his fellow boatmen were moored. It would be a triumphant arrival, for the *Santa Maddelena* was freshly painted in most distinguished crimson and freshest green, and could be counted on to make the others look most satisfactorily shabby. Paint was no longer easy to come by, and had it not been for the good Francesco, who had charge of such things in the Admiralty dockyard, Paolo's poor *Santa Maddelena* might well have been as shabby as the rest of the dghaisas in Grand Harbour.

Lazily Paolo reached behind him into the bows. He pulled out a small wicker basket and took from it a loaf. The loaf was in two parts and the middle of each part had been scooped out and filled with a mixture of lettuce, tomatoes and oil. Paolo took up one half and inspected the contents with approval. Then he settled himself more comfortably . . .

After eating he wiped his mouth on a sunburned forearm, leaned back and dozed.

The blazing afternoon was well advanced when the *Santa Maddelena* slid smoothly into Dockyard Creek. Standing upright amidships, Paolo leaned on his oars in short, quick strokes and gazed out idly over the bows. The *Santa Maddelena* glided past the first of three destroyers which were lying to their buoys in the creek. Some distance ahead, a cluster of moored dghaisas began to assume shape and identity.

Then, as Paolo passed the *Savage*—the second of the destroyers—a loud shout rang out on the afternoon air.

"Ao dghaisa!"

Paolo ceased rowing and gazed contemplatively at the *Savage*. At the head of her ladder he saw the quartermaster standing with his hands cupped around his mouth, in the act of hailing. A moment later a second shout rang out across the water and echoed from the quiet houses at the harbour's edge.

"Ao dghaisa!"

But Paolo was still more than half-inclined to ignore the summons. He urgently desired to show off the new splendours of the *Santa Maddelena* to his waterfront rivals, and he had no desire at all to have a lot of rough sailors kicking his beautiful new paint around before it had been seen, admired and envied. And not many days previously he had had difficulty in extracting his rightful fare from a group of seamen from this very ship.

But following upon these thoughts came another. After all, thought Paolo, a fare was a fare, and even a prince of dghaisa-men must live. With a faint gesture of resignation he leaned on his port oar and the *Santa Maddelena* slowly began to turn in a wide circle.

Paolo hung on to the destroyer's ladder while his passengers got in. There were four of them. Paolo regarded them impassively. Two of them looked suspiciously like those he had had trouble with before. Well, he decided, if they were, they would not get away with anything this time.

When the last of the four was seated, Paolo shoved off and started to push the *Santa Maddelena* steadily across the harbour.

Stolidly he kept to his oars, ignoring his passengers. The drowsing Valletta waterfront grew steadily nearer.

Then, when they were not more than ten yards from the Customs House Steps, Paolo, with a dexterous twist of the wrists, brought the *Santa Maddelena's* course parallel to the quayside, and, leaning back on his oars, arrested the boat's progress. With the way off her the *Santa Maddelena* lay motionless on the water. Paolo's passengers, who had been preparing to get out, looked at him in surprise.

"What's the idea?" asked one of them.

"Pay now," said Paolo quietly. "Pay now, please—one shillin'."

"What the . . .?" All four of the seamen were glaring at Paolo now, but Paolo remained steadfast.

"Pay now . . ."

"Why, you miserable little rat . . ."

"Pay now," said Paolo.

For a moment the four in the stern ceased looking at Paolo and looked at each other instead. Then there was a sudden, violent upheaval, and an instant later Paolo found himself lying on the floorboards of the *Santa Maddelena* with very little idea of what had happened. A figure loomed above him, grabbing the oars, and in a matter of seconds the *Santa Maddelena* was alongside the steps, her passengers had leaped out and were moving off rapidly along the waterfront. The sound of their laughter came cruelly to Paolo's ears.

Paolo sat up, choking with rage and mortification. Automatically he drew the oars inboard to safety, and then for an anguished minute he sat motionless, holding with one hand to the lowest of the steps. His fiery, Latin-Oriental temperament urged him to pursue his aggressors with every curse and vilification known to his harbour eloquence, but with a tremendous effort he restrained himself. He had appeared foolish enough already. He would not give those bell-bottomed devils any further cause to mock at him.

The devils in question were now crossing the waterfront road with the obvious intention of striking up into the town.

Already, faced with the serious problem of choosing a bar from the many which offered, they had almost forgotten the incident of the *Santa Maddelena*.

Calmer now, Paolo watched them until they turned into the Via San Niclau and vanished from sight. Then, as though their disappearance had broken a spell, he hastily secured the *Santa Maddelena* to a ringbolt in the harbour wall, leaped urgently out, and hurried off in pursuit of the vanished foe. The few loungers on the waterfront regarded him with some interest, for it was a phenomenon to see a dghaisaman hurrying on land (or on water for that matter). But Paolo ignored them and made straight for the corner of the Via San Niclau at his best turn of speed. As he rounded it he looked anxiously ahead. Then his pace slackened.

The blue devils were still in sight, proceeding in a leisurely fashion. They were just beginning to mount the shallow stone steps which led to the upper town. Paolo decreased his pace still further, to avoid any nearer approach, and advanced with circumspection in the shadow of the wall.

The chase ended suddenly. With satisfaction Paolo watched the four seamen disappear through the doorway of the "Blue Anchor", a small bar about half-way up the steps. Paolo moved forward more rapidly, took the steps nimbly, two at a time, and slid unobtrusively in through the same narrow entrance.

The little bar was crowded and thick with smoke. Behind the bar counter Saviour Comozzi, proprietor, mopped alternately the wet, polished wood and his gleaming, beaded forehead.

Standing just inside the door, Paolo peered through the smoke and located his quarry at a table in the farther corner. They were deep in talk as they waited for drinks, and every few seconds they laughed uproariously together. At each burst of merriment Paolo seethed inwardly.

But once he had located them he did not look again in their direction. Instead, he moved discreetly up to the bar, and when Saviour had a moment to spare beckoned to him.

Saviour slid his stomach along the counter towards the door and looked inquiringly at Paolo.

Paolo talked quickly and urgently, and Saviour's face was the ample mirror of his many conflicting emotions. Surprise, disbelief, laughter and anger all moved mercurially across that vast and mostly gleaming countenance. Paolo threw his whole heart and soul into ever more urgent and graphic explanations and entreaties. Then, when he finally stopped, Saviour looked at him hard and strangely, as though he thought him completely and hopelessly mad. Paolo looked back beseechingly, until finally Saviour threw up his arms and his eyebrows, passed a damp cloth across his forehead, frowned, scratched his nose and nodded. Whereupon Paolo immediately grinned broadly and vanished.

For the bell-bottomed devils the evening seemed to be turning out far better than they could possibly have hoped. When they shouted for their second drink Saviour came over and told them, in a dramatic but somewhat bewildered fashion, that a mysterious benefactor had appeared, demanding that any drinks the four might care to have should be placed to his account in token of the gratitude he had always felt to such heroic defenders of his humble island. No, the benefactor was no longer present, and could not be thanked, except through Saviour, who would willingly convey any message they might wish to send, though he could not pretend to understand what it was all about. But meanwhile, any drinks they might care to have. . . .

The heroes cared to have quite a lot, and the evening grew steadily more beery and unrestrained, until instinct told them that their revel must be drawing to a close. For the ship's company of the *Savage* leave ended at midnight, although it is hardly to be expected that they would have remembered even so much had it not been that the captain of the *Savage* was notoriously hard on men adrift from leave. This one fact penetrated their consciousness just sufficiently to cause them to stagger to their feet and stumble out of the doorway with loud but incoherent farewells to Saviour. Saviour watched them go, wondering still, until the hands and the eyebrows came up again and he turned to mop down the bar for the last time.

The air of a summer night in Malta is like wine, but wine is not to be recommended for those who are already full of beer. The cool dark hit the heroes like a blow, and for a few minutes they swayed weakly. But the urgent necessity of getting back still presented itself more or less coherently, and they staggered off doggedly down the steps, into the Via San Niclau, and thence to the waterfront.

Here fortune appeared to favour them, for although normally at this hour it is not an easy matter to get a dghaisa, a long black shadow glided immediately out from the Customs House Steps and slid along the low wall at their feet. Thankfully they tumbled in and subsided in a comatose condition in the stern.

As he pushed out across the harbour Paolo surveyed his inert cargo with grim satisfaction. They were very far gone. Not one of them had in fact been able to tell Paolo where to take them. But Paolo knew well enough. He rowed on steadily, and soon a dark shape grew out of the night.

It needed a great deal of prodding to get the four of them up the destroyer's ladder, but at last it was achieved, and the four seamen stood together on the shadowy quarterdeck vainly endeavouring to collect themselves. Vaguely they registered the absence of the quartermaster as a happy accident which might enable them to get below without being caught. After one false start in the wrong direction they at last stumbled off forrard along the starboard side.

Once they were safely aboard Paolo pushed gently off a little and watched them for a moment. Then, with a secret smile, he leaned on his oars again and moved slowly away. He was tired and would have to be up early.

But a warm sense of achievement made his weariness a pleasant thing.

The harbour was still covered in soft white mist when Paolo stepped into the *Santa Maddelena* again. It was very early, and the traffic of the harbour was not yet stirring. He got out the oars and pushed slowly off from the quay.

Soon a vague shape loomed indistinctly through the mist. This shape was the battered remains of a British destroyer which had been completely demolished forrard of the bridge structure by a direct hit during a heavy air attack. But the watertight bulkheads had held and she still floated. She had been lying idly at this mooring for many months, useless and deserted.

Deserted?

Well, Paolo had passed her every day during the time she had lain there, and there had never been the slightest signs of life. But there were most definite signs of life now. Vague figures on her quarterdeck were indulging in the most extraordinary activity. Paolo turned slightly to port and approached slowly. He could now make out four figures, all of them gesticulating wildly. Then a desperate hail came forlornly through the mist.

"Ao dghaisa!"

Paolo glided to within twenty yards of the derelict destroyer, and then stopped.

"Come on and take us orf!" roared a voice from the hulk. Paolo ignored this demand and stood at his oars, watching silently.

"Hi! You there! *TAKE US ORF!*" There was a distinct note of entreaty this time. Paolo moved a yard or two nearer.

"Dghaisaman," he said suddenly, in a loud, clear voice, "is not rat!"

There was complete silence for a moment, and then a solitary, astonished voice came from the group.

"Oh, my Gawd! It's . . .!"

"Take us orf!" broke in another voice, pleadingly. "Come on, there's a good feller."

"Rat yesterday, good feller today," said Paolo coldly, and backed away a yard or two. This was greeted with a furious outburst of shouts and cries.

AO DGHAISA

"*TAKE US ORF!*" The castaways made a final effort, a concerted, despairing shout. Paolo moved in again, closer this time. He stopped a bare five yards from the ship.

"Pay now," said Paolo.

"For Gawd's sake!" said the biggest seaman—Paolo had a shrewd idea it was he who had caused his ignominious descent to the *Santa Maddelena's* floorboards the previous afternoon. "We'll pay yer! Only chop-chop! We're more'n six hours adrift already!"

"Ten shillin'," said Paolo, edging closer still.

"Why, you robbin' so-and-so . . .!" began the big seaman, but then he added hastily, as Paolo showed signs of withdrawing again, ". . . All right! Only git alongside!"

Paolo took up the port oar and shoved the blade up on to the destroyer's quarterdeck.

"Ten shillin'," he repeated.

The four figures in the ship's stern went into a huddle then, and after a moment or so the big seaman broke away with a grimy ten-shilling note in his hand. With a gesture of disgust he slapped it on to Paolo's oar. It clung to the wet blade and Paolo drew it carefully inboard, removed it, wiped it, and put it in his belt. The four seamen watched his deliberation with something of the patience of despair. Then at last Paolo deigned to bring the *Santa Maddelena* alongside. The four dropped down into the stern with most remarkable speed and sat there in abject gloom. Paolo pushed carefully off.

Eleven o'clock. The sun beat down upon Grand Harbour as fiercely as it had done the day before. Paolo lay in the bows of the *Santa Maddelena* not more than a hundred yards off the starboard beam of the *Savage*. He was watching the ship with interest. Gold braid was glinting on the quarterdeck, where a certain amount of activity was taking place. A small table had been positioned just abaft the door of the wardroom lobby. A tall, commanding figure now stood behind it, and other figures were ranged on either side. As Paolo well knew, the captain of the *Savage* was seeing defaulters.

Just forrard of "Y" gun stood a small group of bell-bottomed figures who looked vaguely familiar to Paolo. Yes, there were four of them; and as he watched, one of these figures moved forward and stood to attention before the table and removed his cap. The mumble of question and answer came faintly across the sunlit water.

Paolo watched happily as each of the four figures moved forward to stand before the table. He glowed with satisfaction as each cap came off. He chuckled as each figure was dismissed and moved slowly off forrard—their disconsolate manner was apparent even at that distance. He watched until at last the table was removed and the quarterdeck was once more deserted, except for the familiar figures of the quartermaster and the boatswain's mate. Then, with a sigh of complete satisfaction, he stretched luxuriously and reached behind him for his wicker basket. He was hungry.

COMMANDER JOSEPH BARTOSIK

EAGLES FLY HIGH

The *Orzel* was the largest Polish submarine before the war. Her name meant "Eagle". On the eve of war, which the Poles knew was coming, they christened their latest warship after their national emblem: the royal bird.

Long before the actual outbreak of hostilities, the Germans forced upon Poland a war of nerves. From Christmas, 1938, onwards, the Polish Fleet was kept in a state of constant alert.

For almost nine months the *Orzel* carried out one patrol after another. Meanwhile in the *Orzel* the strain and the tension aged many of her crew, and before autumn came the Chief Engineer's hair turned white, although he was only just over thirty.

At dawn on the memorable day—September 1st, 1939—the *Orzel* was lying in harbour, resting after her latest patrol. Her Captain was ill, but refused to leave the ship. "It will soon be over," he told the doctor, who wanted to move him to hospital.

Just before daybreak the moon set and patches of fog began to rise. On top of the hill called Oxywie, which dominates the harbour, the granite statue of the Son of Man was already emerging from the dark when a roar of aircraft engines approached the ship. A squadron of bombers flew low over the harbour, showing black crosses on their wings. The *Orzel* and all the other warships at once opened fire.

The noise of gunfire was still shaking the mist when an alarm message was received in the submarine's W/T office.

It came from the small Polish garrison stationed at Danzig and read: "Am being attacked, S O S." Almost simultaneously the code word "Dragon" was flashed from the C.-in-C. It meant: "The war has begun. Carry out your orders. Good luck to you all."

There was a short whistle on the bridge, a signal for the men standing by to "let go" the ropes. As the ship passed the breakwater, hundreds of seagulls circled round her with disturbed cries. Once clear of the channel the *Orzel* submerged and set her course to the east.

The sector appointed to her was only some five miles away, roughly midway between Gdynia and the peninsula of Hel. It was an exposed position, guarding the entrance to the inner Polish waters.

When the *Orzel* reached her station, German aircraft were already over the bay, flying in groups of three and coming in very low. The shallowness of the sea, not more than twenty-five fathoms, and the light transparent colour of the Baltic water, greatly hindered the submarine's movements. For the three days of her operations there she was repeatedly attacked from the air, while by night the presence of enemy M.T.B.s caused numerous submerging alarms and made the recharging of batteries an uneasy problem.

On the morning of the fourth day the C.-in-C. ashore ordered the *Orzel* to a new sector farther to the north in the outer approaches to the Bay of Danzig. While under way the *Orzel* was detected by aircraft and subjected to an exceptionally violent attack. In an attempt to defy enemy surface craft which joined the attack, all machinery was stopped, including the gyro-compasses. The explosion of a depth-charge just over the ship threw her down until her bows hit the bottom of the sea. All lights went out and water began to come in through the exhaust valve of the main diesel engine. All through the attack, which lasted for several hours, the enemy propellers could be heard overhead. It was not until after sunset that the *Orzel* was able to come to the surface. Then by the light of the moon a patch of oil could be seen on the water. It meant that the tanks were leaking, betraying the position of the ship all the time.

For the next ten days the *Orzel* remained in the new sector, operating between Sweden and the Polish coast, intercepting enemy merchantmen and naval units. At the same time the Chief Engineer made every effort to repair the damage the ship had suffered.

Suddenly the Captain's illness took a critical turn. As all Polish harbours were already cut off by the enemy, the C.-in-C. ashore ordered the sick officer to be landed in a neutral port. The First Lieutenant, who for the last three days had been virtually in command, chose Tallinn, the capital of Estonia.

On the night of September 14th, after having obtained the consent of the Estonian authorities and their promise to give all necessary assistance, the *Orzel* entered the port. There was a German merchantman named *Thalatta* in the harbour; on seeing the Polish warship she at once hauled down the swastika and in great haste painted over her recognition signals on the funnel.

No sooner had the Captain been driven away in a Red Cross ambulance than two senior Estonian officers arrived on board. They stated that as the German *Thalatta* was about to sail, the Polish *Orzel* would not be allowed to leave Tallinn until forty-eight hours after the German ship's departure. "These," they declared, "were the exigencies of international law."

The next afternoon the *Orzel* was moved to another place and moored between five Estonian warships. It was obvious to the new Commanding Officer that the Estonians—with whom Poland had an unofficial treaty of mutual assistance— were likely to yield to the demands of the German Minister. As a precaution he ordered all ciphers and secret documents to be destroyed.

Hardly an hour later the Estonian Admiral notified the Captain that the *Orzel* and her crew would have to be interned. Armed Estonian guards were at once placed on her deck and at the gangway ashore. Lorries brought a detachment of Estonian sailors, who within a few hours unloaded all the ship's ammunition, took away the gun breeches, rifles, fourteen torpedoes and all charts and navigational books.

The same day the ship's wireless gave the news that the Russian armies had broken into Poland. It was a depressing day for the crew of the *Orzel*.

The disembarking of the armament was still in progress when the British Military Attaché in Tallinn, accompanied by an Estonian official, came to see the ship. After his visit two cards were found on the wardroom table. On the front was the Attaché's name and rank, but on the back they showed some handwritten words: these were "Good luck" and "God bless you." This unexpected message brought a new light to their hearts. Watching the trolleys as one by one they removed the torpedoes with which they had hoped to avenge the injuries of their country, they felt that the time had come to act.

In secret—so as not to raise the suspicion of the sentries—a plan of escape was worked out and parts distributed. The Commanding Officer himself suddenly displayed great anxiety about the davit, with the result that ten minutes later, when the next torpedo was being lifted, the wire broke in half. The Estonians accepted it as an accident and postponed further unloading until the following morning, leaving six of the *Orzel's* twenty torpedoes still on board.

In the evening the ship's company went to their hammocks as usual, and by 2200 loud snoring resounded everywhere. The two Estonian sentries were—no doubt—well pleased with their prisoners.

Soon after midnight an Estonian officer called at the *Orzel's* gangway to make sure that everything was in order. After he had gone the sentry in the control-room hardly managed to keep awake, lulled by the monotonous ticking of the navigational clock. Suddenly there was a bang behind him, and before he realised what was happening he and his comrade had been knocked down, gagged and disarmed.

In one moment the whole crew were on their feet, carrying out their prearranged orders. The Chief Electrician, with an axe in his hand, ran ashore to the place where a thick cable branched off from a big, red-painted box. A few seconds later there was a terrific flash, followed by complete darkness; all the lights in the harbour went out. At this signal the mooring wires were cut—including the one which connected the *Orzel* with the Estonian warship on her port side—and the drum of the capstan whirled wildly away. The engine telegraph on the bridge tinkled once, and then again: "Full ahead both."

First a hissing sound of the compressed air was heard, followed by a deafening roar of the diesel engines. A fresh draught of air swept down the main hatch. The ship started moving, her bows almost touching the Estonian destroyer as they slipped past her.

The darkness of the harbour was now complete, with dense low clouds hiding the rest of the stars. The Captain had no charts, but he knew that somewhere on his course two dangerous shallow places were awaiting him. Once clear of the quay revolutions were reduced and a slow speed ahead maintained. The breakwater was just coming into sight and the *Orzel's* nose was about a foot above the water when a violent bump shook the ship. She was aground, sitting on a rock. The Estonian warships sounded an alarm. Soon several searchlights were switched on and started sweeping the surface of the outer harbour. It was not difficult for them to find the *Orzel*, immobilised in the middle of the entrance. Machine-gun and rifle fire at once opened from several directions, and bullets pattered on the bridge and hull.

In this hopeless situation Nature came to the rescue. A fresh breeze blowing from astern took the smoke and the fumes of the diesel exhausts and carried them ahead so as to hide the ship's low silhouette behind a dense screen of smoke.

"Flood the after tanks," ordered the Captain, while the pumps were still howling away trying to empty the forward ballast tanks; both engines were sent to "full speed astern". Fired at all the time, the ship moved gently an inch, then another, then a whole foot. Gradually she slipped back and was water-borne again.

As course had to be altered after she had passed the break-water, the smoke no longer covered the *Orzel*. Instead, she came into the blinding beams of several searchlights. There was a thunder in the air followed by the tremendous explosion of a 14-inch shell, which landed only about two cables away from the ship's side.

The channel was about half a mile long and too shallow for the *Orzel* to submerge. As she moved along it the splashes and explosions of the shells from the shore battery were getting nearer and nearer. The Captain—a stopwatch in his hand—counted the time of flight of each salvo. There were still three cables to go, then two cables, then one. . . .

At last the Captain pressed the button. A series of long buzzer sounds were heard all over the ship. The diesel engines came to a standstill, and the electric motors took over. A deep silence fell suddenly upon the ship. The hatch in the conning-tower was shut, and gradually in the beam of the searchlight the *Orzel's* silhouette grew smaller and smaller until it disappeared completely beneath the swollen surface of Riga Bay.

In front of them stretched a narrow sea, full of shoals and rocks, with an irregular bottom. They faced it without a single chart to guide them, and the only help they could get was from their echo-sounding machine. During the weeks which followed the life of them all depended largely on the proper functioning of that tiny set.

The Estonians chased the *Orzel* for twenty-four hours. Aircraft and warships were used in the search, and from time to time the explosion of depth-charges shook the sea. As the propellers of the pursuers could be heard all the time, the *Orzel* stopped her machinery and lay still on the bottom. By the following evening the submarine got as far as the entrance to the Gulf of Finland. Then just as her conning-tower was breaking surface three warships were sighted following close astern. She dived again at once and remained motionless for some time. The sound of the propellers approached, came right overhead, then slowly went away on the other side.

As their noise died away in the distance, the Captain and his fifty-four men realised that at last they were free. The *Eagle*, although her talons had been blunted, was now taking off for a new flight.

The news received by wireless was heart-breaking; except for Warsaw, which, besieged and on fire, was still holding out, all Poland was in the hands of the enemy. On top of this the German wireless put out its own version of the *Orzel's* escape. According to this the treacherous Poles had murdered the defenceless Estonian sentries and had escaped, violating international law and breaking the word of honour they had given the Estonians.

This lie roused a feeling of extreme indignation among the ship's company. They wanted to protest and to tell the whole world that the Germans were lying. Originally they had intended to land the two Estonian guards secretly on the Estonian coast, but now they altered the plan.

On the night of September 21st they closed the lighthouse of Ostergarn on the Swedish island of Gotland. When a mile and a half off the shore they lowered their dinghy on the smooth surface of the sea. The two Estonians were put into the boat, supplied with food and several bottles of whisky, with money sufficient to cover the expense of their journey back to Tallinn, and above all with a letter to the Swedish Commander-in-Chief.

The submarine waited for an hour and a half to make sure that the two had landed safely. After that the *Orzel* proceeded south, nearer to the enemy coast.

The first problem to be solved was that of navigation. A search of the drawers in which the confiscated charts had been kept yielded an important discovery; behind one of the shelves a German "List of Lights" was lying. It must have slipped there and the Estonians never noticed it. With the help of this book the Navigating Officer made what he called the "Map of the Baltic, No. 1".

It was a strange map; it showed neither coastline nor sandbanks. The only thing one could see on it were isolated dotted points marking the positions of various buoys and lighthouses. The enormous blank space between these had soon to be filled from experience.

One day, as he was not sure of his position, the Captain decided to go north until he could see land, but several hours later the submarine bumped into a submerged rock and started heading south. This unlucky place was marked on the map and the name of the shoal inscribed: "Kamienny Kres polnocnych szlakow", which in English means "Stony End of Northerly Courses".

The small bay in Gotland where the two Estonians had been landed received the name of the "Gulf of Two Estonians".

One day towards the end of September the *Orzel* sighted an armed German ship south of the Swedish island of Öland. While manoeuvring for position to attack her with torpedoes the *Orzel* hit a sandbank. The Captain tried to climb over it, but the conning-tower unfortunately broke water. Undiscouraged, he hoisted a signal ordering the merchantman to stop. The German obeyed, but almost immediately the *Orzel's* Wireless Officer overheard a very close wireless transmission and within ten minutes, while the *Orzel* was still struggling on the sandbank, a Heinkel bomber appeared overhead and started circling. At last the submarine slid off the bank into deep water, but the merchantman was now miles away, making off at full speed. On the map this place was named "The Bank of Fears".

Gradually many more names that spoke for themselves filled the white sheet. This strangest map ever made had its own "Cape of Good Hope" and its own "Calvary".

Before September came to an end the last link between the

Orzel and the country was cut. With the words of the national anthem, "Poland has not perished as long as we live", the Warsaw station closed its last broadcast. After twenty-seven days of bitter fighting the capital of Poland was silent. Two days later the naval stronghold of Hel also fell. There was something tragic in the silence. The sailors in the *Orzel* knew that the battle for Poland was over and lost. But not the war. . . .

The store of fuel oil was gradually decreasing. So were provisions and the compressed oxygen in the steel bottles. But the most acute of all was the problem of fresh water. To distil it from the sea water was possible only when the engines were working at high speed, which was undesirable and meant a high consumption of fuel.

After the crew had been using salt water for washing for a week so little fresh water remained in the tanks on October 6th that it was barely enough to make the last tea for all of them. The Captain was now forced to take the decision which he knew sooner or later he would have to face. Having heard through the B.B.C. that other Polish warships had fought their way through to Great Britain, he decided to take his ship there.

Anyone who has been to the Baltic realises how difficult from the navigational point of view is the passage through the Danish Straits. The *Orzel* was going to risk it without a single chart and right under the nose of the enemy who—the crew felt certain—was keeping a close lookout on the narrow waterway. The other two alternatives, to seek an internment in a neutral port or to surrender to the enemy, were never even considered.

The very evening that the *Orzel* was ready to enter the Sound the B.B.C. announced that a ship had been sunk off Malmö. This confirmed the Captain's previous suspicion that the Sound had been mined by the Germans. In order to avoid the main tracks the *Orzel* entered Swedish territorial waters to risk the coastwise rocks without a chart rather than try to navigate his ship through a minefield by night.

The water was too shallow for the *Orzel* to submerge, so she had to proceed on the surface.

On the way several German and Swedish warships were seen. From time to time they would switch on their search-lights and sweep over the surface of the sea. One beam moving from astern approached the *Orzel* and almost touched the cloud of smoke from the diesel exhaust. The light stopped, trembled for a moment or two, and then slowly moved away again.

Suddenly the brown line on the echo-sounding screen jumped up at a steep angle. Before the engines could be stopped the depth of the sea dropped to sixteen feet. There was a violent shock, and all lights on the port side went off. The *Orzel* was aground.

By now the beam of the searchlight was again closing the ship. "All hands on deck," was the order. The only men to remain below were three engineers in the diesel compart-ment. When life-jackets were distributed the Captain ordered the remaining ballast tanks to be blown. Then he told the "Chief" to set both diesels to the maximum output of which they were capable. "No safety margin to be left" were his words. The engines roared as never before. The darkened ships on the horizon must have heard them, but meanwhile the submarine's hull jumped once, then again, and for a third time. Scraping on the bottom and shaking, the *Orzel* climbed over the obstruction.

Before midnight a flood of lights could be seen blazing on the horizon to the west. This was Copenhagen, capital of neutral Denmark, enjoying a gay Saturday night.

The contours of Elsinore Castle were still visible in the darkness when a low, black object was sighted ahead. It was a German M.T.B. The *Orzel* dived at once. But the Germans must have noticed her, as they started a regular search. For no fewer than twenty hours the noise of German propellers vibrated on the plates of the submarine's hull while she lay on the shallow bottom with all life stopped in her, waiting for the pursuer to depart.

As there was a considerable sea traffic in the Skagerrak for the next twenty-four hours, the *Orzel* patrolled north and south hoping to find an enemy. While some fifteen miles east of the Skaw lightship she ran into a German minefield. The scraping of the mine-wires against the hull resounded uncomfortably inside the submarine.

When the store of fuel oil dropped to two days' supply course was set to the west. The passage across the North Sea was rough, and no enemy was seen either at sea or in the air. It was Saturday, October 14th, and the *Orzel's* fifty-fourth day of war, when at 1100, some thirty miles east of the Isle of May, a silhouette of a warship was reported. Recognition signals were exchanged: it was H.M.S. *Valorous*, which had come out to meet the Polish submarine and escort her into Rosyth.

After a short refitting period in dock the *Orzel* resumed her operational duties from British bases. She carried out seven more patrols off the coast of Norway and in the Skagerrak, sinking enemy merchantmen and carrying out contraband control duties. She was the first ship to detect the coming German invasion of Norway by sinking at the entrance to the Oslo Fjord the 7,000-ton transport vessel the *Rio de Janeiro*, laden with troops, some twenty-four hours before the actual landings began.

On May 23rd, 1940, the *Orzel* sailed for her eighth patrol. From this operation she did not return. The Admiralty stated officially: "No signals received since sailing." The British Admiral Commanding Submarines, summing up her service, said: "The dash and efficiency with which she performed all her duties merit the highest praise, and the part she played was a very valuable contribution to the Allied war effort."

There were, however, some who refused to believe that the *Orzel* was lost. Those were the colleagues of the missing sailors. Until the last day of the war the sailors of the Polish Navy believed that the *Orzel* had fought her way back to the Baltic and returned to Gdynia. Unnoticed by the Germans—

they imagined—she lay on the bottom of the harbour, while her crew found their way to Warsaw to deliver a message of hope to those who were dying in the dungeons and behind barbed wire, to tell them that Victory would come. . . .

Whatever the truth, one thing is certain, that in the naval annals the story of the *Orzel* will not be forgotten.

THOMAS WOODROFFE

IN THE MIDDLE WATCH

A strong easterly gale blowing against the ebb tide had raised an awkward lumpy sea, making the Officer of the Middle Watch very anxious for the safety of the picket boat, which was threatening at any moment to rise on some higher sea and crash up into the boom to which it was made fast. He paced the dark quarter-deck with the wind howling about his ears, cursing his luck that in the very first watch he should be called upon to keep in this, his new ship, it should choose to blow a gale. He was in two minds whether to send the picket boat into the Dock-yard for the night or not. With his collar turned up round his ears and his hands stuck deep into his pockets he stared gloomily into the darkness, then up at the lowering sky; every now and again he stepped out on to the upper plat-form of the starboard gangway from where, because it jutted out over the ship's side, he could see how the boat was riding without having to make a journey forward. She seemed to be all right; perhaps he wouldn't send her in just yet; and if he did, should he tell the Commander? Even his short experience told him to let sleeping Commanders lie and tell them in the morning. In any case your head was bound to be bitten off.

Under the lee of the after turret a little group consisting of the Quartermaster, the Boatswain's Mate, and the Corporal of the Watch were huddled closely together like sheep under a hedge, and were passing the time, until the Boatswain's Mate went up to the galley to get cocoa, in carrying on a one-sided argument as to who should fill the inside-left position in the ship's football team on the coming Saturday.

The ship had been beaten the previous afternoon, chiefly owing to the poor shooting of the inside-left, a young marine fresh from the depot, with a glowing reputation. Perhaps the rough fields of the North and the unconventional methods of the players in the Fleet had upset this pride of Eastney— the fact remains that he was useless, and the Quartermaster was delivering himself of a long tirade on the iniquity of playing a man on his reputation alone. The Corporal made several ineffectual attempts to stand up for his corps mate, but his objections were always brushed aside. The Boat- swain's Mate added nothing to the conversation; he gazed at his heavy seaboots and loudly sucked his teeth.

The Flag Lieutenant, whose cabin was just under the ladder, let his detective story slide off his bunk to the deck, and, wakened by the noise, switched off the light, turned over, and dropped quickly off to sleep again, thankful that he'd done with watchkeeping for ever.

A few feet farther aft, his lord and master, the Admiral, switched off the light in his much more palatial abode after studying for the twentieth time a letter from his old friend X., now at the Admiralty—a letter which ended, ". . . so I think it practically certain that you will get China; in fact, you'd better look over your whites". China! The Admiral had always wanted one day to be Commander-in-Chief, China; he loved the East and he dropped contentedly off to sleep to dream of subservient Orientals bowing to the might of Britain as exemplified in the person of Sir Hector Blamfield, K.C.M.G., etc. etc.

And so, except for a few sweating stokers down below and some watchkeepers, the whole ship's company slept peace- fully, even the erring inside-left, though he stirred restlessly in his unaccustomed hammock.

Now it is a well-worn truism that little things often produce great results; and the fact that the grating on the platform of the starboard accommodation ladder had gradually worked loose owing to a succession of seas hitting up against it from underneath, until it finally disappeared altogether and floated awkwardly away into the night, might be considered an insufficient reason for turning the peaceful slumbers of a large proportion of the ship's complement into a period of wakeful bedlam. But so it was. This little wooden grating fits into an iron frame which juts out from the ship's side horizontally over the water.

The Officer of the Watch, in his ceaseless pacing up and down, stepped out on to the platform for yet another uneasy glance at the picket boat. But instead of the picket boat, he saw a galaxy of stars as something caught him a sickening jolt under the chin. He felt himself dropping through the air; then he felt his right ankle wrenched painfully as he landed smack on his back in the water, and as he went under he swallowed what seemed to him to be most of the Firth of Forth.

He struggled madly for a second or two, but his right foot was firmly trapped; he had not the vaguest notion what had happened, but, dizzy and breathless as he was, he managed to get his head above water, and, what is more, to keep it there by reaching forward and grabbing a stay, though every second or so a sea would come with a threatening swish and break over his head to leave him gasping. At last he realised more or less what had happened. He could just make out the dim outline of the ladder above him. He was continually washed against the side of the ship by succeeding seas; his right foot in its leather seaboot was tightly wedged between the side and one of the iron stays supporting the bottom of the ladder. His position, similar to that of an oarsman at the beginning of a stroke, was not one that he could maintain for long. He felt sick and weak; he struggled ineffectually to clear his foot, but soon gave that up; once he let go his hold, only to submerge immediately, and he regained his precarious position with difficulty. "Help! help!" he shouted feebly, but his voice was blown away by the gale so that no trace of its mournful wail reached the ears of the little group on the other side of the turret. The howling wind and the "crash, crash, swish" of the breaking seas drowned his cries or made them sound like the plaintive croak of some wakeful gull.

He felt that at any moment he would have to let go and then it would be all up with him; he was getting numbed by the cold and he wondered if drowning were the pleasant death everyone stoutly maintained that it was, though most of the upholders of the theory, he reflected, could not abide a ducking. He had just decided that it was about time his past life did something about flashing by him when he was startled to hear a grunt up above and something like a bare foot hit him hard between the eyes and nearly stunned him. He felt as if his neck was broken. He took another draught of the Firth as he lost his hold and went under. By a supreme effort he managed to raise himself again, but his brain refused to work; he could not think what had hit him or why; he just felt cold and deadly, deadly tired and very sick. Someone seemed to be swimming away from the ship; he must be getting delirious; swish!—another mouthful; his ankle was hurting now. What an absurd death, drowning a few feet from hundreds of his fellow-beings—he was inches, no, only one inch, just the thickness of the plate of the ship's side, from some sleeping shipmate—it was fantastic, it was unfair. He tried to hammer with his fist against the iron plate in a despairing effort to wake someone. He hammered madly, he screamed. Then he subsided and was on the point of bursting into tears when something again, and very similar, hit him bang between the eyes. This was too much. He let go and drifted away into unconsciousness.

The Flag Lieutenant, always a light sleeper, stirred restlessly. Then he woke up and listened. A voice was calling something. He sat up fully awake and turned on the light over his head. It was not coming from the flat outside; it sounded like a feeble cry for help far away; yes, there it was again. He opened his scuttle and peered out into the darkness. The light from his cabin threw a feeble beam over the water, lighting up the white crest of a muddy-brown wave as it hissed past him down the ship's side. He could see nobody, but he heard the cry again. Somebody was out there in the ditch, and that somebody appeared to be drowning. He leaped out of bed and rushed up on to the quarter-deck in his pyjamas. He was almost blown back down the ladder by the chilly blast that met him. He peered through the inky blackness and then, more by instinct than anything else, ran quickly to the starboard ladder, his bare feet just missing deckbolts and other obstructions on the way.

As he stepped out on to the platform he was hit on the side of the head, a brutally hard object caught him in the ribs, his foot met something soft and cold and then he found himself under the iciest water he had ever known. He kicked vigorously and came up gasping and dizzy. He could not make out what had happened. He had some hazy notion that the ship had blown up. All he was certain of was that he had fallen overboard most inexplicably, and he remembered the dictum that if you fall overboard you should swim away from the ship's side at once to avoid being smashed up by the propellers. Quite forgetting that the ship was at anchor, he struck out lustily and in a few seconds was some way from the ship. Then he started to collect his wits and remembered the cries for help. He turned. There was the dark mass looming up. He began to swim back.

A thousand supplicating Orientals were crying for mercy, their foreheads beating the ground with every prayer. Then the scene focused on one particularly miserable object who beat his breast, whacked his forehead on the ground, and with every prostration cried out—oddly enough in English—"Help. . . . Help." Then, the Admiral woke up. But there was a faint cry of a sort. The Admiral cocked his ear. Yes. There it was. He wondered angrily who in thunder had fallen overboard and why no one seemed to be doing anything about it. What was the Service coming to? Here was his flagship with people drowning all round, and apparently not a damn soul cared a hoot. The Admiral, when roused, moved

quickly and liked to see to things for himself, as not a few of
his juniors knew to their cost. He was known irreverently but
affectionately as "Old Fireworks" by the little group behind
the turret, and when he was living up to his name the crew
of the flagship, though outwardly terrified, secretly used to be
filled with admiration at the wealth of his vocabulary. He
boiled over with rage and, jumping out of his handsome brass
bedstead, streaked past an astonished sentry outside the cabin,
who swallowed his fag-end in his fright, and clumped heavily
up the ladder.

He stepped out into the cold darkness and bellowed for the
Officer of the Watch. But there was no answering cry of
"Sir" and the scurry of hurrying feet. He grew rapidly
angrier and thundered out again, but his voice, even his, was
powerless against the gale, and it tailed away down-wind.

The Quartermaster's monologue was only half done, he
was well into his stride.

"This ship's dam' slack," thought the Admiral, as he made
his way blasphemously to the starboard ladder. Again the
faint cry met his ears and he too stepped out on to the platform to see if he could make out anything. He felt suddenly
as if he had stepped into a lift that happened not to be there,
and his remarks were cut short by the saltiest nastiest water
he had ever tasted. He came up blowing like a whale, with a
resolution that he'd have everybody's blood for this, starting
with his Flag Captain and ending with the ship's cat. Then he
felt something in the water beside him. He felt round until
he grasped the bottom of the ladder and found an inert
somebody who appeared to have no interest in the proceedings. He got the corpse, as he supposed, on to the lower platform by an effort, and peered into the face of a total stranger.
"Who are you?" he said. "What are you doing here?" He
could not for the life of him make out how someone quite
unknown could happen to drown at the foot of the gangway
reserved exclusively for his own use.

Just as he was clambering on to the ladder himself he heard
the sounds of someone swimming towards the ship and was

astounded to see his Flag Lieutenant appearing out of the darkness as if he had been for a bathe. The Admiral blinked, and the thought shot through his mind that perhaps he'd better cut down his brandy a bit after dinner.

"I've been over the side, sir," announced the newcomer superfluously, spitting out mouthfuls of water between the words.

"So it seems," replied the Admiral, convinced that Flags had gone quite mad. "Anyhow, if you've had enough you'd better give me a hand here."

Flags scrambled out and caught sight of the corpse, who at that moment sat up and was sick.

"Who the hell is it?" asked the Admiral. "Where's everybody? What is all this midnight bathing? Where have you been?"

"Don't know him from Adam, sir," said Flags through chattering teeth. Then he gazed dumbly at the apparition whom he failed to recognise by the fitful gleams of the moon.

"Who are you, dammit? What are you doing here?" went on the Admiral, growing more and more furious. He was chilled and shaken and seemed to have burst into a bathing party of lunatics.

The Officer of the Watch opened his eyes and gazed with a puzzled stare at these two apparitions in dripping pyjamas. He was promptly sick again.

Between them they got him up the ladder and safely across the gaping man-trap at the top, on to the quarter-deck. Here the Admiral was on his home ground and let himself go like a bull moose.

"Officer of the Watch! Quartermaster! Boatswain's Mate!" he bellowed. "What's up with this —— ship? Where's anybody at all?"

A faint rumble caused the Quartermaster to halt for a moment in the enunciation of his theories on team building.

"Wot wos that, Stripey?" he asked the Corporal.

"Dunno. Sounds like it wos someone calling."

"O.O.W. mos' likely. Wants 'is cocoa. 'Arf a mo'."

The Quartermaster walked serenely round the turret, and to his horror saw some ghostly figures at the gangway. He stopped, a horrible crinkly sensation creeping down his spine. From the remarks that issued from one of them they appeared to have come straight from the nether regions. He swallowed hard, reminded himself that he was living in enlightened days, and went slowly up to see who it was.

Then he gave a horrified gasp. Holding a dripping and unconscious Officer of the Watch in one hand and waving the other over his head was the Admiral, and in pyjamas.

"Cripes!" he ejaculated. "It's Old Fireworks!" and fled.

He ran forward along the battery, and, feeling that he ought to do something more constructive and actuated by the memory of dripping, excited figures at the gangway, called away the lifeboat. "Man overboard. Awaaaay lifeboat's crew," he piped as he ran.

"My sacred aunt," roared the Admiral, "everyone's gone insane. I'll have the whole ship under arrest." He shook the Officer of the Watch fiercely and again bellowed at him. "Who the hell *are* you, sir?"

"Smith, sir," replied the mystified unfortunate. "I think I must have fallen overboard."

"Think?" shouted his rescuer. "Here, Flags, for God's sake go and find someone sane."

The Flag Lieutenant agreed that someone else ought to be dragged into this. He was just recovering from the shock of meeting his Admiral in dripping pyjamas sitting at the bottom of the ladder swearing at a perfect stranger. He burst into the Commander's cabin. The Commander turned on his light and sat up. He saw Flags trying to say something; he was dripping wet and bleeding profusely from a cut on the side of the head.

"I've been over the side and so has the Admiral," he blurted out.

The Commander felt for his bell and surreptitiously rang for the sentry.

"Quite, quite. That's all right, old man. Now you just sit down quietly here and you'll be all right in a jiffy. You wait here a second and I'll get the doctor." He jumped out of bed and made for the door. At that moment Flags crumpled up into a heap on the deck of the cabin in a pool of salt water and blood. Flags had fainted.

"Something dashed odd been happening here," thought the Commander, and, telling the sentry who had just appeared to get the Surgeon Commander, he ran up on deck.

Then he thought that he too must have gone mad. The quarter-deck lights were on and showed the Admiral, whose usually purple face had by now gone a bright blue, holding up a drooping Officer of the Watch and bellowing like a wounded buffalo. The lifeboat had just let go the falls and was being pulled lustily down to the gangway by a tousle-headed crew in underpants and flannels, with their lifebelts on anyhow.

He ran over to the Admiral and stood at a safe distance.

"Who's this Smith?" asked the Admiral fiercely.

"That's the Officer of the Watch, sir," replied the Commander, mystified.

"Then what the hades is he doing sitting in the ditch all night? Don't go near the gangway, the grating's out."

At this moment the Quartermaster appeared, looking rather like an early Christian at the entrance to the arena.

"There's the lunatic," roared the Admiral. "Commander, that man is insane. He is not responsible. He must be put under restraint. I no sooner rescue this Smith than this other idiot must disappear yelling 'Man overboard'. I've had enough. I'm going below. I'll want an explanation of all this in the morning."

He stumped off below, shouting for his steward. "Hot brandy, hot blankets, hot-water bottles," he ordered, as he disappeared into his cabin.

The lifeboat made fast and its crew found their hammocks again. Another Officer of the Watch appeared, and gradually peace was restored. Peace for all, except for the Surgeon who had to solve the problem of warding off apoplexy and double pneumonia from an impatient Sir Hector.

By the morning the Admiral, who had cured himself by consuming vast quantities of old brandy, felt in a more equable frame of mind. He realised that he had a story that he could use whenever he dined out.

The incident was considered closed.

LIEUT. MICHAEL PARKER

A TRAWLER'S PIG

Some pigs are sea-sick, it seems; but Denis was happily immune. Of course, he started young. The Murmansk reindeer recently borne on the books of one of H.M. submarines may have made a more exotic shipmate, but what Denis lacked in glamour he made up for in character. So much was clear from the start. Securely trussed, the guinea-fowl and the chickens gave no trouble at all. But Denis, then aged five weeks, was quicksilver.

His last and most spectacular escape occurred while we were settling with the French farmer's wife. Our seamanlike knots and hitches and the closed 15-cwt. truck might have baffled Harry Houdini, but not Denis. . . . The ensuing chase, poignantly reminiscent of the Gadarene episode described in Mark v, 11–13, culminated less disastrously. We thundered down a "steep place" in full cry and had him cornered at last on Afric's sunlit strand, 'twixt the devil—in the shape of three moist but determined officers—and the deep blue Mediterranean.

We bore our purchases back triumphantly to the ship, and issued instructions to the coxswain. Denis was bedded down comfortably enough on some clean straw in the spud-locker. The rest of the livestock was dispersed "as convenient". For a fortnight the ship, with its squawks and grunts from unexpected quarters, rivalled the Children's Hour in its more bucolic moments.

The new draft demands a word of explanation. It was early December 1942, and we were based on Bone in Algeria, at that time the First Army's forward supply port. Though the Hun's Stukas and E-boats were evidently determined that this Christmas should not prove a dull one, amenities were notably lacking. So we decided that, even if Christmas and the New Year were to be spent at sea, at least there should be something to supplement compo rations. Roast chicken and guinea-fowl, albeit no "first footing", should console our Scotsmen at Hogmanay.

Christmas found us stooging peacefully to and fro. (We might have felt less peaceful had we been aware that our patrol lay on top of an unpleasingly shallow minefield laid by E-boats.)

Denis enjoyed the sunshine and made a leisurely breakfast of potato peelings, quite unaware of his impending fate. However, when the moment approached, dark and mutinous looks were observed among the ship's company. The butcher-designate, a burly engineman, who had been heard to reveal with seeming authority some of the secrets of the slaughter-house, now hung back, his confidence strangely evaporated. Another volunteer was called for and amid general relief none stepped forward. Thus was Denis's reprieve signed; and as the poultry proved ample for two dinners, everybody was happy.

Denis had soon become a favourite. When and by whom he was christened I do not recall, and in the choice of names only one dissentient voice, that of our Number Three, was raised. He took a lot of convincing that George, or Augustine (after St. Augustine of Hippo, or Bone), were less suitable names. This officer's name happened, of course, to be Denis too. We soon discovered that it was a matter of tradition. All sailors are superstitious, and any fool will tell you how unlucky it is to sleep with your feet forward or to carry a parson. Similarly, the word "pig" must never be breathed on board ship. "Denis" if you will; but never "pig". All ship's pigs are Denis, regardless of sex or numbers—if there are ten pigs on board they are all Denis.

For a trawler one is enough. Ours soon outgrew his temporary billet in the spud-locker, and was turned loose on deck. His favourite spot was a sheltered "caboose" over the boiler-room casing, where the heat of the steel deck was much to his liking. He always slept there, and I used to look forward to his welcoming grunts as I passed by to keep a night-watch on the bridge (for he knew us all as well as any dog). And I would stop and give him a friendly scratch on the back or tum.

One day, after we had had the good fortune to bring down a Heinkel, we were to be honoured with a visit by a High Personage. The ship was scrubbed and shining, the paint-work immaculate; but Number One was clearly concerned about Denis. Not all senior officers are pig-minded. So with strange oaths on one side and outraged squeals on the other, Denis—now a portly figure—was uncomfortably wedged into the spud-locker for the duration of the inspection. All went well until the crocodile filed past, when our familiar footsteps were greeted by a perfect crescendo of grunts. Our hearts stopped beating as the Personage somewhat nervously lifted the lid. Turning to the C.O. he gravely inquired, "Where, may I ask, do you stow the cow?"

Less important callers, especially if they had looked upon the wine when it was red, would invariably exclaim in startled tones, "Good heavens! What's that?" as unwilling to believe the evidence of one's eyes.

Frequent visitors at Algiers were a delightful French couple, who instantly succumbed to Denis's charms. On the dreadful day when he had to undergo a certain *petite opération* and his protests brought all work in the dockyard to a standstill, it was an able Gaulliste vet introduced by them who performed. Two days later Denis was his old self, and as a consolation prize Madame had made for him a little French sailor's cap with a red pom-pom on top, and an elastic to go under his chin. He wore it only on ceremonial occasions such as entering and leaving harbour, when he fell in with the crew on the forecastle. And very smart he looked, too, with his coat glistening white, and his cap at a jaunty angle.

He was not always immaculate. A gregarious soul, he hated to be left out, and coaling ship was his passion. He loved coal, ate it by the pound, wallowed in it and tossed it playfully around. Fortunately, coal is good for pigs—its external application was our headache. Exhausted, happy and black, Denis would consent to be "dhobied out" only if sustained with slabs of chocolate, of which he was inordinately fond. It was an expensive operation, as he had a similar capacity for pusser's soap, which went the same way as the "nutty" if vigilance was for a moment relaxed. However, his radiant appearance—until the next time—was our reward.

To my shame, Denis was the first pig I had met *qua* pig and not *qua* pork; and I am astonished that qualities of these animals are not more widely known. Denis would answer to his name and follow you like a dog. He was always ready for a game or to be made a fuss of. If a sailor had chocolate in his pocket, Denis's unusual sense of smell never failed. I have seen one of our stokers streaking round the deck with a piece of "nutty" and the pig thundering after, flat out. With a twenty-degree roll either side, these mad marine steeplechases were as exciting as the Grand National any day.

The sea was in his blood. Once we were lying alongside the Môle du Passageur, Algiers, and decided to give Denis a "run ashore" on the green grass in the middle. With much prodding and heaving, we edged him down the brow and coaxed him on to the grass. Left to enjoy himself, he gave one hunted look round, then trundled back at full speed to the gangway, where he lay at the sentry's feet until, to his evident relief, he was put back aboard. The next time he left the ship was the last.

When the hands turned to in the morning, Denis was already at his post—the swill-tub—fulfilling his duties. At action stations his *sang-froid* was an example. Bombs could fall all round, but he never batted a bristly. His unwavering morale and unimpaired appetite at the stickiest moments were an inspiration to us all.

Denis grew and grew, and trawlers are not big ships. The hard decision was finally made that he must go. I will not dwell on that distressing parting. Afterwards the ship was dull and deserted. His new home was with friends at Philippe-ville. There, old salt that he was, he pined for three days, refusing to eat and rooting up most of the garden, including some precious rosebushes, in his chagrin. Finally, he settled down "to enjoy the blessings of the land with the fruits of his labours".

That poor Denis has by now gone the way of all pork is, I fear, inevitable. But I like to think of him, his funny hat with the red pom-pom rakishly tilted, basking in the sun and sniffing the fresh sea-breeze of some piggy heaven, where celestial coal and swill abound, and in which ever and anon some ethereal Stoker One will float down bearing ambrosial "nutty" for his refreshment.

JOHN DAVIES

BROOKLYN UNDER FIRE

I doubt whether it is very widely known that during the recent war two major New England cities—New York and Boston—found themselves under fire from weapons of the British Navy. And, moreover, by way of adding insult, under fire from weapons designed and built for the ungrateful Limeys in American plants and factories.

The first assault was delivered in New York—more particularly in Brooklyn—during the early months of 1943. The ship concerned was an ancient and undistinguished corvette which was then refitting in the Brooklyn Navy Yard.

Strange things were happening to destroyers and corvettes in those days. All sorts of new and mysterious equipment was being fitted, and by no means the least mysterious item was a strange piece of apparatus which looked like a cross between a four-poster and a fakir's bed of nails. This was the Hedgehog, our latest anti-submarine weapon. Its function was to hurl a number of bombs into the air in such a fashion that, after a graceful parabola, they fell into the water immediately above the suspected U-boat. (And don't laugh—a lot of U-boats were sunk even thus.)

But at the time of which I speak this weapon was only just coming into service, and it must be confessed that it was almost as much a secret to those entrusted with its installation in ships as it was to the rest of the lubberly world at large. It was a complicated affair, and its teething troubles were many and obscure.

Now the corvette in question was one of the first ships to receive this addition to its fo'c'sle, and in due course a technical officer from the British Admiralty Delegation in Washington appeared to carry out the necessary trials. He spent a long, cold day prodding into the entrails of the weapon (where he found a quite extraordinary amount of electrical equipment) but round about tea-time one thing had become pretty obvious to him. The gadget wouldn't work. And so, it being round about tea-time, he yielded to the blandishments of a most solicitous ship's officer and went aft to the wardroom, leaving a zealous petty officer to continue investigations.

Now, as everyone knows, when a petty officer technician is faced with a piece of apparatus which will not work, his impulse is to thrust a screwdriver into its entrails and see what happens. . . .

It happened in this case all right. The petty officer was staggered and astonished by four mighty explosions occurring in rapid succession within a few feet of him. Sipping his second cup in the wardroom, the technical officer suddenly heard Nemesis rap loudly, four times.

He rushed on deck. A deceptive peace prevailed. He rushed to the fo'c'sle. The petty officer was still holding his screwdriver. The technical officer looked at the secret weapon. Four bombs had vanished.

And then a tragic groan escaped from him, for he noted now what he had not noted before, namely that the ship's bows, and therefore the lethal bedstead, pointed directly shoreward, and, moreover, pointed directly at a vast army barracks. And a mounting clamour was coming from the direction of the barracks. In the distance a siren wailed. With another groan the technical officer dashed shorewards. . . .

A hundred or so American soldiers, whiling away their after-parade leisure in their dormitory on the top floor of the barracks, were somewhat surprised when a medium-sized bomb suddenly fell through the roof on to the floor between the beds and skidded at lightning speed until it came to rest with a crash against the door. And as an aircraft's motors were at that moment heard overhead, there was some excuse for their thinking the worst. Not that they had ever really believed before that the Japs could make it. But now they dashed as one man for lower and safer levels.

All the world knows that New Yorkers love a sensation, and they certainly made the most of it this time. The police arrived. The civil defence people arrived. The F.B.I. arrived.

And in due course our technical officer arrived.

It had been a nerve-racking and laborious dash up from the ship, but on the way inspiration had come to him. On arrival he immediately gathered together the bosses of the barracks, the police, the F.B.I., the civil defence, and spoke to them in a hushed and impressive tone.

"Now this," he said, "is a secret weapon. A most secret weapon. It would be most undesirable if . . ."

It worked perfectly.

The same ingenious weapon was responsible for a certain amount of diversion in Boston's Navy Yard. A sub-lieutenant in a British frigate was a little too anxious to get acquainted with his new toy, and this time six bombs went sailing through the air. One landed in a cauldron of soup in the Navy Yard restaurant, a second on the roof of the machine shop, a third and fourth on another British ship (which at least showed impartiality); and an American lieutenant, seeing the fifth and sixth coming, threw himself flat on his face in a very large puddle.

The first I heard of all this was when, answering my telephone, I heard a slightly dishevelled voice requesting my presence. And then, I fear, I yielded to temptation.

"It'll take me half an hour to get over," I said. "Your bomb-safety officer will have to take charge until I arrive."

It wasn't fair, because in this area, remote from any but the most slight possibility of air attack, the title of bomb-safety officer was strictly one of courtesy only. Each American officer in the Navy Yard added this to his official duties for a day every month or so. Most of them hadn't even the remotest acquaintance with bombs.

But I got there in less than half an hour, and there was no doubt the bomb-safety officer was very glad to see me. He was standing beside one of the bombs which had fallen in the road and was looking at it as though it were a rattlesnake.

"It's all right," I said, " . . . it's a dummy. Sand-filled."

The unfairness was that I had known that all along. That particular ship hadn't any others.

It was probably the enticing newness of things on these lease-lend ships that occasionally caused things to go bang. A few weeks later a gunner's mate found a new four-inch gun too much for him, and a four-inch armour-piercing shell sped on its way into the heart of Boston. We worked out from the elevation and training of the gun its probable landing place, and were distressed to find that it seemed bound for a very thickly populated district.

And there it was that we found it—in the middle of a cemetery.

The only other incident of which I was a witness was somewhat less spectacular. From his pet Oerlikon an enthusiastic able seaman fired two rounds, which ricocheted off one of the ship's davits and passed noisily beneath the noses of two American petty officers. As a result the ship's gunnery officer was called to account by the officer in charge of the yard.

"Well, what have you to say?"

"Well, sir," said the gunner (he was pretty hard-bitten, with twenty-five years' service behind him), " . . . all I can say is that if it had been British ammunition that davit would have been cut in half and someone would have got killed."

The Americans took all our pleasantries very well.

GUY MORGAN

ALBERT AND THE GERMANS

This is the true story of Albert, born in captivity at the age of thirty-five in May, 1943, and probably the last British prisoner-of-war in Germany.

For Albert never figured in any camp roll or official list. That was his particular blessing.

Albert was John's brain-child, and only an artist's vision and mastery of materials could have produced a man like Albert, in his time the most celebrated character of Marlag "O", the camp for British naval officers in Germany.

Marlag "O" was a difficult camp to escape from. It was a small camp—a mere dozen huts on a rectangular cinder-patch three hundred yards by a hundred and twenty. The soil was sandy, with water at eleven feet, and, to prevent tunnelling, the Germans had dug a ten-foot ditch round the perimeter outside the wire and had buried microphones at intervals in it.

The wire was floodlit at night. At dusk there was a curfew, and dogs were released inside the camp to enforce it.

Tunnelling, of course, continued, more as a relaxation than as a serious operation, for the odds were all against it.

The obvious opportunity to escape was from the outside, which meant the weekly bath-party when those desiring hot showers were marched in parties of thirty every Thursday through the fore-lager out of the main gate and up the hill to the bath-house, that stood in a cornfield a couple of hundred yards away and served three camps.

As this was the only occasion that officers saw the outside of their camp, many plans of escape were from time to time based on it, but the Germans were no fools and took strict precautions.

Towels and overcoats were subject to search in the fore-lager; many counts and re-counts were held, and, finally, the Obergefreiter at the main gate handed a chit with the numbers written on it to the Feldwebel in charge of the ample escort. The guards accompanied us into the changing-rooms and practically under the showers themselves. The whole outing lasted under thirty minutes.

Moreover, there was a faction of ardent ablutionists in the camp who placed general cleanliness above individual freedom and deprecated the use of the bath-party for escaping, fearing the loss of this weekly facility as a reprisal.

The best escapes are usually the result of improvisation based on personal observation of routine. Accordingly, in May, 1943, it was duly noted by all those interested in such things that the Germans had grown slack at searching the towels and washing-gear of the weekly bath-parties.

When John announced that he could make a life-size model prisoner-of-war, sufficiently lifelike to pass close scrutiny, able to march in file, in detachable sections easy to assemble, dismantle, and conceal about the person, no one took him very seriously. If you consider that such a character would have to pass muster before a dozen guards at a range of six or seven paces, and would have to march two hundred yards in broad daylight, the attitude of the sceptics was understandable.

Undeterred, John set to work, and soon Albert began to take shape under his hands.

From the start Albert was a masterpiece of improvisation. Copies of the *Volkischer Beobachter* were soaked in size and the resultant papier-mâché was moulded round a sockful of sand into a human head. Oil paints gave him his complexion.

Half-sections of a ping-pong ball made realistically convex-eyeballs. His eyelids were cunningly weighted from behind like a sleeping doll's, so that he blinked when disturbed, just like any tired old warrior.

The eye pupils had the authentic lack-lustre of a five-year

prisoner about to take his 260th Thursday shower. They had been done with water-colour. Our own hair went to cover his poor bald pate, and we zealously plucked our eyelashes and eyebrows for his adornment.

It is extraordinary what you get up to when you have all the time in the world and there is nothing doing any minute of the day.

Albert grew, not only in lifelike lineament, but in personality. I think the fact that he was always a secret tenant of the room gave him his importance in our company. We were always conscious of his presence, but never more so than when Good-time Charlie, Nut-brown, Franz the Waiter, or any other of our decrepit old Barracke-führers were in the room negotiating some black-market deal.

Even when he was so high, a severed and precocious head with cigarette dropping negligently from his lips, Albert had character, and it was possible to place him accurately against his social background.

He had worked on the Stock Exchange in peacetime (though some claimed that the selling of second-hand cars in Great Portland Street had given him his slightly contemptuous suavity). He was married, but it had not taken, and he kept a small yacht at Burnham-on-Crouch as a diversion.

As far as the Navy went, he was definitely a big-ship man, and, though only a lieutenant, bore the unmistakable stamp of permanent pre-war Volunteer Reserve. We even suspected there was a period in his naval past when he had been on some Admiral's staff, he had such a knowing look.

He soon had his personal niche in our conversation.

"Sorry, old man, I've got a date with Albert tonight", "You can't borrow those—those are Albert's", or "I bet old Albert's a devil with the women in his quiet way".

Albert's torso was a relatively simple affair. A khaki greatcoat was fitted with a wire frame so that it could be worn by someone else, yet, when taken off, would still retain the shape of a human body. The head could be clipped on to the frame at the neck.

ALBERT AND THE GERMANS

His lower limbs were the subject of perpetual debate. A pair of ammunition boots were filled with sand and attached by gaiters to the legs of a pair of battledress trousers, the waist-band of which could be hooked on the frame inside the coat.

John had a theory that, given time, he could design a walking mechanism, but this was abandoned on the sound theory that during routine inspections a guard would never look below the waist; he would count heads only.

The fact that Albert's feet would drag and swing grotesquely would be unlikely to attract the attention of guards happy in the knowledge that the number of rhythmically bobbing heads tallied exactly with the figure written on the Obergefreiter's chit. Albert would have to ambulate as best he could, arm-in-arm with the two outside men of his file.

The plan was quite simple.

Albert should go up to the bath-house piecemeal, someone wearing his greatcoat, someone his cap, a third concealing his head in the folds of his towel, a fourth with the nether limbs rolled neatly under his arm.

The officer who was to escape would be wearing his regulation going-away kit (Swedish seaman) under his battledress and immediately on arrival at the bath-house would secrete himself in an outside closet which, judging by the cobwebs on the door, had not been used for many months.

After our communal shower Albert would be assembled and would emerge with the rest of the party.

There would be a tricky moment when he actually came through the narrow doorway in full face of the guards waiting to count us. But with incidental horseplay and sensational offers of cut-price deals in cigarettes, we hoped momentarily to divert their attention. It was in our favour that they would be completely unsuspecting.

Once safely in the ranks, Albert would march down to the camp engaged in animated conversation by his outside numbers. Nodding and blinking in the sunlight like an old stager, he would pass cursory inspection at the main gate, and so into the camp, leaving the escapee to emerge from an unguarded bath-house at his leisure and, with papers provided by excellent cartographers in the camp, catch the next train to Lübeck or Swinemünde.

Inside the camp, it would be a relatively simple matter for Albert to fall in three times a day on roll-calls until danger of the escape being connected with the bath-party had been averted.

The plans were perfected. Albert's drill and timing were worked out to the last detail.

For once we prayed for rain. Our prayers were answered, but not on Thursdays. Soon it would be too late for the reasonable wearing of greatcoats. We had to take a chance.

The day of Albert's first outing dawned brilliantly sunny. By midday there was only the barest wisp of cloud in the sky, albeit members of all bath-parties seemed strangely nervous of casting a clout and unduly fearful of a change in the weather. Greatcoats were *de rigueur* that day.

Albert came through with flying colours. Even those in the know found it difficult to spot him as the party returned down the hill.

"Blondie", who remained behind, reached Lübeck without incident (though the Gestapo caught him there), and when, three days later, Albert ceased falling in for roll-calls, the Germans, whose inability to count must have saved thousands of lives, failed to notice for an extra roll-call that the numbers were short.

Then, after a minute search of the camp, they set a party unrolling enormous coils of barbed wire on the top of the roof, confident that they had blocked yet another possible exit.

There seemed no limit to Albert's capabilities, and a whole series of escapes was planned for successive Thursdays.

But Fate took a hand and played one of those unpredictable little tricks against which the best-laid plan is never proof.

The German guards' lunch issue of sausage was bad that day. As we marched up to the bath-house we little guessed from the normal expression of bovine apathy on their faces that sausage even at that moment was claiming simultaneous lebensraum in six German stomachs.

"Mitch", a Canadian air-gunner, hiding in the closet, was surprised by a German guard bent on an errand of some urgency. Albert, alas, had already fallen in outside.

Then the fun started. We had been counted and found correct. The Feldwebel shouted and waved his chit. The guards ran up and down our ranks like excited dachshunds. They counted us forwards; they counted us backwards; they counted us sideways; they counted the files and multiplied by ten, until the napes of their necks outshone the poppies in the corn at the roadside.

One too few was bad enough; one too many was impossible. All this and indigestion too was intolerable.

Then suddenly and beautifully, at a moment when all backs were turned, Albert disintegrated in the ranks. One moment he was there; there was a slight scuffle, a sigh of relief; the next moment there was an empty space and a row of innocent faces; among the guards consternation, bewilderment, frank disbelief. The Feldwebel was near tears. Surely the *wurst* could not have been that bad!

Exhausted by shouting and mathematics, they marched us down the hill. At times the puzzled eyes of the Feldwebel narrowed to a diamond point of intelligence. He was thinking very hard.

"I think there is a man with a mask," he reported, without conviction, to the Obergefreiter at the gate. It did not make sense, but it was as near as he could get.

As soon as they ordered a search we knew that Albert's hours were numbered. A crowd collected behind the wire in the camp to watch the fun.

Half the party were searched without discovery. Neither Albert's greatcoat nor his legs aroused suspicion. The head was the problem.

Then, as the rear rank began to dwindle before the searchers, a slight heeling movement of the feet was observed by the spectators, and a round object shot out, like a football from a scrum or a rabbit from a cornfield at reaping-time, and vanished under the raised flooring of a hut behind. One of the guards saw it flash by and ran to retrieve it. His expression, as he held up Albert's severed, blinking head, was a joy to see.

The Germans, as always when they thought they had been too clever for us, were delighted with Albert, and interested only in the ingenuity of the project. Albert was borne away in triumph to the Kommandant.

It was not German brains but German bowels that had beaten us.

We heard later that Albert, reassembled, sat in state in the corner of the Kommandant's office, wearing a German cap and greatcoat and smoking a German cigarette, the prize exhibit and plaything for every visiting Admiral from Bremen, Kiel and Wilhelmshaven.

Later still we heard that Albert had been sent to a war museum in Berlin.

So if any Russian scientists are at this moment trying to fathom the secret of yet another suspected V-weapon—an automatic soldier—we could reassure them.

Besides, we think Albert deserves repatriation.

With a few minor adjustments Albert is just the type for Parliament.

E. M. HEARD

CONVERSATION IN VALHALLA

The plump foot protruding from the arbour stirred slightly as the latest arrival hurried past, and a chubby face, surmounted by a curled wig, was thrust out, looking after her with more curiosity than courtesy.

Another also evidenced curiosity, but more discreetly, and in acknowledgment of her flurried gesture lifted his cocked hat with a remarkable blending of punctilio, correctness, gallantry and deference.

The occupant of the arbour, observing all this with a mixture of envy and regret, coughed as the small slight figure passed. It paused, while the plump gentleman sprang up and bowed with much deference.

"I have, strangely, not met you before, Sir," observed the stroller, "but"—cordially—"I believe I address Mr. Pepys and am happy to have that honour——"

"Nay, my Lord Nelson, the honour's mine," broke in Pepys eagerly, "but I'm flattered."

"Nay—nay; 'tis an honour to meet one who has striven for our great country as you, Sir," said Nelson.

"We have both served the Navy, Sir; but what Englishman could but desire heartily the honour of speech with Nelson of the Nile?"

"Tut-tut," said Nelson, evidently pleased, yet sincere in what he said. "I had the inestimable privilege of commanding the finest Fleet, the best seamen, the world's ever seen—or ever will, Sir!—and Heaven has been pleased to grant me victory for our country and some personal honour.—But, Sir,' tis strange to see such a new Member as has just entered."

"Aye, Sir. A comely wench, I thought, and wondrous neat and trim. Would such had existed in our day!" said Mr. Pepys with unregenerate zest.

"Nay, Sir," said Nelson coldly and stiffly, "*my* days, at least, were not fitting for a refined young female to have any intimate contact with the Fleet. Women, Sir,—what discipline can be held in a Fleet with women about? Fleets, Sir, exist to fight—what the devil business has a woman with that? These grim sights and sounds——"

"I think, Lord Nelson, you wrong the fair sex. The rouges are none so dainty and can endure much. Could you ha' seen 'em in the week of the Great Fire, Sir—how bold after their goods, you'd never scorn 'em. And surely the wenches ha' much good report in this present conflict Below."

"Aye, aye. 'Tis true, I have been unjust. Men or women, what matter? 'Tis the will to serve that counts (my midshipmen—children only!)—yet my soul revolts at the thought of women—in danger."

"Nay, since when has your Lordship considered danger?"

"We are men, Sir!" said Nelson sternly.

"Your Lordship"—roguishly—"will ha' noticed many women have much courage!"

"True! True!" flashed Nelson. "I *have* known such—the courage of a man, the tenderness and graciousness of a woman—undaunted by the greatest odds, the most imminent danger—but those were two rare women, Sir!"

"Come, Sir! They are much like us—perhaps less subject to temptation sometimes—we are sad creatures——"

Through Nelson's frosty disapproval Pepys hastened on. "Yet, Sir, I do protest I ha' known many a wench that might ha' distinguished herself had she but worn breeches——"

"'Tis true, and since our country has been in such sore straits as we have heard"—his eyes clouded again—"ill it beseems me, a derelict cripple, to decry those serving! Do not think, Mr. Pepys, I would be hostile or unfair; God forbid I should have any but the best of goodwill to those rendering our country service. Yet it grieves me that even their own countrywomen should ever have to help *Englishmen* to defend England."

"Nay, Sir, you mistake. Did not those recently come tell us how things stand? 'Tis the men that still fight the ships—and ever will, I do believe—but you'd not have good men wasted ashore, Sir?"

"No, by God! 'Tis on the sea that they are wanted!" said Nelson, stirred.

"Aye, Sir. Whereas, were we not ever hampered by the rogues ashore feeding like vampires on our seamen? These wenches are at least of the Service—and the Fleet's not weakened!"

"Ah, Sir," said Nelson, cordially, "I verily believe, had we had you at the Admiralty in my day, my men had been better served."

"God knows I'd ha' done my best, Sir! But 'tis dreary work, though thousands of these wenches do it."

"Thousands!" echoed Nelson.

"Aye, shore establishments, Sir. And our Wren at least saluted you!"

"Aye, aye—perhaps not quite according to the book, eh? But we must all learn. My midshipmen used to go wrong sometimes—though we got them out of that."

"Mayhap even a man might be flurried, unexpectedly coming on your Lordship."

"*Flurried!* What the devil business has a seaman to be *flurried*? No, these women, playing at being sailors——"

Following Mr. Pepys' gesture he swung round, snatching off his hat to acknowledge again the Wren's salute, but with a choleric air and muttered "This is unbearable!" almost unconsciously, it seemed, addressed her in a startlingly stentorian voice.

"You there! Er—Wren—madam."

"Sir!" The Wren, blushing furiously, halted, coming to attention with a galvanic precision she certainly could not often have attained.

"You're in naval uniform—aren't you acquainted with Service customs—madam—— What *is* your correct address?" Incertitude evidently added fuel to the fire.

"Wren, Sir." She had herself in hand now.

"Er—Wren. Don't you know you only salute on first meeting an officer?"

"Yes, Sir."

"Then why have you done so again? You've already saluted me."

"I understood, Sir"—the Wren, trembling with nervousness, spoke with resolute steadiness—"that was aboard ship or in an establishment."

"That is so. Well?"

"That was—why I saluted—Sir."

Nelson glowered.

"Explain yourself!"

The Wren tried to speak, her lip trembling, swallowed, and started again.

"I thought this was in public, Sir, and I understood one had to salute anyway in public. We always had to; and after all I—I thought—I mean, you are like the C.-in-C., only more so——" (gulp). "I'm very sorry, Sir, if I've done wrong."

"No, no! My dear child"—Nelson's tone changed as he took in the scarlet face, the conflict of "Service" manner and feminine sensitiveness—"don't distress yourself. We get most disgracefully bearish, away from feminine society." He did not seem to realise his inconsistency. "Tell us how you come to be here."

"I don't know, Sir."

"But—you must have done something."

"No, Sir."

"My dear child," said Mr. Pepys, who had looked on with varied emotions chasing each other over his rubicund countenance, "don't you know where you are?"

Relieved from the aweing necessity of addressing an angry and very senior officer, combining in himself the shattering qualities of an Admiral of Admirals and a long-worshipped (and now offended!) idol, the Wren replied with more verve.

"I haven't the faintest idea!"

"My good child, this is Valhalla!"

"Val—*what*?"

"Valhalla!"

"But—it can't—I thought Valhalla—Wotan—oh, how can I be?"

"Ah, my dear, vulgar errors. 'Tis a sort of post-mortem club for Service people."

"But"—she wrinkled her brows—"how can I be *there*? The last thing I remember, they said we'd have to swim for it."

"Swim!" said Nelson in a voice like thunder.

"Yes, Sir," stiffening again.

"Where were you?"

"Our ship was attacked—there was a lot of firing——"

Nelson snapped out:

"I said, where were you?"

"Oh—at sea, Sir. They put us below, saying it was safer—the ship must have been hit, the captain ordered 'Abandon ship'. We were going up——" She fumbled in her mind. "The others were ahead, I was last—then something happened and everything seemed to dissolve."

"What were you doing in a ship at sea?"

Strangely the hard metallic voice did not now seem to scare the Wren.

"Foreign draft, Sir."

"They sent you——"

"No, we were all volunteers, Sir."

"My God!" muttered Mr. Pepys.

"Your ship sank?" pursued Nelson.

"I—suppose so."

"It was a warship?"

"Yes, Sir."

"How many? Where?"

"I don't know where. Perhaps twenty or thirty."

Nelson turned abruptly away. Mr. Pepys turned to her with very winning kindness.

"You are in the right place, my child. Try to bear with us. We become rather set and old in our ways. Let me have the privilege of escorting you."

He trotted the Wren off in manner kind and cheery. Nelson stood fixedly, his gaze abstracted. So Mr. Pepys found him on return.

He started and turned.

"Good God, Mr. Pepys—what a tale to hear!"

"'Tis, alas, very usual in war, Sir."

"Usual, Sir, *usual*? Never in my day."

"Sir, Sir, 'tis tragic; but women ha' been lost at sea before. You feel this much——"

Nelson moved restlessly.

"Feel it. To think of it! If I could only have been there—surely something could. . . . *What* was the captain about, accepting action in such circumstances."

"Nowadays, Sir, 'tis not easy to choose—these submarines."

"But women! Sunk—lost at sea!"

"Yourself said just now, Sir, 'playing at sailors'," reminded Mr. Pepys softly.

"God forgive me."

There was a silence, then Nelson added, "At least this will have stopped such folly."

"Folly?"

"Sending women afloat in wartime, Sir."

"Nay, Sir. The Wren said many more such drafts have since gone. Wrens are in all the ports your Lordship knows so well—Alexandria, Gibraltar, the East——"

"I—do—not—know," said Nelson slowly. "You said before—in Home ports."

"Aye, Sir, every port in England. Victualling yards, slop rooms, workshops, pay offices, ship repairs, signals—many thousands."

"Incredible!" said Nelson slowly.

"You must remember, Sir, the great and terrible emergency."

"Aye—but such hardships——"

"Not the hardships of our days, Sir. Remember these new devices—'tis oft more skill than strength, now. Nor do all face such perils—but 'tis more monotony and weariness most contend with, I'll warrant. That is no mean thing, Sir."

Nelson mused:

"She was a neat little thing—she spoke up and did not vapour or argue."

"She seemed very quick, Sir, in picking up and interpreting those sound signals we hear from Below."

"Signals!" Nelson flashed into vivid interest. "Did she? And well?"

"Very well, I judged, though I know little of 'em."

"An exacting branch, Signals, and more so now," Nelson muttered. "Hard work and quick wits——"

"Aye, Sir. She said she had served over a year, also, as a steward."

"Why?"

"No employment in the Signal Branch, Sir, and she was so eager to serve. She said 'I was so keen' (anxious I understand by that) 'to get in. Everybody's been in the Navy. My great-grandfather was killed at Copenhagen. But I did long to do Signals, it was all I could do to—er—er—"stick it". I was so thrilled when I actually got into SIGNALS'——"

"So thrilled, was she? Poor child," Nelson said. "And then——?"

"She joined this draft, Sir."

"And——?"

"And——" said Mr. Pepys and paused significantly.

"Ah! Poor child," said Nelson again, softly. "And then—that."

"Aye, Sir. I asked, 'Don't you regret now?' and she answered, 'Oh, no. My mother will understand. I haven't a brother—there was no one else. There are plenty more women. And everyone was needed then.' And then, Sir—it seemed monstrous sad—she said again, 'My mother will understand. It couldn't be helped. Somebody has to stay and somebody to go. I don't regret—anything!'"

There was a long pause.

Then Nelson said in a very low voice:

"After all, I think they are not unworthy of their fathers and forefathers, and the Navy need not be ashamed to own them."

EDWARD YOUNG

FAR-EASTERN PATROL

We lived the next few days in an atmosphere of anti-climax until orders came through that H-class submarines were to cease operational patrols forthwith and join the Seventh Submarine Flotilla, which consisted only of training submarines and was based at Rothesay in the Clyde estuary. Harwich was to be abandoned as a submarine base. We packed our gear and sailed up the East Coast, round the north of Scotland to the Clyde, spending a week or two at Dundee on the way. It must have been about the beginning of December when we arrived off Rothesay and secured alongside H.M.S. *Cyclops*.

In normal times Rothesay is a popular summer resort. Now the lovely bay, with its long prospect of Loch Striven and the blue hills of Argyll, was dominated by the dirty coal-burning merchant-ship that had been converted into an inadequate and uncomfortable submarine depot ship. Only the wartime shortage of shipping had saved old *Cyclops* from the scrap-heap. Throughout the submarine service she was known, almost affectionately, as the "Cycle-box". Once a year she was taken to sea on exercise, to disprove (some said unkindly) the rumour that she was aground on a self-made reef of empty tins. But between these annual jaunts she rode peacefully at anchor, with her submarines berthed on either side of her, a mother hen with her chicks, disturbed only by the frequent gales and squalls which came sweeping down the hills and churned the bay into an angry ferment, so that the submarines began bumping badly and had to lie off.

The purpose of the Seventh Submarine Flotilla was two-fold: to give sea-training to new submarine officers and ratings, and at the same time to provide live practice targets for destroyers and other escort craft. Many of the boats in this flotilla were therefore dispersed at the various bases where anti-submarine forces carried out their training. So we spent the next few winter months up and down the rugged and beautiful coastline of Western Scotland, dividing our time between Rothesay, Campbeltown, Ardrishaig and Tobermory, acting as "clockwork mouse" to the crews of destroyers and corvettes who were being trained in the use of asdic. Each morning we proceeded to the exercise area, followed by the surface ships, and then dived to eighty feet for perhaps two hours at a time, usually on a prearranged course, while the asdic instructors initiated officers and ratings into the art of "pinging" on us, picking up an echo from our hull, plotting our movements, and making dummy attacks.

This was inordinately dull work for us. When off watch we spent most of the day sleeping. But gradually we grew so accustomed to submarine life (away from the depot ship we lived entirely in the boat for weeks on end) that diving and surfacing became second nature. And sometimes we managed to get in a practice attack on the surface ships at the end of the day.

There were continual changes in the crew, as is inevitable in a training flotilla, and by February I was the only officer left in *H.28* out of the four that had taken her on her last patrol. Jock Tait left to join an operational boat: our paths thereafter crossed only briefly once or twice; and in the end I heard that he had been lost on patrol. I took over the duties of navigator. We also had a change of First Lieutenant, and shortly afterwards Wingfield went off to take command of a new U-class submarine called *Umpire* and was relieved by Lieut. L. W. A. Bennington.

Bennington, who already wore a D.S.C., had been Number One of the submarine *Triumph* just over a year earlier when she struck a mine in the Skagerrak. They were on the surface on a very dark night, charging batteries as usual, and Bennington was officer-of-the-watch on the bridge. He saw the horned mine poised on the crest of a wave ahead of him, too late to do anything but shield his face. There was a tremendous explosion: it seemed certain they were done for. But to his amazement the boat remained on the surface. Inspection of the damage revealed that eighteen feet of the bow had been blown off, but the for'ard bulkhead, split and leaking badly, was by some miracle still holding. The torpedoes had not detonated (in a T-boat there were eight of them ready for firing in the bow tubes), but one had been blasted clean out of its tube, another had nothing left but its tail, and the T.N.T. warhead of a third had been utterly crushed. Amidships there was a ten-foot vertical crack in the pressure hull. And after all this they discovered a seaman still snoring in his hammock only ten yards from the point of the explosion. They were in a sorry state. They could not dive, and it was all the pumps could do to cope with the flooding from the leaks. The Captain, Lieut.-Commander J. W. McCoy, wirelessed for help, and they set off for home across the North Sea. They were sighted by German aircraft next morning, but as the enemy began to attack they were met by air escort and destroyers, and struggled into the Firth of Forth late the following night.

Bennington was short and stocky, with fair hair, a ruddy complexion and a dark chuckle. He talked endlessly in his deep voice about submarines and the submarine service, which for him was a kind of religion: the Royal Navy was immeasurably superior to the other services, and within the Navy the submarine branch was the most efficient and potentially the most powerful as a striking force. He never spoke of "subs" or "tubes" or "boats"; submarines were "submarines" and no nonsense. He was a quiet but strict disciplinarian, and had an unobtrusive way of showing his appreciation of good work. He professed to have no interest in women, and liked nothing better, when ashore, than to sit drinking beer and talking submarines by the hour. He was a terrible man to wake in the morning; when we were living in the boat he would lie in his bunk smoking cigarettes and drinking cup after cup of tea until two minutes before harbour stations, when he would miraculously appear on the dot of time and give orders with his accustomed precision. He never to my knowledge ate breakfast.

He was a wonderful teacher; from him I learnt much which stood me in good stead when I eventually had a command of my own. We got on well together. But in April, almost exactly six months after I had joined *H.28*, a signal came ordering me to report to Chatham. Wingfield had asked for me as his Third Hand in *Umpire*.

Umpire's dockyard trials had been successfully completed, including the usual static basin dive to prove that the hull was water-tight. The last welding leads had been removed, the bunks, cupboards and other wooden fittings were a bright mahogany gleam, new curtains hung in the messes, and the whole boat was resplendent with fresh-smelling paintwork, white inside and battleship grey outside.

Mervyn Wingfield was plainly delighted with his new command, though he tried to conceal his pleasure behind a demeanour of severity and icy reserve. The First Lieutenant, Peter Bannister, I had not met before; he was tall, energetic and humorous, easy to get on with. Tony Godden, the navigator, had been in the same training class with me at Fort Blockhouse; I was delighted now to find we were in the same boat, for he was a most amusing and endearing shipmate, and we had many good evenings ashore together during our stay in Chatham.

Umpire moved out at last into the River Medway on a day towards the end of July, spick and span, a brand-new white ensign flying, bound north-about for the Clyde, where we were to carry out sea trials and training with the Third Flotilla based at Dunoon, before setting forth on a "working-up" operational patrol in the North Sea. After that, the Mediterranean.

We stopped overnight at Sheerness to wait for a convoy of merchant-ships leaving the Thames the next day. In the morning we got under way early and found the convoy congregating off Southend under an escort of motor launches and Admiralty trawlers. We took up our station astern, and by the time we turned the corner at Shoeburyness the convoy had more or less sorted itself out.

All day we moved up the East Coast, passing Burnham, Clacton, Walton-on-the-Naze, Harwich, Felixstowe, Orfordness, and when we were somewhere off Aldeburgh a German bomber came in low from seaward and began attacking the leading ships of the convoy. I was officer-of-the-watch at the time, and in accordance with our convoy instructions gave the order to dive.

Now, we had never dived before at sea and under way. Normally a brand-new submarine carries out numerous dives in slow motion, with the crew already at diving stations, before it is committed to a full-speed dive. We had to make our first dive on the klaxon, and it is to the great credit of all concerned—the Chatham men who built her; Wingfield, who as Captain had thought ahead and trained his officers and men to his satisfaction; Bannister, who as Number One had organized the crew in their duties and had also worked out the first trim; and the crew, who went calmly to diving stations and performed their jobs correctly—it is to the credit of all these that *Umpire's* first dive was a complete success. Within two minutes Bannister had caught a trim and the Captain was able to concentrate on the periscope. We did not want to stay down longer than we need, because the convoy was drawing ahead of us. Five minutes later the Heinkel seemed to have vanished, so we surfaced and pressed on to regain our station in the convoy, which had sustained no damage from the attack.

We felt very pleased with ourselves, and boyishly proud of our boat that had behaved so well. Then, about nightfall, one of the diesels developed trouble and had to be stopped. At first this did not affect our speed, our propulsion being diesel-electric, and we continued to maintain our station. But as the evening wore on, the engine-room staff were unsuccessful in their attempts to get the defective engine going. The other one produced insufficient power by itself to balance the batteries' output when driving two propellers, and we were obliged at last to reduce our speed. The Captain flashed a signal to the Commodore of the convoy, reporting the situation. An M.L. was detailed to drop back and act as our escort, and we were to catch up as soon as possible.

We knew from the latest W/T situation report that, some twenty miles to the north of us, a southbound convoy was approaching down the same buoyed channel. The two convoys were due to meet somewhere about midnight.

The international rule at sea is that in a channel-way ships must keep to the starboard side. Ships meeting in a channel should therefore pass *port to port*. It was revealed afterwards that when the two convoys met, some miles ahead of us, they passed on the *wrong* side, starboard to starboard. So when Tony Godden, the officer-of-the-watch, presently sent down a message that the southbound convoy was approaching, Wingfield was surprised to find on reaching the bridge that the on-coming convoy was not on our port bow, as he expected, but right ahead, with part of it actually extending across our starboard bow. It was a calm night, very dark, but with reasonably good visibility; lights could have been seen at a fair distance. But the German E-boats were raiding the East Coast convoys nearly every night, and no one was showing any lights. Our escorting M.L. had lost touch with us some time earlier. We were quite alone and almost invisible to other ships even at close range.

The normal action would have been to alter course to starboard, but this would have taken us across the bows of the approaching merchant-ships and we might not have had room to get clear. Wingfield altered a few degrees to port, and the first six ships of the convoy passed safely down our starboard side about two hundred yards away. Although we did not know it, our own convoy, now several miles ahead, had taken the same action.

Suddenly a dark shape appeared ahead of us, detached

from the nearest column of the convoy. Examining it through his binoculars, Wingfield saw that it was a trawler, presumably part of the convoy's escort, and that we were directly in its path. In the next second he realized that it was alarmingly near to us and apparently unaware of our presence. He had to decide quickly what to do. The trawler was fine on his starboard bow and seemed certain to pass dangerously close. By the rule of the road it was the trawler's right of way and our duty to keep clear. According to the rules Wingfield should have altered course to starboard, but only two hundred yards to starboard was the endless line of southbound merchant-ships forming an impenetrable barrier. With every ship fully darkened, this was a predicament not visualized by the authors of the Regulations for Preventing Collision at Sea. Wingfield ordered "Hard-a-port". But, even as we began to turn, the trawler seemed to see us, low and dark in the water, and turned instinctively to starboard. This made collision inevitable. Wingfield yelled his last order down the voice-pipe. "Full astern together!'—but before the order could be carried out, the bows of the trawler struck *Umpire* with a sickening metallic crash, some twenty or thirty feet abaft the starboard bow. The submarine lurched to port, and for a few seconds the two vessels stayed locked together, held by the impetus of the trawler's headway. During these seconds Wingfield clutched the trawler's side as it swung in towards him, and shouted furiously, "You bloody bastard, you've sunk a British submarine!" Then the trawler fell away, and Wingfield found his boat sinking under him by the head. In less than thirty seconds she plunged under, leaving Wingfield, Godden and the two look-outs in the water. In the darkness there was shouting and confusion, but the four kept together at first. But presently one and then the other of the look-outs dropped out of the small circle. Tony Godden, who was wearing long fur-lined seaboots, gasped out that he could not kick them free and that he was sinking. For a while Wingfield helped to support him, but Tony finally let go and sank out of sight. It seemed a long time before the trawler's boat appeared, and Wingfield was unconscious when he was hauled on board. When he came to and realized that he, the Captain, was apparently the sole survivor, his feelings can be imagined.

When the Captain left the wardroom to go up on the bridge in response to Tony's message about the approaching convoy, Peter Bannister and I were sitting at the wardroom table, decoding a routine wireless signal that had been passed to us by the telegraphist on watch.

The wardroom was divided from the control-room only by a thin steel partition, and by curtains from the passage-way; at sea these curtains were drawn back, and Peter and I could hear the helmsman repeat the orders which came to him down the voice-pipe from the bridge.

When we heard him repeat the Captain's emergency order, "Hard-a-port", we pushed back our chairs and stood up, our eyes meeting in question and alarm. We stumbled out into the passage-way, and Peter at once gave the order to "Shut water-tight doors!" Almost immediately we heard another urgent yell down the voice-pipe, but before this last order from the bridge could be repeated by the helmsman there was a violent crash for'ard in the torpedo-stowage compartment, followed by the blue-white flare and muffled thump of an electrical explosion. The boat rocked to port, stayed there a few seconds, and then slid drunkenly forward and over to starboard as she began her plunge to the bottom. If the water were deep here, its weight would crush us like an egg-shell. Most of the lights had gone out. Then men were running past us from the next compartment, Peter was yelling "Shut that door!" and I had my hand on it, letting the men run through, disobeying Peter because I hadn't the courage to deny any of them a chance so long as the water was not yet actually at their heels. Somehow the further door to the damaged compartment had shut, whether blown to by the explosion or deliberately shut from the inside by a last nameless act of self-sacrifice as the sea came flooding in, we shall never know. "Shut that bloody door!" repeated Peter in a fury, but by now all the men from the intervening compartment were through. With some difficulty, because of the angle of the boat, I pulled the door up towards me and clamped it shut.

I turned, and struggled up the tilting deck into the control-room. The boat was listing to starboard and sloping forward at an angle of about ten degrees. Water was pouring in from what seemed to be a hundred places. Peter was struggling with the outboard battery-ventilation-valve overhead, desperately seeking an explanation for this inrush of water, and acutely aware of the fatal danger of chlorine gas if the sea-water should find its way into the battery cells under the deck. I reached up to help him, glad in my numbed state of something positive to do. But the valve was already shut, as we knew it should have been, and we must look elsewhere for the breach in our defences. To my paralysed brain it seemed that the shock of the collision had cracked the hull and started rivets along the whole length of the ship. Surprisingly enough, no water was coming down the conning-tower; presumably the upper hatch had fallen shut when the boat took on a list immediately before she went under.

Peter was now calling for more light, and one or two of the men searched about for the emergency hand-lamps. I remembered that I had a torch in my drawer in the wardroom, so I retraced my steps, moving with difficulty down the wet and sloping deck. In the passage-way the water was already knee-deep. I sloshed through it and pulled myself up into the ward-room. Streams of ice-green water were cascading from some-where overhead, drenching the beautiful new curtains and bunks in a universal deluge. If I had brought a conscious intelligence to bear on the source of this waterfall I should have hit on something that ought to have been obvious to all of us. But not until the whole thing was over did I realize that all this water must have been coming from the *ventilation shaft*, now open to sea pressure through the damaged torpedo-stowage compartment. By reaching up my hand over the Captain's bunk I could have shut the valve on the bulkhead quite easily, and the flow of water would have stopped. But my brain, as though stunned by the catastrophe, had become incapable of constructive thought.

I found the torch and splashed my way back to the control-room. As I did so, it occurred to me to wonder what depth we were at. I shone the torch on the depth-gauges and found, to my surprise, that they were both reading only a little over sixty feet. This meant we were in very shallow water, with the bow presumably resting on the bottom at something like eighty feet. I asked Peter whether it was possible to *blow* her up. It seemed unlikely, since we had been at full buoyancy at the time of the collision, and a vast quantity of water must have entered for'ard to have overcome that buoyancy so suddenly. It was obvious that a large gash had been torn at the top of the pressure hull in the torpedo-stowage compartment, and that the compartment had filled up in a matter of seconds. We should never get her up with all that weight of water in her. However, Peter thought it would do no harm to try, so one by one he opened up the valves of the high-pressure air-panel until all five ballast tanks and the two main internal tanks were blowing. But it was no use: the depth-gauges did not even flicker.

The sea continued to pour in on us, with a terrible and relentless noise, and the water in the compartment grew deeper every minute. As the level crept up the starboard side, live electrical contacts began spitting venomously, with little lightning flashes. Vaguely I wondered if we were all going to be electrocuted.

In the half-darkness the men had become anonymous groping figures, desperately coming and going. There was no panic, but most of us, I think, were suffering from a sort of mental concussion. I discovered one man trying to force open the water-tight door that I had shut earlier. "My pal's in there," he was moaning, "my pal's in there." "It's no good," I told him; "she's filled right up for'ard and there's no one left alive on the other side of that door." He turned away, sobbing a little.

For some reason we decided it would be useful if we could

find more torches. I knew there must be one or two others somewhere in the wardroom, so I made yet another expedition down the slope, wading through the pool that was now waist-deep and already covering the lowest tiers of drawers under our bunks. I spent some time in the wardroom, shivering with fear and cold, ransacking every drawer and cupboard, pushing aside the forsaken paraphernalia of personal belongings—underclothes, razors, pipes, photographs of wives and girl-friends. But I could find only one torch that was still dry and working. Holding it clear of the water, I returned to the control-room.

It was deserted.

The door into the engine-room was shut. Had I spent longer in the wardroom than I thought? Perhaps they had all escaped from the engine-room escape hatch, without realizing that I had been left behind. Even if they had not yet left the submarine, they might already have started flooding the compartment in preparation for an escape, and if the flooding had gone beyond a certain point it would be impossible to get that door open again. I listened, but could hear nothing beyond the monotonous, pitiless sound of pouring water. In this terrible moment I must have come very near to panic.

I could at least try hammering on the engine-room door. Looking round for a heavy instrument, I found a valve spanner and began moving aft towards the door. As I did so I heard a voice quite close to me say, "Christ, who's that?" I looked up and found I was standing under the conning-tower. In it, to my infinite relief, I saw Peter with an able seaman and one of the E.R.A.s. "Where the hell have you come from?" said Peter. "Where the hell's everybody gone?" I retorted. "Any room for me up there?" "We ought to be able to squeeze you in. The others are going to escape from the engine-room."

I climbed up through the lower hatch, grateful as never before for the company of my fellow-creatures. Four of us in the tiny space made a tight squeeze. Peter at the top of the ladder with his head jammed up against the upper hatch, the

A.B. half-way up the ladder with his bottom wedged against the side of the tower, leaving just room for me and the E.R.A. standing at the foot of the tower, with our feet on the edge of the lower hatch-opening. The E.R.A. was in a bad way, vomiting continuously and hardly able to stand.

In the centre of the upper hatch was a small port, or round window, made of glass thick enough to withstand tremendous pressure. Number One said that he could see a glimmer of light through it, and supposed it to be caused by a searchlight from some vessel waiting overhead. This encouraged him to think we ought to be able to swim to the surface and be picked up without much difficulty. We knew the control-room depth-gauges were reading just over sixty feet; the upper hatch was something like fifteen feet higher than the normal surface waterline (the point of reference for the depth-gauges) and was therefore probably only about forty-five feet from the surface, say the height of eight men standing on top of each other. It ought to be easy.

"Shut the lower lid," said Peter, "and let's just think this out." I bent down, shut the hatch and pulled the clip over. We then discussed exactly what we were going to do. We agreed that to wear Davis escape gear would be an unnecessary complication in the confined space. One of the dangers was that on our way up we might crack our skulls on the cross-bar between the periscope standards, but we decided there was little chance of this owing to the starboard list. We hoped (vainly, as it turned out) that we might be assisted in our rise to the surface by the bubble of air which would be released from the conning-tower as the hatch opened. The drill was simple. Peter would open the hatch, and as the water came in each man would fill his lungs with air and climb out as fast as he could. Except for the poor E.R.A., who was sick beyond comfort or encouragement, we were by now quite calm, even cheerful.

How long we considered the situation I cannot remember; but at last Peter said, "Well, the next thing is to see if we can open this hatch against the sea pressure." Bracing himself against the side of the tower, he pushed upwards with all his strength. The hatch remained firmly shut. Somehow we must raise the pressure inside the tower.

It occurred to me that while we had been talking the pressure had still been building up in the control-room below us, owing to the continuing inrush of water. I eased off the clip of the hatch under my feet, and sure enough there came the sharp hiss of air forcing its way into the tower. I allowed the air to come in until, after a minute or two, I became aware of a peculiar, faint smell. Perhaps it was merely the odour of fear, but my first thought was that the sea-water had at last found its way into the batteries. "Hullo," I said; "I think I can smell chlorine gas." "All right," said Peter; "shut the lid again and I'll have another shot at opening this one." This time he managed without much effort to lift the hatch slightly off its seat, allowing a trickle of water to come through.

"O.K.," said Peter. "Well, boys, take your time. There's no hurry. You say when you feel you're ready."

I said I was for having a go at once, before we weakened ourselves any further by breathing foul air, and the others agreed. We stripped down to vest, pants and socks.

"Ready?" asked Peter.

"Ready," we all replied, though I think the E.R.A. had reached the point in his sickness where he wanted to die more than anything else.

"Right. Stand by," said Peter cheerfully. "Here we go for fourteen days' survivor's leave. We're off!"—and he pushed up the lid with all his strength.

I took as deep a breath as I could, and then the sea crashed in on us. There was a roaring in my ears, a blackness everywhere, and there was nothing for it but to fight for life with all one's primitive instincts of survival. Hauling myself up by the rungs of the ladder, I found my head obstructed by the A.B.'s bottom. With the strength of a desperate man I pushed up at him, his heel struck me in the face, I pushed again, and then we were through the hatch and clear of the submarine. I swam upwards with quick, jerky breast-strokes. It seemed a terrible distance. Time stretched out of its normal span until I thought my lungs must surely crack before I reached the surface. And then suddenly I was there, coughing, spluttering, gasping in great draughts of the sweet night air and drinking in the blessed sight of the stars shining in the immensity of space.

The sea was fairly calm, with no more than a gentle popple. Seeing two heads in the water not far away, I called out and found they were Peter and the A.B., both in good heart. Of the E.R.A. there was no sign. We could make out the dark shapes of several ships around us, so we began shouting to attract attention. Some of them were throwing searchlights on the water, and one of these seemed to me nearer than the rest. "Come on," I said, "let's swim to that nearest one," and began swimming towards it with my rather feeble side-stroke. I pressed on for a few minutes, imagining the other two were following me, but after a while I turned and could see no sign of them, although I heard them shouting at intervals not far off. The vessel I was making for was farther away than I had thought. I am not a strong swimmer, so I turned over on to my back and relaxed into an easy backward leg-stroke, calling "Help!" at the top of my voice from time to time. Sometimes a wave lopped over my head and I swallowed a little more water. I seemed to be swimming for a long time. Whenever I looked round, the ship seemed to be as far away as ever. Surely, after all this, I was not going to drown in sight of safety? I began to feel rather exhausted. Suddenly I heard voices shouting, the churning of propellers going astern, and I turned to find a searchlight blazing in my eyes and below it the shape of an M.L. quite close, with a scrambling-net down over the side and men running along the deck. A heaving-line shot out, I grabbed it and was hauled in. A sailor clambered down the net and helped me on to the deck, where I fell into the arms of two R.N.V.R. officers. Exhausted and groaning for breath, with my lungs half full of sea-water, I must have appeared in a worse state than I was, but while they wrapped me in blankets and hustled me below I managed to tell them that there were some more of us out there in the water and many others still down in the submarine trying to escape from the engine-room.

In a cabin below they rubbed me down, gave me dry clothes, and put me into a bunk, where I lay shivering from delayed shock. About half an hour later they came and told me our men were starting to come up from the bottom. I couldn't bear to stay in my bunk while this was happening, so I wrapped myself in a blanket and tottered along to find out what the situation was. They were coming up at fairly frequent intervals, strange Martian creatures with their D.S.E.A.[1] goggles and oxygen bags, and rendered almost unrecognizable by black oil which had floated up from the bilges when they flooded the engine-room for the escape. But they were in extraordinarily good spirits, half intoxicated with their unexpected return to life. Every one of them was full of praise for the way in which the Chief E.R.A. and the Torpedo Gunner's Mate had organized the escaping party and carried out the escape drill. When finally these two reached the surface, the Chief E.R.A. last of all, they reported there was no one left in the engine-room. There had been enough D.S.E.A. sets for all but two of the party. Two men had volunteered to go up without them, each holding on to the legs of one of the others; one of these was never seen again. A final roll-call showed that the only other casualty of the engine-room party of twenty was a civilian technician from Chatham dockyard, who had joined *Umpire* as passenger for the trip north: the Chief E.R.A. and the T.G.M. had fitted him with a D.S.E.A. set and patiently explained its simple operation to him several times, but the man was so unnerved by the catastrophe that, although he succeeded in getting out through the hatch, he failed to reach the surface. But altogether the engine-room escape was a remarkable justification of the submarine escape drill.

It was only afterwards I discovered that, half-way through the escape, the Chief E.R.A. thought it would be advisable to

[1] Davis Submerged Escape Apparatus.

make sure none of the escapers was getting caught up in any obstruction outside the hatch. He therefore clipped on the oxygen mouthpiece of his D.S.E.A. set, made his way up through the hatch, walked about on the outside casing of the submarine in the vicinity of the hatch, and then, although he could easily and without shame have made his ascent to safety, he climbed down through the hatch into the engine-room once more and carried on with the business of super-vising the escape of the remaining men. Not until every other man had left the compartment did he make his own get-away.

For his part in the escape Chief E. R. A. Killen was later awarded the British Empire Medal.

It was not until the M.L. landed us at Yarmouth that I heard Peter Bannister was missing. I had been told that another vessel had rescued some survivors from the water, and I had assumed these were Peter and the A.B. who had been with us. In fact only the A.B. had been picked up. When I saw him later at Yarmouth, he said that he and Peter had swum together for some time and that when they were rescued he had thought Peter was immediately behind. A long search failed to find him. I was staggered by this news, for Peter was a strong swimmer and had seemed in excellent fettle when we spoke together on the surface. To have got so far and be lost at the last moment was an appalling tragedy.

It was daylight when we reached Yarmouth and were met by Lieut.-Commander J. F. B. Brown, who had flown up from submarine headquarters in London to get the facts at first hand. During the day, in the intervals of answering questions, we enjoyed the generous hospitality of the Naval Base.

That evening I strolled alone after dinner in a small grassy courtyard. A gentle drizzle of rain was falling, and it was what one would call a miserable evening, but to me the sound of the soft rain falling like a benediction on the living grass seemed inexpressibly sad and sweet, and life itself so desirable that I could not imagine myself ever again being dissatisfied with it. For the first time I knew the delirious joy of not being dead.

At the same time I felt that in the emergency I had failed to act in the manner expected of a submarine officer. Running over again and again the sequence of events following the moment of collision, I was tortured by two nagging thoughts. First, why had I not had the sense to realize that all the water coming into the control-room had been pouring in through the ship's ventilation system? Secondly—and this has haunted me ever since—I knew that I should have been in the engine-room with the men.

There was also the problem of the future. At first I was sure I never wanted to see the inside of a submarine again. But the conviction grew in me that to ask to leave the submarine service would be such an admission of defeat that I should never recover my self-respect. For the purely egoistic reason of patching up my pride, I therefore decided to remain in sub-marines—if I was allowed to. On the principle of imme-diately remounting the horse that has thrown you, I resolved to ask to be sent on an operational patrol as soon as possible.

With thoughts like these crowding my brain, I was still awake when Wingfield walked into my cabin about midnight. He had just landed, having stayed on the scene of the collision until nightfall. He was looking ten years older, grey and haggard from worry and lack of sleep. He told me how Tony Godden had been drowned, and asked about Peter Bannister. I told him the story up to the point where we had separated after reaching the surface. He said the final casualty total was two officers and twenty men, almost half the ship's complement.

The next day, after further interrogation, they sent us off on fourteen days' leave. In the middle of it we were recalled to attend the official Board of Inquiry at Chatham, a dreary and gruelling experience.[1] At the end of my leave I reported to H.M.S. *Dolphin* at Gosport, and in answer to my request for an early return to sea I was appointed to relieve Freddie

[1] The Admiralty apparently did not attach too much blame to Wing-field, for he was given another command soon afterwards and remained in command of operational submarines until the end of 1944, winning a D.S.O. and two D.S.C.s.

Sherwood[1] as Torpedo Officer of the submarine *Sealion*, then based on Fort Blockhouse and operating off the French coast under the command of the famous bearded Ben Bryant.

When we sailed for our next patrol we had on board an R.A.F. inflatable rubber dinghy and three extra passengers: an Army major, a naval rating and a native of Sumatra. We were under secret orders for an unusual mission.

Leaving Trincomalee at dusk on May 6th we travelled all the way across the Indian Ocean on the surface as usual. During the afternoon of the 9th white cumulus clouds billowing up over the horizon on the starboard bow showed that we were approaching the northern mountains of Sumatra. Soon after dark, radar reported land echoes thirty miles ahead, and by midnight we had made our landfall and fixed our position. Slowing down so as to arrive at the right place just before dawn, we passed to the north of Pulo Bras and dived in the middle of Bengal Passage, about eight miles west of Pulo Weh, our objective.

Pulo Weh is an island off the north-west tip of Sumatra. Commanding the bay on the north side is the port of Sabang, which at that time was occupied by the Japanese as a naval base. The object of our Special Operation was to land an "agent"—the Sumatran native—to obtain information about the facilities and defences of the port. The Sumatran had volunteered for the job and had been under training in India for several months. We were to land him on the south side of the island and pick him up at the same spot four days later. The landing party consisted of the Major and the naval rating, a Leading Seaman. They were to row the Sumatran ashore in the rubber dinghy and then return to the submarine. We had rehearsed the drill at Trincomalee a day or two before sailing, and it was just as well that we had.

After diving we went deep to wait for daylight, closing slowly in towards the island. A little later we came up to

---

[1] Lieut. F. C. Sherwood, the first Royal Canadian Naval Volunteer Reserve officer to join submarines in this war.

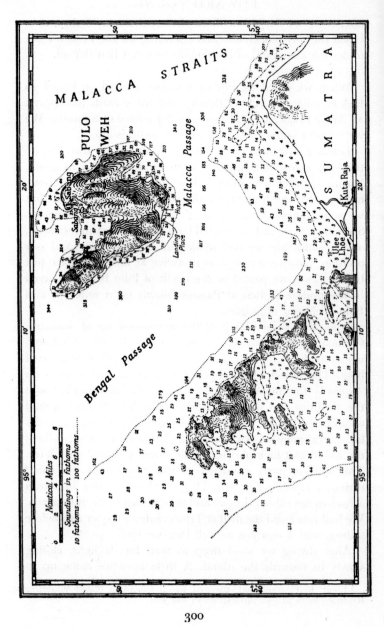

thirty-two feet and examined it carefully through the periscope. The land rose steeply from the shore to a high ridge
which ran like a spine down the whole length of the nearest
arm of the island, rising gradually to a pair of humps in the
south-west corner. Silhouetted in the half-light it had the
semblance of a gigantic stranded whale. It was thickly wooded
everywhere, and when the dawn came up behind the land
and threw a pink flush all over the sea and sky, we saw that
the steep slopes of the shore were covered in luxuriant foliage
which came tumbling right down to the water's edge, with
rust-coloured rocks showing here and there amongst the vivid
green. Although no swell was apparent to seaward we could
see an occasional surf exploding lazily against the rocks and
drenching the overhanging creepers. No place for a landing
here. Even if a landing were possible, no one could have
forced a way through the jungle undergrowth which climbed
abruptly to the skyline. We steered in until we were no more
than a mile off-shore, and then turned south-east along the
coast.

Our inspection was interrupted by three small river cargo-
steamers which appeared from the northward and passed in
line abroast down Bengal Passage within a mile or two of our
position. They would have made a perfect gunnery target,
but we were obliged to keep quiet until the Special Operation
was over, and therefore had to watch them go by unmolested.

I spent most of the morning trying to train the Major in the
use of the periscope. He appeared to have no sense of how
long he had had the periscope up, and time after time I was
obliged to tell him rather sharply to lower it. He seemed
oblivious of the fact that the whole operation might be
jeopardized if the periscope were spotted from the shore. Nor
was he very intelligent in the matter of identifying landmarks.
Spread all over the wardroom table was a large-scale aerial
photographic survey of the whole island, and the Admiralty
chart was open on the chart-table; the Major and I took it
in turns to look through the periscope and then brood over
the plans.

We had already selected a possible landing-place on the south-west coast of the island. Here the photograph showed what appeared to be a sandy beach with a wide clearing in the jungle behind it, and issuing from the clearing a path which led in the direction of Sabang, following a valley between the two humping hills. I hoped it would be possible to use these hills for fixing our position off the landing place at night.

Accordingly we followed the coast until at noon we were opposite the place we had chosen. The soundings on the chart showed deep water up to a short distance from the shore. We closed to within four cables (800 yards) and through the high-power periscope were able to see everything in great detail. The beach was there all right, a fine stretch of white sand, with palm-trees nodding over it, and on the slope of the hill behind it a large open space clear of jungle. We could even identify the track leading up between the two hills. But at the top of the beach was a group of straw-thatched huts, and we could clearly see the dark-skinned inhabitants moving about among the trees. The place was unhealthily over-populated from our point of view. Moreover, a little to the right of this village, where the hill curved forward, I noticed a small square construction set high up on the bluff which sloped steeply down to the sea. It looked suspiciously like an observation post or gun-emplacement, perhaps both.

However, we had earlier observed a narrow strip of beach about three-quarters of a mile back, and we now returned to examine its possibilities. It seemed to suit our purpose excellently. The two hills were still well placed to give me a fix by night, and immediately behind the beach was another small but conspicuous patch of clearing in the jungle which, if we were lucky, might stand out in the dark and provide a leading-mark for the boat party. I took careful bearings of all useful landmarks, and then retired slowly to seaward, satisfied that we ought to be able to get the party ashore at the right spot.

We surfaced three miles to seaward when it was quite dark. We had agreed to wait for moonrise before sending the boat

party in, for they would need a little light to identify the beach
we had chosen and find the inland path without stumbling on
the village. The moon would rise behind the island, so there
was no danger of our being silhouetted towards the shore. We
had an hour to wait. I decided to make use of the time by putting in a short battery charge. Not only should we be making
our approach to the beach on the motors, but if we were unlucky enough to run into an anti-submarine patrol we might
be forced to dive and spend the rest of the night being hunted.
Every amp we could get back into the battery now would be
valuable, and at the same time the engines would be drawing
fresh air into the submarine.

I stayed up on the bridge while we cruised slowly back and
forth, three or four miles out from the shore. Down below the
boat party were making their final preparations. We were not
at full buoyancy, but trimmed down to reduce our silhouette,
to simplify the launching of the boat and to enable us to dive
more quickly if we ran into trouble. Being lower in the water
than usual, the engine exhausts were submerged and muffled,
and threw up continuous little fountains of spray. While the
officer-of-the-watch and the look-outs concentrated to seaward, I trained my binoculars along the murky shore and tried
to identify the landing-place. After some minutes I thought I
could just make out the patch of clearing which was to be our
leading-mark. The island was black and sinister. From time
to time lights flickered among the huts under the palm-trees.
It was very quiet.

Presently I was aware of a gradual lightening of the sky
behind the right-hand hill. I looked at my watch and saw that
it was nearly eight o'clock. The moon was about to rise.

"Control-room! First Lieutenant on the voice-pipe."

"First Lieutenant speaking, sir."

"Number One, tell the boat party to stand by. Open the
fore hatch and get the boat up on deck. When the boat is
through, shut and secure the hatch as quickly as possible."

"Ay, ay, sir."

"Control-room, break the charge, out both engine clutches."

The noise from the exhausts died away. I was pleased to notice that a little breeze had got up and was ruffling the face of the sea to a darker grey. This would help to make the dinghy less conspicuous during its approach to the shore.

"Bridge! Both engine clutches out, main motors ready."

"Slow ahead together."

As I brought the submarine round on to a course which aimed straight at the patch of clearing, I looked for'ard and saw the lid of the fore hatch swing open. Wade and the Second Coxswain stepped out, and began hauling up the deflated dinghy. This hatch was the one normally used for loading torpedoes and conveniently led down into the submarine at a forward-sloping angle. It was the only hatch which could have been used for getting the boat out, since all the others were vertical. But being so close to the water-line, it was a dangerous hatch to have open at sea. As long as it was open we were in a vulnerable position, and I was very relieved when the loose folds of the dinghy were safely up on deck and the hatch slammed to. So many dark figures had emerged after the dinghy that it now seemed as though half the crew were down there on the forecasing, but in fact there were only six men: the three members of the boat party, with Wade and two of our men to give them a helping hand. The Major pulled the string which released the compressed-air bottle inside the rubber skin, there was an explosive hiss and the dinghy ballooned out with an alarming suddenness, nearly slithering off the casing as it did so.

I proposed to take the submarine to within half a mile of the shore before launching the boat. Even so they would have a heavy pull before them, but it would be madness to take the submarine in any closer. We still had a mile and a half to go when the Major came softly aft to the bridge to report that all was ready. With his blackened face he looked like a desperado out of a boys' adventure story. We made a final check on our watches and ran quickly once more over the arrangements. He and his Leading Seaman would row the Sumatran ashore. I would wait in the vicinity for half an hour in case of trouble, then retire to seaward to continue the battery charge. Meanwhile, having concealed the boat, they would push inland to find the path, and when the Sumatran was safely on his way to Sabang, return to the beach. Three hours from the time of the first launching I would return to pick them up. As we might have difficulty in sighting the dinghy, the Major would flash his torch towards us, making the letter R—short, long, short.

The moon was just beginning to appear over the shoulder of the hill. We had timed it perfectly. The patch of clearing was now easily visible, but its bearing had moved a little to the right, showing that a slight current was taking us sideways towards the north-west. I pointed this out to the Major and warned him he would have to allow for this on his way in. In the darkness the island seemed appallingly close, the skyline rearing high and black before us, but I had memorized the crucial bearings and knew we were still outside the half-mile limit.

When the bearings were nearly on I stopped the motors, waited until the way was off the ship, and then gave the order to launch the boat. It slipped into the water with no trouble. The three men climbed gingerly down into it and within half a minute they were away, the Major and the Leading Seaman with an oar each, pulling steadily for the land, and the cheerful little Sumatran sitting erect in the stern steering with a paddle. I immediately ordered "Half astern together", and began to retire discreetly to a safer distance. Through my binoculars I watched the boat pursuing a somewhat erratic course until I lost it against the dark line of the shore; but they seemed in the end to be making for the right spot. I waited half an hour as agreed, a mile and a half to seaward, then turned north-west into the middle of Bengal Passage and re-started the battery charge.

We were due to pick them up at ten minutes to midnight. Half an hour beforehand I began to return towards the landing-place, but keeping three miles offshore. The moon was now very bright indeed, and I hoped we should not have to go in quite so close as we had done before. To our surprise, fifteen minutes before the appointed time we suddenly saw the letter R flashing at us from not very far away, and there they were already half-way out from the shore and coming to meet us. We swung towards them, and ten minutes later they were both back on board and the dinghy had been deflated and taken down through the fore hatch.

The adventurers were delighted with the way everything had gone according to plan. They had had no trouble in hitting the right beach and concealing the boat in the undergrowth. In less than twenty minutes they had found the track leading up between the hills. They had gone a little way along it with the Sumatran and finally left him to make his own way in the best of spirits. Returning to the beach, they had stayed hidden for a time, but then decided they would prefer to wait for us out on the water.

I now turned away from the island and, after running out until we were well in the middle of Bengal Passage, set course eastward to pass out through Malacca Passage, the strait which divides Pulo Weh from the mainland. Part One of the Special Operation had been carried out successfully.

We now had four days to waste, during which we could make no attacks on shipping, lest we attract anti-submarine patrols to the area and endanger Part Two of the operation. So we moved round the corner, eastward along the north coast of Sumatra, examining the shore at our leisure. We investigated the little port of Sigli, but saw nothing of interest except a small vacant jetty and a number of corrugated-iron warehouses. Farther east we found a place where the only railway line in northern Sumatra ran close to the sea and crossed a small bridge within easy gun range. The bridge would be a tempting gunnery target for the last day of a patrol, particularly if the action were timed to coincide with the railway time-table. West-bound trains were sighted at 1100 and 1300. It was galling not to be able to attack them.

Early in the morning of the fourth day we returned towards the scene of our operation, diving before dawn in the middle of

Malacca Passage. During the day we moved round the corner to have another look at our landing-place, and after night-fall surfaced well out to sea. We were not due to pick up the Sumatran until midnight, so we spent the intervening hours charging batteries about six miles west of the island. With half an hour to go we stopped the charge, prepared the dinghy on deck ready for launching, with the Major and the Leading Seaman standing by, and stationed ourselves about a mile from the shore to await the agent's signal—the letter N (a long and a short), which he was to flash by torch at intervals of a minute, starting exactly at midnight.

The suspense of the last five minutes was almost unen-durable, and several times I had to put my watch to my ear to make sure it was still going. But at last both the luminous hands were pointing firmly to twelve, and it was midnight.

It was a terrible anticlimax when no signal came. Perhaps his watch was slow. But the minutes passed and nothing hap-pened. The moon began to rise over the hill and threw our patch of clearing into prominence. The Major came aft along the casing and climbed up beside me on the bridge. It was certainly beginning to look as though something had gone wrong. There was just a chance that the Sumatran had for some reason been unable to get back to the beach on time. This possibility had of course been foreseen, and it had been agreed that if either party were prevented from keeping the rendezvous a second and final attempt would be made the following night. I said, "Well, Major, if he hasn't shown himself by half-past we'll pack up for tonight and give him another chance tomorrow."

Precisely at the half-hour, and just as I was about to give the orders for going astern and falling out the boat party, we saw the signal, a long and a short, winking at us from the shore, clear and unmistakable. But there was something peculiar about the exactness of that half-hour delay which made us pause and consider.

Our clocks and watches were still keeping Ceylon time (six and a half hours ahead of Greenwich). Being so much farther east, one would have expected Sabang local time to be ahead of Ceylon. It ought to have been well past midnight. However, man can decide to keep whatever time he likes, and it was possible the Japanese here were keeping a time that was half an hour *behind* ours. Perhaps it was a Jap who was making the signal, unaware of the difference in time. Perhaps the Sumatran had been caught and tortured and forced to give the whole show away. Perhaps he had turned traitor.

On the other hand, it was still possible that there was a more innocent explanation. His watch might have stopped, and in restarting it he might have set it by a local clock. Or again he might have been delayed in his return to the beach and the exactness of the half-hour was just a coincidence.

However, there was in any case another disturbing feature of the signal. It was coming not from the landing-place but from a position well to the right. It was in fact so much to the right that it was bang in the middle of the beach in front of the village. If the game *had* been given away, it seemed that the Japs were nevertheless not sure of the right spot. But perhaps the Sumatran had only just got back to this side of the island and had not had time to find the correct beach.

Whether he was all right or not, we still did not want to land the boat right in front of that village. So we decided to postpone the pick-up until the following night, hoping that in the meantime he would be able to re-discover the original beach. Accordingly we withdrew, and continued the battery charge out in the deep field.

I thought it better to patrol well away from the island during the following day. After diving in the early hours we kept over to the southern side of Bengal Passage. Half-way through the morning a small ferry-boat came out from Ulee Lhoe, the little port at which the Sumatra railway terminated, crossed the strait and disappeared round the eastern edge of Pulo Weh. This was probably the connecting-link between the railway and Sabang. Looking at the passengers as the boat passed within a mile of us, I reflected that they had probably been aboard one of the trains we had seen farther along the coast, and that if it had not been for the operation in hand we might have surfaced and taken one or two useful prisoners. Perhaps there would be another chance later in the patrol when the operation was over. I decided to spend the rest of the daylight hours investigating this port of Ulee Lhoe, which the ferry had just left. And here occurred a curious incident which puzzled me at the time but took on a new significance in the light of what happened later.

Towards evening we were patrolling about two and a half miles north of the place, in a depth of about thirty fathoms, when two apparently innocent motor fishing-vessels cast off from the jetty and began to move slowly in line abreast towards our position, stopping occasionally and then coming on again. I feel certain now that they were some form of anti-submarine patrol, but at the time I was completely at a loss to account for their behaviour. It was more than a coincidence. Yet I was confident that our periscope could not have been spotted, for there was a considerable lop on the sea and we were two and a half miles from the shore. It was possible that our propeller noise had been detected on shore hydrophones, but in that depth of water it seemed unlikely. Somewhat disturbed, I retired north-westward until I had lost sight of them in the falling dusk.

At midnight we were sitting once more opposite the landing-place. This time, in case of trouble, we had the gun's crew standing by at the gun, with a shell all ready in the breech.

When the signal again came exactly half an hour late we were faced with an extremely difficult decision. As Captain of the submarine I had an over-riding power of veto. If I considered that the situation exposed the submarine to too great a risk it was my duty to call off the operation. On the other hand, I had no power to order the Major to proceed with it if he on his side thought the odds against success were too great. The circumstances were now, to say the least, extremely suspicious. At the same time, we still had no positive proof that anything had gone seriously wrong. The flashing signal on this second night, although not quite in the right spot, was at least much nearer to it and certainly a good quarter-mile away from the village. I did not see how I could abandon the operation on the evidence available. I should have to justify such a decision to Captain Ionides on my return, and the more I thought about it the more I realized my reasons would look pretty feeble. Besides, we had a duty to the Sumatran, who had after all taken a bigger risk than any of us. We could not leave him so callously to what would undoubtedly be a ghastly fate at the hands of the Japanese. It seemed to me that we were bound to give him the benefit of any doubt we might have.

Standing together on the bridge, the Major and I argued the problem back and forth for a good five minutes. He had the wind-up properly. I could hardly blame him for that; it was he, and not I, who would have to go in to the beach; the smell of treachery was in the air, and the island loomed ominously before us in the dark like a crouching beast waiting to spring. But however much I might sympathize, I was convinced it was his duty to go forward with the operation. One thing was certain: this was no time for dithering. The longer we waited the greater the risk.

All this time the signal was flashing from the shore. Finally I lost all patience.

"Major, it's for you to decide. But I can't keep my ship waiting here all night while you make up your mind. If you don't take the boat away in five minutes I shall call off the operation and report my views to the Staff when we get back."

He turned without a word, went for'ard and told his Leading Seaman to stand by. In that moment I admired him very much. He was extremely frightened, but in cold blood he was going ahead with the job he had to do, and you can't be braver than that. I ordered "Half ahead together", and we began moving in. This time I took the submarine to within eight hundred yards of the shore before giving Wade the order to launch the boat.

As they pulled away I felt I was probably sending them to

their death, but the die was cast, and I had too many other things to worry about now. We were still pointing towards the shore; if there were trouble and we had to dive quickly we might hit the bottom in the shoaling water. Yet I couldn't turn my stern to the shore, for if I did we shouldn't be able to fire the gun, which was for'ard of the bridge. So I manœuvred the motors until we swung slowly round to port and came to rest roughly parallel with the beach. From that position a half-turn to port would take us immediately into deeper soundings. The recognition signal was still flashing away, much too brightly, I thought . . . N . . . N . . . N . . . N . . . and with increasing frequency as the boat drew nearer to the shore. Wade and Blake were up beside me on the bridge, Blake at his post as Gunnery Officer, looking down at the men waiting in silence on the gun platform. I told him to train the gun on the flashing torch and be ready to open fire at the first sign of trouble. The barrel swivelled round until it was pointing out on the starboard beam. I still had my binoculars fixed on the boat, but presently lost sight of it against the dark reflection of the land.

When the torch stopped flashing, the darkness of the island sprang out blacker and more intense than ever. We waited for the climax in a silence that was as taut as a wire stretched almost to snapping point—a wire that might have been strung between my binoculars and that point on the shore-line where I had last seen the boat. And then suddenly in the lenses I saw a black dot on the water, emerging from the shadows and moving towards us. It was the boat returning. For a moment I dared to hope that all was well. But then that torch started up again . . . N . . . N . . . N . . . flashing much faster now, moving a little towards the left along the shore, and at once it was certain that something was wrong.

In the same instant the silence split asunder and the whole basin of the hill erupted into a crackle of noise and flame. We found ourselves the focal point of a radial cross-fire from four machine-guns set in an arc round the lower slopes behind the shore. Fiery streams of tracer stuttered towards us across the water, accelerating swiftly, ricocheting off the sea like molten pebbles, whipping over the periscope standards. And simultaneously, from the emplacement high up on the bluff astern of us, came the sharp boom of a larger-calibre gun, probably a four-inch. Fortunately this gun seemed to have no idea of our range, and its shells went hurtling over our heads and far into the seaward darkness. The general shindy, after the long silence, was appalling.

Blake was yelling in my ear.

"Open fire, sir?"

"Yes, open fire."

We cracked off a shell and saw it burst on the slope of the hill in a muffled shower of sparks. Over. "Down 200 . . . Fire!" The second round landed near the spot where the torch had been flashing. But we were unequally matched for a shooting contest: we could not hope to silence five guns whose exact positions were not easy to pin-point. Already machine-gun bullets were striking the casing of the submarine, and sooner or later we should have casualties among the gun's crew. There seemed no point in exposing the men if they could serve no useful purpose. So I ordered them to fall out, and sent everybody down below except Wade.

One of the machine-guns had shifted its fire to the dinghy, which at this point seemed to be about four hundred yards away. Now that I could see the boat clearly with the naked eye, I realized that there was only one man in it. This was disastrous. And it seemed impossible that the one man now rowing with such desperate haste could get through to us without being hit.

I was extremely frightened. It was my first experience of being under machine-gun fire, and instead of acting up to tradition and standing boldly and calmly at the front of the bridge regardless of danger, I sheltered myself as well as I could behind the for'ard periscope standard, cocking an eye occasionally to see how the boat was getting on. I was in something of a quandary. I had to think of my duty to the ship. We had run into what was obviously a prepared ambush, and at any moment we might find our retreat cut off by a hidden fleet of submarine-chasers. All my instincts were to dive and get the hell out of it, and I daresay that if I had done so there and then my action would have received official approval. I was responsible for fifty men and a valuable ship; one unlucky hit on the pressure hull from the four-inch gun would be fatal to us. Ought I to continue risking *Storm* for the sake of one man?

The correct answer was undoubtedly No, yet somehow I could not bring myself to desert him while there was a sporting chance. The big gun was still overestimating our range, its shells roaring well over our heads with a noise like an express train. I compromised by deciding that I would wait so long as this gun showed no signs of finding our range. The machine-guns could do no serious harm to the submarine itself.

Someone was calling up the voice-pipe. It was Number One.

"Are you all right, sir?"

"Yes," I replied testily, "of course I'm all right."

But Number One was quite correct to ask. For all he knew Wade and I might both have been dead, and they would have looked silly waiting below for orders if there was no one alive up top to give them.

The boat was coming on at a maddeningly slow speed, but with every yard he put between himself and the shore the rower's chances were increasing. When he was about one hundred yards away I recognized him without doubt as the Major, and then suddenly saw the Leading Seaman in the water, hanging on to the stern of the boat and swimming with his free arm. Wade and I were now wildly agitated; it was like the last lap of a neck-and-neck race, but a hundred times more exciting. We yelled crazy words of encouragement which they could not possibly hear above the din. I even urged the Major to get out and swim, though what good that would have done I cannot now imagine.

At last the incredible was coming true. They had run the gauntlet. They were within a few yards of us, and the Major was turning his head to choose the best place for coming alongside. I sent Wade down on to the fore-casing to give them a hand up, and in a few moments they were scrambling over the ballast tank and up on to the casing. "Get them up to the bridge," I shouted. "Don't worry about the boat." And then:

"Control-room! Full ahead together. Hard-a-port. Steer 210." As the submarine gathered headway I caught a glimpse of the abandoned dinghy drifting down the starboard side.

The Major and the Leading Seaman were completely done in. Retching and groaning, they struggled through the little door at the front of the bridge, staggered past me and somehow got themselves into the hatch and down the ladder.

I ordered Wade to follow them. He had been splendid.

"Control-room! DIVE, DIVE, DIVE!"

As I pulled the hatch down over my head I could still hear the four-inch shells screaming overhead and the bullets whining and pinging all round us. In a few seconds we should be safe under water. Landing hurriedly on the control-room deck I ordered "Thirty-two feet" and told Blake to switch on the echo-sounder, for I was not sure how much water we had below us. As the machine recorded the increasing depth so we went gradually deeper too, keeping about twenty feet between us and the sea's bottom, finally steadying at eighty feet.

What now? I was still expecting a flotilla of anti-submarine vessels to close in on us. We slowed down and listened, but heard nothing. Feeling it was imperative to get as far from the scene as possible before daylight, since I was sure submarine-chasers would soon be on the spot, I made a bold decision to surface almost at once and get away on the main engines.

When we came up, only two miles from the shore, the firing had ceased. At this distance we were not visible against the background of the islands to the westward, and our surfacing produced no reaction from the enemy. We started the engines without further ado and proceeded at full speed to the southward. Five miles from the shore we doubled back eastward and passed out through the Malacca Passage.

It was remarkable that we had got away without a single casualty, but the most surprising feature of the whole incident was that we had seen no enemy ship of any kind. Perhaps the

Jap soldiery were jealous of their naval forces and hoped to win the kudos of sinking us unaided. If so, they had been very stupid: properly organized land-and-sea co-operation should have had us absolutely cold.

When we dived that dawn, we were nearly forty miles away, well off the northern coast of Sumatra in the Malacca Straits. We badly needed a restful day to soothe our nerves and recover lost sleep, so I decided to spend May 16th patrolling quietly a good four miles off shore.

When the Major and the Leading Seaman had recovered from the shock of their experience, I elicited from them the story of what had happened when they reached the beach.

As they neared the shore they got the impression that the flashing light was moving gradually left, and finally it seemed to recede into what appeared to be a little creek, thickly surrounded with trees and bushes, and very dark. When the boat touched bottom, the Leading Seaman got out and waded through the water up to the entrance of the creek. The torch was still flashing. And then he heard the Sumatran's voice, more high-pitched than usual and calling out in an agitated manner from the head of the creek. He said he was wounded and would have to be carried.

"It will take both of you. The Major must come too," he said.

The Leading Seaman didn't like the sound of this, and returned to the boat for consultation. While they were discussing the situation in low tones they became aware of rustling and crackling noises in the undergrowth to the side of the creek.

"The whole thing stinks to me," said the Major. "Come on, we're going to beat it. Jump in."

And he started rowing away from the shore as fast as he could. Shortly afterwards the torch began its damned flashing again, and then pandemonium broke loose. Presently, when the machine-gun fire began to get pretty close, they decided that the Leading Seaman should hop out and swim astern, both to reduce the target and to give them a second chance if one of them should be hit. They were terrified that at any moment we would dive and not realize they were on their way out to us.

We speculated miserably on what had happened to the Sumatran. It was of course possible that he had deliberately betrayed us, but from the description of the way he had spoken in the creek it looked rather as if he had somehow got caught, spilt the beans under torture, and had then been forced to act as a decoy, probably with a revolver at his back. The thought of his probable fate cast a gloom over our spirits for the remainder of the patrol.

And the remainder of the patrol was gloomy indeed. We knew that the whole neighbourhood would be alerted by now, and it was extremely unlikely that any targets would come our way for some time. On the night of the 16th I ran out to seaward and sent a signal to Trincomalee reporting the failure of the operation, and then went off to pass two days at the extreme eastern end of my area, off Diamond Point.

On the 19th we returned to Pulo Weh, and spent the next four days patrolling off its eastern and north-eastern coast— the opposite side of the island from the scene of our abortive operation. On the 21st expectations were aroused by the sighting of a torpedo-boat which entered Sabang from the eastward, but although we thereafter kept a close watch on the harbour entrance he did not reappear with the merchant-ship we hoped he had come to escort. On all these days we wallowed in a heavy south-westerly swell caused by the onset of the monsoon period in the Indian Ocean.

One afternoon when I was doing a spell of periscope watchkeeping, as I usually did once a day if things were quiet, I found myself surrounded by a lively school of porpoises. The well was particularly heavy that day, and the planesmen were having difficulty in keeping the submarine at a steady depth, sometimes dropping her several feet and leaving me staring up at the underside of the tumbling surface. I had often looked through the periscope under water, watched the light filtering down through the pale green water like afternoon sunshine into a forest of beech-trees, and gazed up at that quicksilver roof which refraction made so unexpectedly opaque. I had seen it from below on calm, windless days when it was as hard and definite as a sheet of mirrored glass, reflecting every speck of solid matter that drifted close to the surface, every mote of dust, every scrap of spongy seaweed, every jelly-fish, every water-logged twig. I had seen it under the lash of tropical rain-storms, when the greyed silver was spangled with a million dancing pricks of light; and I had seen it many times in rough weather when it reared up and away from the periscope and as quickly dropped back towards it with a violence that was all the more impressive because of the absolute silence. On this day off Sabang the sea was so rough that the whole surface was broken into a tossing welter of foam, one mass of water falling on another in a soundless avalanche of froth. To the majesty of a breaking sea viewed from below was added the incomparable spectacle of porpoises leaping. There were six or seven of them at a time within my field of vision, and they were jumping clean out of the water across the troughs of the waves, re-entering it smoothly with a trailing plume of white bubbles. Once by a coincidence the periscope broke surface and dipped again simultaneously with one of these porpoises, and I was able to follow its leap from beginning to end, the seemingly effortless forward and upward thrust from the powerful tail, the brief thrilling flight through the air, and the clean plunge at the finish. The whole school was moving forward in parallel curves, leaping one after the other, over and under in a grace-ful rhythm of *perpetuum mobile*, like the crank-shaft of a slow-moving engine, until presently they had all gone past us and on into the impenetrable green under-water darkness beyond my vision. This was the only occasion on which I ever saw fish through the periscope—I suppose they are normally frightened away by the great mass of the hull—and I am glad to have been the privileged observer of that day's magnificent sub-marine display.

FAR-EASTERN PATROL

We were all mightily relieved when the signal came ordering us to leave patrol. The Major had in the meantime gone down with an attack of dengue fever. We reached Trincomalee on May 29th, thoroughly fed up with ourselves, and so ended *Storm's* only "cloak-and-dagger" experience.